M000306511

Apparatus for Teaching Physics

A Collection of
"Apparatus for Teaching Physics"
Columns
from *The Physics Teacher*, 1987-1998

edited by
Karl C. Mamola

The Bay School Library
35 Keyes Avenue
San Francisco, CA 94129

Apparatus for Teaching Physics

(A Collection of "Apparatus for Teaching Physics" Columns from *The Physics Teacher*, 1987-1998)
© 1998 American Association of Physics Teachers
Published by:
    American Association of Physics Teachers
    One Physics Ellipse
    College Park, MD 20740
    U.S.A.
    301-209-3300
    www.aapt.org

Apparatus for Teaching Physics Column Editor for *The Physics Teacher* from 1985 to May 1992 was Walter Connolly, professor emeritus, Department of Physics and Astronomy at Appalachian State University, Boone, NC. The Column Editor from September 1992 to present is Karl C. Mamola, professor, Department of Physics and Astronomy, at Appalachian State University.

Because this work is a compilation of articles that span an 11-year period, the accuracy of the content information for authors or for vendors mentioned in the articles cannot be guaranteed. Catalog numbers and prices included in articles were correct when originally published, but may no longer reflect current prices or availability. People should contact the appropriate vendor to verify product information. AAPT assumes no liability for incorrect information.

Interior Layout: by Jane Chambers and Rebecca Heller Rados
Cover Design: by Christine Rogers

ISBN #: 0-917853-90-3

Apparatus for Teaching Physics
Table of Contents

Chapter 1. MECHANICS

Kinematics

Forces, Newton's Laws

Rotational Motion, Centripetal Force, Angular Momentum

Oscillatory Motion, Elastic Forces

Momentum, Energy

Fluids

Other Mechanics Apparatus

Chapter 2. WAVES AND SOUND

Chapter 3. THERMAL PHYSICS

Chapter 4. ELECTRICITY AND MAGNETISM

Electric Charge, Electrostatics

Capacitance, Resistance, Circuits

Magnets, Magnetic Fields

Induced emf, Lenz's Law

Chapter 5. LIGHT AND COLOR

Light Rays, Reflection, Refraction

Mirrors, Lenses

Wave Optics, Diffraction, Interference

Spectra, Color Mixing

Other Optics Apparatus

Preface

The "Apparatus for Teaching Physics" Column of *The Physics Teacher* is a forum in which teachers may share their new and creative ideas regarding the instructional apparatus they use. High-school, college, and university physics teachers worldwide have contributed to the column's pages. The articles appearing in the column include descriptions of new instructional apparatus as well as discussions of innovative uses of standard, well-known equipment. While many commercial items are included, most of the articles deal with home-made apparatus that can be easily constructed using low-cost, readily available components. The emphasis is on demonstration and laboratory apparatus useful primarily in the introductory physics course. Karl Mamola is the current column editor. He was preceded by a number of outstanding members of the physics teaching community, most recently by Walter Connolly who edited the Apparatus Column from January 1985 until May 1992.

This volume contains reprints of Apparatus Column articles that were published during the period January 1987–May 1998. Apparatus Column articles from earlier years were included in previous reprint collections produced by the AAPT (e.g., *A Potpourri of Physics Teaching Ideas, Selections of Reprints* from *The Physics Teacher,* April, 1963–December, 1986). Articles were selected for inclusion in the present volume based primarily on their degree of applicability to the high school and/or introductory college physics course and the current availability of the apparatus/components described.

The articles in this collection have been loosely arranged according to topic. There are five major headings, with various subgroupings. They appear in the approximate order in which the topics are frequently taught in the introductory physics course. Of course, apparatus found under one heading may often be useful in other areas as well. Some items that have more general, rather than specific uses, have been included under "Other Apparatus" headings.

Production of this volume was carried out by Jane Chambers, Rebecca Heller Rados and Christine Rogers of the Communications Department of the AAPT. Cliff Swartz and Walt Connolly gave invaluable encouragement and advice throughout all phases of the project.

Kinematics

Simple Free Fall Apparatus*

J. Fox, N. Gaggini, and J. Eddy, Department of Physics, Indiana
University of Pennsylvania, Indiana, PA 15705

Secondary school teachers report that their students are always interested in measuring accurately the acceleration due to gravity. The method commonly used
involves dropping an object through a set of photocell gates. In a recent article on
Faraday's law a study was made of the voltage induced in a coil through which a cylindrical magnet was dropped.[1] We have expanded upon that idea to develop a simple and
inexpensive method of measuring the acceleration due to gravity.

Fig. 1 illustrates a 1.2-m-long, 16-mm outside-diameter glass tube that has three coils
wrapped around it. The coils each consist of 180 turns of #36 magnet wire. By wrapping
the glass tube a number of times with masking tape, leaving a space of 3.0 mm, it is easy
to wind the 180 turns within the 3.0-mm space. The dimensions between the coil centers
are shown in Fig. 1. The coils are connected in series with a 1000-Ω resistor. The leads
are connected directly to a 12-bit computer interface board.[2] The voltage output from the
coils as a result of dropping a magnet through the glass tube is shown in Fig. 2.

The analysis is straightforward. The voltage vs. time data are printed, and the time of
fall from the first coil to the second and from the first to the third are recorded. Knowing

*This work partially supported by NSF Grant TEI 8550224.

the distance S_2 from the first coil to the second and the distance S_3 from the first coil to the third, the equations of motion can be written:

$$S_2 = v_0t_2 + 1/2g(t_2)^2$$

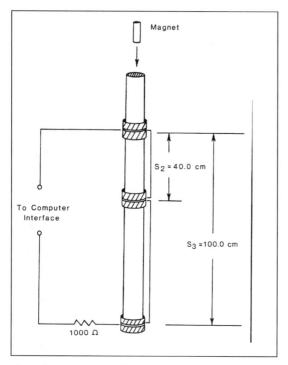

Fig. 1. Glass tube with coils made from 180 turns of #36 magnet wire wound between cylinders of tape used as a coil form. The distances shown are from coil center to coil center. The figure is not drawn to scale. The 1000-Ω resistor is used to avoid shorting the input of the interface.

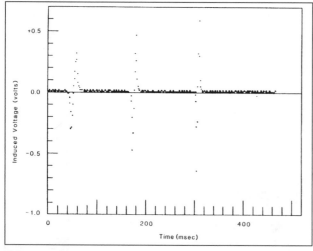

Fig. 2. The voltage induced in the coils as a function of time. Note that the induced voltage increases with the increasing speed of the falling magnet.

$$S_3 = v_0t_3 + 1/2g(t_3)^2.$$

Eliminating v_0 yields:

$$g = 2[(S_3/t_3) - (S_2/t_2)]/(t_3 - t_2).$$

The average value obtained for g after 13 trials was (972 ± 7) cm/s² where the uncertainty reported is the standard deviation of the mean. This corresponds to an uncertainty of less than 1% and can be attributed to our inability to resolve the times to better than 1% using the software supplied with the interface. It is also seen, however, that some small systematic error exists. This error is primarily associated with the measurement of the coil separation. The coils are not wound uniformly, so the exact "magnetic" center to center separation of the coils is uncertain by ± 1 mm. This uncertainty is sufficient to explain the systematic error.

The apparatus is extremely simple, the data are acquired rapidly, and the analysis is straightforward. Resolution could be improved by using a longer tube. Some variations of the experiment are possible. First, measuring the time from the positive to negative peaks of the induced voltage permits the student to determine the "instantaneous" velocity as the magnet passes each of the coils. The effective length of the 2.7-cm magnet is approximately 2.4 cm.[1] That velocity, divided by the time it takes for the magnet to pass between the coils also yields a value for g, but it lacks the accuracy (approximately 5% for this method) of the method described above. This is due to the lack of precision in measuring such small periods of time. Second, the student can calculate backwards to determine the velocity of the magnet at the release point ($v_0 = 0$). Third, the loss of gravitational potential energy can be compared to the kinetic energy of the falling magnet as it passes the first coil. Finally, one could suspend the magnet by a soft spring to obtain a record of the position of the oscillating magnet within one of the coils. This is truly a simple and inexpensive device that opens the door to many experiments that can be explored by the secondary school student.

References

1. R.C. Nicklin, *Am. J. Phys.* **54**, 422 (1986).
2. Advanced Interface Board, Vernier Software, 2920 S.W. 89th St., Portland, OR 97225.

An Easier Way to Measure *g* with a Spark Timer

John Olson, *Rockhurst College, Kansas City, MO 64110-2508*

To measure the acceleration due to gravity, general-physics students commonly use an apparatus that has a flat vertical metal plate with a wire running parallel to it. The plate and wire are connected to a spark timer, and a piece of spark-sensitive paper tape covers the plate. A metal plummet, which *almost* fills the gap between the plate and the wire, is dropped for a distance of about a meter, completing the spark gap and recording the plummet's position at uniform time intervals as it falls. This experiment for beginning physics students accomplishes three things very effectively: it verifies that the distance traveled by something subject to a constant force varies directly as the square of the time ($S = 0.5\ at^2$); it shows, through measurement of the distances traveled between sparks, that the speed of a falling object increases at a linear rate; and it obtains a good measurement of *g*.

This apparatus, nevertheless, has some practical problems. To avoid error due to friction, the metal plummet must not touch either the paper (on one side) or the wire (on the other). It must, however, be close enough to each of them for the high voltage to spark across and produce a dot on the paper tape. These tolerances are really too fine to be maintained when the device is in regular use by students: eventually the plummet falls, for part of the distance, too far from either the wire or the metal plate to produce a spark. The adjustments needed to remedy this are delicate and not easily done, resulting in frustration for both students and lab instructor.

An alternative device (see Figs. 1 and 2), modeled on a PSSC method of measuring *g*, uses a spark timer instead of a carbon-disk timer. Attach a weight to a strip of spark-sen-

Fig. 2. Close-up of the spark gap. Two strips of flexible plastic guide the tape through the gap with very little friction.

Fig. 1. Rockhurst students Lan Tran and Jennifer Moore prepare to drop a weighted strip of waxed-paper tape through a stationary spark gap.

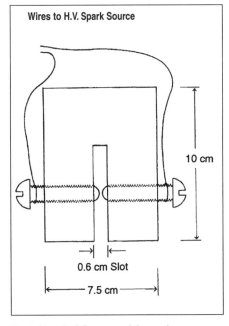

Wires to H.V. Spark Source

10 cm

0.6 cm Slot

7.5 cm

Fig. 3. (Top view) Geometry of the spark gap.

sitive tape and drop it through a *fixed* spark gap. This procedure almost guarantees that every timing pulse produces a spark and leaves its record on the tape, and the adjustments necessary to assure this are relatively easy. The heart of this apparatus is a block of wood with a slot for the waxed-paper tape (see Fig. 3). The wood has two bolts in it that almost meet in the slot and which form the high-voltage spark gap. The ends of the two bolts are ground to be hemispheres and can be threaded closer together or farther apart as needed to optimize the spark. Two strips of flexible plastic (cut from a bleach bottle) serve as a low-friction funnel to guide the tape into the spark gap. The spark gap is mounted on a vertical board in such a way as to be about one meter above the

floor, and an "alligator" paper clip is mounted about one meter directly above the gap to hold the end of the tape (prior to dropping).

This device has been in service at Rockhurst for three years and has given no trouble at all. Students usually get their data tapes made in just a few minutes, and the number of "failures" is very small. Typical student results for the acceleration due to gravity are within one percent of the accepted value. Moreover, the apparatus is inexpensive and easily constructed: the prototype of the pictured device was assembled in just a few hours by the young man in Fig. 1, and (though rougher in appearance than the device pictured) it worked quite well. If you already have a spark timer, this arrangement has much to recommend it.

Free-Fall Measurement with a Solenoid as Starting Device

Fritz Schoch and *Walter Winiger*, Kantonsschule, Heerbrugg, Ch-9435, Switzerland

I f a solenoid is used as a starting device for a sphere (ball bearing) in a free-fall apparatus, there is a problem with the residual magnetism of the iron core of the magnet. Unwanted magnetic forces will act on the falling sphere as the body starts to fall (Fig. 1).

To gain some knowledge about this phenomenon, we measured the falltime t_f as a function of the initial current (I) through the solenoid. The extrapolation to $I = 0$ gave t_{fo}, which in turn gave a reasonably accurate value for g (Fig. 2).

t_{fo} was calculated with a linear regression function $I = I_{min} = 82$ mA was about the smallest current possible just to

hold the sphere.

With the height h = 2.759 m and $t_{fo} = 0.750$ s we got 9.81 ms^{-2} which is about 0.5% greater than the local g value of 9.806 ms^{-2}. If we take into account air resistance and buoyancy, we get 9.84 ms^{-2} which is about 3% greater than the official value. This indicates that the extrapolation to $I = 0$ does not yield a perfect t_{fo}, which is also expected for physical reasons.

Nevertheless, our results are better than those obtained if no extrapolation had been made, that is, if we had taken the falltime t_{f1} corresponding to I_{min}.

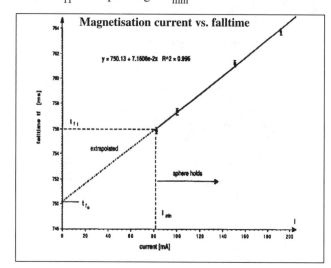

Fig. 1. Magnetic starting device for free-fall apparatus. The watch starts when switch S is closed.

Fig. 2. Graph of current I vs falltime t_f.

The Falling Monkey Problem

William Gombka and *Joseph Steigauf,* Morristown High School, 50 Early St., Morristown, NJ 07960

Every college and most high school physics students have encountered the "falling monkey" problem, but unless the school can afford the $200-plus price tag for the equipment, the students have to rely on the instructor's word that it works. Few actually get to see the "monkey" hit by the "bullet" that is fired at the precise time the monkey drops from a tree.

We have lowered the cost considerably by buying inexpensive items from local stores and modifying equipment intended for other uses.

The dart gun shown in Fig. 1, was purchased at a local toy store for under $5. The contacts, that will form the switch and gapped with a piece of aluminum foil, are the brushes from an old "St. Louis" motor (thin copper or phosphor bronze strips).

The monkey, which happens to be a bear in our case, is cut from plywood (Fig. 2). The solenoid was secured from a local electronics company but could be homemade. Our dc power source is standard physics equipment. So, for a total of about $20 we have put together a demonstration that never ceases to amaze students.

In setting up the demonstration, the dart gun, in its holder, is clamped to the side of a cabinet. The "monkey," in its holder, is clamped to another cabinet about two meters away. The best location both vertically and horizontally can be determined by firing the gun a few times to get a general idea of how far the dart travels.

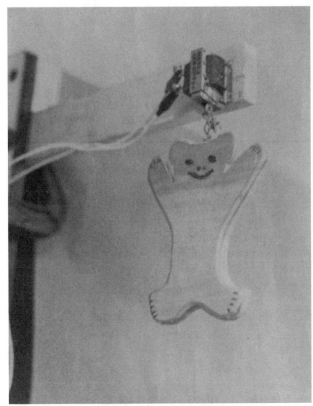

Fig. 2. The monkey being held in place by the solid core of the activated solenoid.

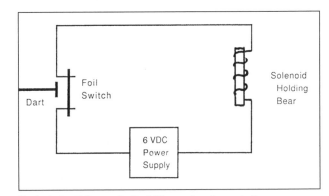

Fig. 3. A circuit diagram for the falling monkey demonstration.

Bell wire can be used to connect the circuit shown in Fig. 3. In our case, we modified an old 3-m (10-ft) extension cord. The ends were soldered to the "St. Louis" brush connections and to alligator clips.

Critical to the entire operation is the switch. By gapping the "St. Louis" brushes with a piece of aluminum foil (Fig. 1), a convenient switch is put into the circuit. As the dart is

Fig. 1. The dart gun mounted and ready to fire. The aluminum foil switch is in place across the "St. Louis" motor brushes.

Fig. 4. The dart gun clamped in an old electric rotator base and elevated at an angle of 30°.

fired, the circuit is opened and the solenoid is turned off, dropping the "monkey."

Minor adjustments to the flight of the dart can be made manually if it is found that the dart is missing the "monkey" either to the left or the right.

Further refinements are possible using a universal mount from an old telescope or an electric rotator base. The gun can be attached to the universal mount and placed on the counter (Fig. 4). The firing angle can then be changed to show that the dart will still hit the monkey. If this variation is tried, it is critical to make sure that the gun is aimed directly at the monkey when the dart is fired.

By measuring the horizontal and vertical distances from the gun to the point where it strikes the "monkey," the initial velocity of the dart can be determined.

A Simple Ink-Jet Gravimeter

J.G. Street, James Fung-A-Fat, and J. E. Faller, Joint Institute for Laboratory Astrophysics, University of Colorado and National Institute of Standards and Technology, Boulder, CO 80309-0440

Elementary textbooks usually devote a large and often early-in-the-book section to the discussion of gravity and gravitation. Because of the familiarity of the idea and also because the free-fall acceleration due to gravity, g, is a useful physical constant, its measurement constitutes a part of many beginning physics courses. The free-fall acceleration due to gravity varies with latitude ($g = 979.608$ cm/s in Boulder, Colorado) and also depends on height (distance from the center of the Earth), as well as on the local rock density and geological situation (mountains, etc.). Because of its usefulness as a geophysical and geological tool and its value in looking for vertical-height changes, the measurement of absolute gravity has evolved to the point where instruments now exist that can measure g at the parts in 10^9 level (a sensitivity of about one cm in height).

Most students learn about gravity from a textbook, supplemented by a pendulum (Galileo-type, "free-fall") experiment that depends on a formula for the period, which is the end product of a reasonable amount of algebra. A true free-fall experiment carried out at other than the most primitive level requires some sort of apparatus. The physics department at the University of Colorado has developed and made their own free-fall apparatus at a cost of between $500 and $600 by utilizing the department's shop facility. Although a commercial direct free-fall apparatus does exist,[1] its cost

probably puts it out of the budget range of all but a few high-school science departments. Large universities can afford to purchase this type of apparatus or have facilities to build one (as did the University of Colorado). However, because "gravity" is something that college students are familiar with and "understand," a free-fall apparatus's usefulness is perhaps more significant at earlier levels of science teaching. The research reported in this paper resolves the apparatus dilemma that faces many high-school and secondary-education science instructors by providing the basis of an easily constructed and inexpensive free-fall apparatus capable of measuring gravity to 0.1 percent accuracy.

The Basic Idea

An ink-jet print head (from a Hewlett-Packard printer) is triggered to discharge small drops of ink at equal time intervals (every 1/60th of a second). A strip of paper attached to a long and rigid mass (long to allow for an adequate data record and rigid to allow for streamlined fall—a 12-in steel ruler will do nicely) is dropped through the ink shower, thus creating a record of spatially separated dots on the paper. Because the mass is accelerating due to gravity, the dots of ink are increasingly further apart as the ruler falls, providing a record of position of the ruler vs time. By measuring the (changing) spacing between the dots, the acceleration of

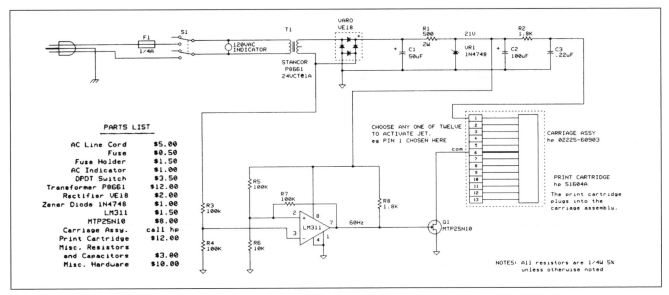

Fig. 1. Circuit diagram for ink-jet gravimeter.

gravity, g, can be determined.

The Necessary Parts

The electrical components for this gravimeter can be purchased at any electronics store. If you have trouble finding the field-effect Transistor (FET) we have listed, any 30-VFET will work. The ink jet (HP 51604A), however, must be ordered from Hewlett-Packard (approximately $11). It is convenient (for purposes of mounting and hooking it up) to also order the carriage assembly (HP 02225-60903). The additional $11 is money well spent, since it will make life a lot easier. The total parts cost for this ink-jet gravimeter is under $60. Individual component prices are shown on the schematic diagram (Fig. 1).

Hewlett-Packard's Ink Jet, also known as their Think Jet or Thermal Ink Jet,[2] discharges ink by means of boiling it, using the heat of a small resistor. This resistor is extremely finicky about the voltage needed to squirt the ink: 22.73 ± 0.21 V. Because it requires distinct pulses, the circuit needed must produce a 60-Hz square wave to drive the FET, which in turn produces the desired ink pulses. A transformer (Stancor P8661) is used to step down the 120-V line voltage to 24 V. A bridge consisting of four diodes rectifies the current, and a 50-μF capacitor filters it. A zener diode sets the voltage to 21 V. Another capacitor (0.224 μF) filters the current again, and a voltage divider sets the voltage. Finally a comparator (which compares a set voltage with the line voltage) creates the 60-Hz square wave.

The ac wall outlet serves the dual purpose of being the power source and the frequency regulator to cause the ink jet to discharge at equal time intervals. The circuit diagram is shown in Fig. 1.

The Actual Measurements

Using the ink-jet gravimeter is simple. After dropping the ruler past the ink jet, one needs only to measure the distances between dots and then apply the simple formula $g = (S_2 - S_1) \, 60^2$, where S_1 is an interval between two dots and S_2 is the next interval. After calculating g for all the intervals on the strip of paper (which should give 10 to 12 values if the record is a foot long), an average of the values yields the final result.

The derivation of the formula simply uses the fundamental free-fall equation

$$S = \tfrac{1}{2}gt^2 + V_0 t \qquad (1)$$

Considering two adjacent intervals, S_1 and S_2, and their sum S^*, we see that

$$S_1 - \tfrac{1}{2}gt^2 + V_0 t \qquad (2)$$

$$S_1 + S_2 \equiv S^* =$$

$$\tfrac{1}{2}g(2t)^2 + V_0 \,(2t) \qquad (3)$$

To eliminate the V_0, we subtract

$$S^* - 2S_1 = gt^2 \qquad (4)$$

or

$$S_1 + S_2 - 2S_1 =$$

$$S_2 - S_1 = gt^2 \qquad (5)$$

Rearranging, we get

$$g = (S_1 - S_2)t^{-2} \qquad (6)$$

and since $t = 1/60$ s, we finally get

$$g = (S_1 - S_2)\, 60^2 \qquad (7)$$

We did several things to improve on the accuracy of the results. Because the data record is only a foot long (you may want to try a longer ruler for a longer record), careful measurements of the displacements are critical; we used standard calipers, readable to 0.001 inches. More important, we found that we got significantly better results when we used a smooth (burn) release technique. We suspended the ruler by a thread, waited until the ruler was stable (no longer swinging), and then burned the string. This method releases the ruler much more evenly than a manual or clamp release (which gave 1.3 percent accuracy). With the burn release, we obtained a value of 978.6 cm/s^2 for g. The accepted reference value for gravity at Boulder, Colorado's altitude is 979.6 cm/s^2, giving us an accuracy of 0.1 percent.

We also investigated the distance from the ink jet beyond which its accuracy is substantially deteriorated. Although we recommend that you drop the ruler as close to the ink jet as possible, the ink squirts maintain their integrity up to 15 mm away. It is important that the entire ruler falls at an equal distance from the ink jet. A twisting and/or tumbling of the ruler while falling will affect the quality of the results.

We hope that this simple and low-cost, ink-jet-based, absolute-gravity measuring device will find broad application because of both its simplicity and the accuracy of measurement obtainable.

Acknowledgments

Author J.G. Street thanks the Undergraduate Opportunities Program at the University of Colorado for the stipend granted to him to work on this project.

References

1. See Central Scientific Company 1990 Catalog, p. 41.
2. *Hewlett Packard Journal*, May 1985.

A Hand-Held, Milk-Carton Accelerometer

John F. Koser, Wayzata Public Schools, 305 Vicksburg Lane, Plymouth, MN 55447-3999

A simple accelerometer for use in amusement park physics activities is described in this note. This accelerometer was student tested at the Minnesota Valleyfair Physics Day in Burnsville, Minnesota.

Henry (Ted) Hale IV, a physics teacher from Blake Upper School in Minneapolis, had earlier designed an accelerometer consisting of a mass attached to a flat piece of spring steel with the opposite end secured to the inside of a rectangular frame so the mass could move in a vertical plane in response to vertical acceleration. If the device was held with the spring steel in a vertical position, the mass would move horizontally when accelerated in the horizontal plane. Calibration was accomplished by holding the frame so that the piece of spring steel was horizontal and marking the position of the mass on a background as its weight deformed the cantilever. This was "one g" or one times the acceleration due to gravity. By inverting the frame, one g in the opposite or negative direction was calibrated. By checking the deformation of a cantilever beam, it was found that the deformation is almost linear with force, so the calibration for one g could be used to calibrate two, three, and four g's accordingly on the same background.

New Developments

While debating ways that students could build inexpensive accelerometers, my colleague (Mike Thorud) and I decided to find a way to make the "Ted Hale 1987 Accelerometer" easy and cheap to construct by large numbers of students as they prepared for our amusement park activity.

The first modification was to find a readily available substitute for the piece of spring steel. I found that the local hobby store carried a supply of several sizes of piano wire so I selected 0.038-cm (0.015-in) diameter wire, the smallest diameter available. By bending this wire in a square-cornered "U" with approximately 10-cm legs and about 0.50 cm in width, a stable (in one plane) substitute for the spring steel piece was constructed. Furthermore, the cost of 0.91 m (3.0 ft) of the wire was all of ten cents.

For a mass, I selected a seven-gram (one-quarter-oz) "split-shot" fishing sinker from my tackle box and squeezed it on the short cross piece of the "U" bend of fine piano wire. Now I had a weight which, if the opposite end from the "U" bend was clamped firmly, would oscillate in a plane, either vertically or horizontally, depending how it

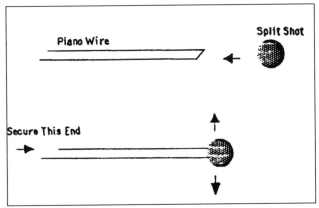

Fig. 1. Pinch the split shot on the crossbar of the bent piano wire. It will bow in one plane but not the other if the free end is secured.

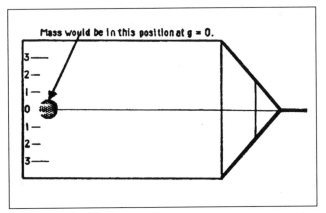

Fig. 3. In this position, the accelerometer will measure vertical acceleration. Depending on the size of split shot chosen, calibrations can be made to four or five g's.

was suspended (Fig. 1).

With a functional spring-mounted swinging weight to indicate acceleration horizontally or vertically, the next obstacle to overcome in creating an inexpensive, easily constructed accelerometer was a modified design for a frame. Hale's had a Plexiglas frame that was neither inexpensive nor easy to construct, although it worked well. Mike Thorud's creative mind saw the ideal container/frame in half of a milk carton. Our next project was to dream up a method of mounting the spring-loaded mass in the milk carton frame. Figure 2 shows the configuration.

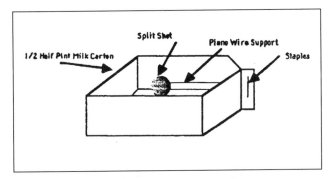

Fig. 2. Assemble the spring mass in a previously cut-in-half school milk carton by first opening the top end and then securely stapling it shut where the piano wire ends pass through.

Calibration

With some checking in an engineering text, it was found that the bending of a cantilever is basically the kind of deformation that the little accelerometer will undergo when a force acts on its suspended mass. Since the vertical defor-

mation (within elastic limits) of the free end of the beam is basically linear in response to the applied force, the calibrations (which are written on the inside of the half milk carton) could easily be determined using gravity to deform the springy wires. In this manner the position of "one g" could be obtained. It was easy then to calibrate the accelerometer in the opposite direction and add calibrations to the expected three or four times gravitational acceleration. In the diagram in Fig. 3, the calibrations are shown with the accelerometer in the vertical position.

Value and Use of the Accelerometer

While the device has the shortcoming that the mass oscillates when in motion, it is possible to see the extreme of the oscillation when it responds to a changing acceleration that reaches a maximum and then decreases. One must approximate the acceleration value, but approximations to the nearest 0.5 g are adequate for amusement park physics applications.

Since the cost for one unit is about three cents for materials and some time, this is a project that anyone could attempt, or that could be attempted in large groups. While it is clear that improvements to this little gadget could be made (possibly some form of damping could be added, or the calibration could be made more precise), it does function. This accelerometer had been "tested under fire" and works quite well, giving reasonable values for the conditions on a fast-moving roller coaster (about four g's at the bottom of the steepest hill). Mike Thorud has definitely improved the device beyond my modifications and certainly made it feasible from the cost and ease of construction points of view. His ingenuity in recognizing a bisected milk carton as a frame provided the spark for this note. What improvements would others suggest?

Accelerometers for Use on an Overhead Projector

Robert Ehrlich, Department of Physics, George Mason University, Fairfax, VA 22030

Inexpensive accelerometers having a strictly mechanical design exist for such purposes as registering the maximum force of impact on packages during shipment, or the acceleration of physics students on amusement park rides—some such designs in fact can be made for only pennies.[1] But our interest here is in accelerometers of simple design that can be moved by hand on an overhead projector and will reveal when their acceleration equals or exceeds a certain value. A basic component in both designs is a small cylindrical plastic box of a type easily obtained from pharmacies, optometrists, and scientific equipment companies.[2]

Ball-on-Washer Accelerometer

The first design is sketched in Fig. 1(a). A small steel washer (hole diameter d) is glued to the bottom center of the plastic box. A stainless steel ball (of diameter D) will be placed atop the washer. If the cylindrical box is placed on a flat horizontal surface and accelerated with a constant acceleration a, we can use Newton's Second Law to predict for what magnitude acceleration of the box the ball will fall off the washer. The combination of the vertical weight of the ball, mg, and the horizontal noninertial force $-ma$ acts along the angle with the vertical given by $\tan \theta = a/g$. The net force on the ball no longer is a *restoring* force when $\tan \theta$ exceeds the value d/D. Thus, we expect the ball should fall off the washer when the acceleration satisfies

$$a > g \tan \theta = g \tan\left(\frac{d}{D}\right) \tag{1}$$

In effect, the ball-washer device should act like a threshold accelerometer, which triggers at the acceleration given in Eq. (1), at least in the case of constant accelerations. We used washer hole and ball diameters given by $d = 0.0035$ m and $D = 0.0254$ m, so that the ball should fall off the washer when the horizontal acceleration of the device exceeds $0.14\ g$. In principle, we could check whether Eq. (1) holds for such a device by placing it on a uniformly accelerated

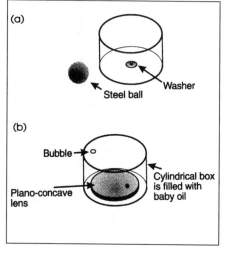

Fig. 1. Two accelerometers for use on overhead projectors. (a)—ball-on-washer design uses small washer (hole diameter $d = 0.0035$ m) glued to bottom of plastic cylindrical box, and stainless steel ball (diameter $D = 0.0254$ m). (b)—ball-on-lens design uses plano-concave lens (radius $r = 0.0286$ m, radius of curvature $R = 0.0872$ m) glued to bottom of plastic cylindrical box that is filled with baby oil. Small stainless steel ball rolls on concave side of lens. Bubble forms in oil at the top of the box and moves in direction opposite that of ball.

cart on an air track and varying the acceleration using hanging weights. However, a static calibration of the device can be done even more simply by placing it on an inclined plane whose tilt is slowly increased to see if the ball rolls off when the angle

$$\theta = \tan^{-1}\left(\frac{d}{D}\right).$$

However, our main interest is in developing an accelerometer for use on an overhead projector, where it is not possible to produce and observe *sustained* uniform accelerations. Two types of motions that can be *approximated* by simple hand motions of the accelerometer on an overhead projector are uniform circular motion (UCM) and simple harmonic motion (SHM). To approximate both types of motion, it helps to synchronize the hand movements with the beat of a metronome set to the desired frequency $\omega = 2\pi f$. For UCM it also helps if the accelerometer is moved along a circle drawn on a transparency, or perhaps touching the inside of an embroidery hoop. In the case of UCM, we would expect to find a constant magnitude acceleration given by $a = \omega^2 r$, and for SHM an acceleration whose magnitude varies linearly with the displacement x according $a = \omega^2 x$. Thus, assuming we could achieve SHM exactly, we would expect that when the accelerometer is moved back and forth with a frequency ω with an increasing amplitude, the ball would stay on the washer as long as the amplitude x satisfied

$$x < \frac{a}{\omega^2} = \frac{g}{\omega^2} \tan\left(\frac{d}{D}\right) \tag{2}$$

In practice, however, the ball usually falls off when the acceleration is no more than about 70 percent of the predicted value. In part, such a discrepancy is a result of an inability to achieve a very close approximation to SHM (or UCM) by simple hand motions. For example, suppose that it is possible to maintain a uniform angular velocity to within ± 20 percent of the desired value with a hand motion. The centripetal acceleration, which depends on the *square* of the angular velocity, would then be constant to no better than about ±40 percent. Hence, under these assumptions, when we move the device by hand so as to have a centripetal acceleration that is 70 percent of the predicted value needed to trigger it, we would find that it is nevertheless triggered after a while because of the 40 percent uncertainty in the acceleration.

Ball-on-Lens Accelerometer

Our second design is shown in Fig. l(b). The device consists of a –3.0 diopter plano-concave lens glued to the bottom of a cylindrical box, whose diameter is about a centimeter larger than that of the lens. A small stainless steel ball is free to roll on the concave surface of the lens. The box is filled with baby oil to damp the oscillations of the ball when it rolls across the lens. Unlike the ballwasher design, which is strictly a threshold accelerometer, the ball-lens design gives an indication of the acceleration (both magnitude and direction) for any value up to a certain maximum that brings the ball to the edge of the lens.

The direction of the acceleration of the device is, of course, opposite to that of the motion of the rolling ball. If you are lucky, a small bubble will form when the device is filled with oil. The direction of motion of the bubble during accelerations is, of course, opposite that of the ball, and in the same direction as the acceleration of the device. (Unfortunately, however, the position of the bubble cannot be used as an indicator of the acceleration magnitude.) An important feature of the design of the device is that the lens diameter is about a centimeter less than the cylindrical box. As a result, when the ball rolls past the edge of the lens it rests in the gap between the lens and the box wall, where it stays until it is manually popped out. Thus, the device not only triggers at a certain threshold acceleration (ball rolling off lens), but it also gives an indication of the acceleration up to the threshold value.

When the ball-lens accelerometer accelerates uniformly with an acceleration a, its equilibrium position on the lens is located at a distance from the center, x, where the tangent of the angle with the horizontal is $\tan \theta = a/g$. If we use the small angle approximation ($\tan \theta \approx \sin \theta = x/R$), where R is the radius of curvature, we see that $a = g(x/R)$. The direct proportionality between x and a in the previous equation shows that the ball's equilibrium distance from the center of the lens is a true indicator of the horizontal acceleration of the device. (In general, the ball does not remain at that equilibrium position, but oscillates about it, which is why a damping fluid is necessary.)

Conclusion

The ball-washer accelerometer has the advantage of using simpler components, and its triggering at the threshold acceleration is more unambiguous. The ball-lens accelerometer has the advantage that it shows both magnitude and direction of accelerations up to the triggering value—the point at which the ball rolls off the lens. When moved by hand in approximate SHM or UCM, both accelerometer versions trigger at accelerations that are roughly 70 percent of the predicted value, owing to an inability to accurately control hand-sustained motions to better than around 20 percent.

References
1. V. Langland, "Accelerometers 2¢ each," *Phys. Teach.* **32**, 309 (1994).
2. Companies such as Carolina Biological, Sigma Scientific, or Fisher Scientific can supply such boxes (used for biological specimens) for under a dollar each if ordered in quantity.

Magnetic Damping of a Mass-Spring Accelerometer

David Simmons, St. John's Jesuit High School, 5901 Airport Highway, Toledo, OH 43615 *and*

Robert R. Speers, Firelands College of Bowling Green State University, 901 Rye Beach Road, Huron, OH 44839

Education based on theoretically derived predictions of the "vertical" g-environments of swings, slides, and roller coasters may be sufficient for the abstract and mathematically inclined student. But students' memories tend to be eternally altered when they simultaneously experience and measure g-environments in exciting situations. An excellent perspective of opportunities for enhanced learning in an amusement park with very inexpensive (dollars/instrument) instantaneous reading mechanical instrumentation is given by Escobar[1] (instrumentation available, for instance, from PASCO scientific[2]). A more expensive, recently developed recording accelerometer/data logger/graphing calculator system was discussed by Reno and Speers.[3] The equipment is available from TI and Vernier Software.[4]

The two approaches are complementary. The mass-spring accelerometer is affordable (about $2) for all students and schools. It is a highly efficient learning instrument since its visible display correlates directly with the perceived g-environment. Although the accelerometer/CBL/graphing

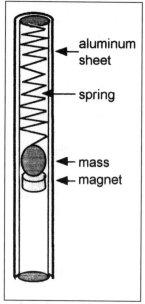

Fig. 1. Damped vertical accelerometer.

calculator system yields more precise data, it is most useful for more advanced students who have well-developed concepts of rollercoaster g-environments and their effects on masses (like brains and stomachs).

The simple mass-spring accelerometer is useful for measuring data that changes no more rapidly than once every five seconds. However, newer roller coasters (for example the Raptor and Mantis at Cedar Point Amusement Park in Ohio) have g-environments so dynamic as to render the simple mass/spring accelerometer nearly useless. The Mantis, for example, includes six major elements including four inversions in less than a minute. The essentially undamped mass/indicator badly overshoots maximum and minimum readings and often goes into resonant oscillation. Our students reported that reading the vertical accelerometer on the Mantis is "impossible." We therefore sought to improve the mass-spring accelerometer by reducing the excess vibration via damping.

A Dampening Damping Experience

Early attempts at damping concentrated on filling the tube with a fluid more viscous than air. Water seemed to be the simplest and safest alternative. However, a water-filled PASCO accelerometer was overdamped and did not accurately record maximum and minimum values. An accidental extreme squeezing of the tube resulted in a wet face during one of the experiments, and a dampening of the experimenter and his enthusiasm for trying more exotic liquids. Informal discussions with several physics teachers at the 1996 Physics Day at Cedar Point revealed that their successes using water, alcohol, and oil were mixed at best. One teacher stated that he liked the results obtained with oil but hated the cleanup. It was suggested that a dense gas (sulfur hexafloride) might provide some damping with a "dry" environment. A mass shape with greater aerodynamic resistance would also be beneficial.

Magnetic Damping

Experience with the Lenz's Law apparatus (wherein the movement of a magnet down an electrically conductive tube is retarded by the magnetic field generated by the current

flow induced in the tube) motivated us to modify the mass/spring accelerometer by adding a neodymium magnet[5] the mass and surrounding it with a conducting foil, sheet, or tube. The amount of conducting foil, sheet, or tube was varied to accomplish the desired amount of damping. (A first-order "analysis" of the effect is to assume that the circumferential Faraday Effect voltage would be constant for a given speed of the magnet, the current would vary as V/R, and therefore the dynamic resistance should vary directly with the reciprocal of the sheet resistance of the tube.)

In the experiments we describe here, the common factors are a simple linear spring[6] and a mass composed of a neodymium magnet epoxied to the bottom of a 9-g sinker (see Fig. 1). For a cheap and easy proof of concept, we wrapped one, two, three, and four thicknesses of heavy household aluminum foil around most of the plastic tube. Noticeable damping was observed, although it was insufficient for the purpose desired.

To enhance the effect, we tried thicker aluminum in the form of a 35-cm long x 19-mm diameter aluminum tube. We sawed a 25-cm cut along the length of the tube, inserted a plastic pointer through the cut, and epoxied the pointer to the bottom of the magnet. Then we calibrated the accelerometer by marking the location of the pointer on the tube as 1 g, doubling the hanging mass and marking the location of the pointer as 2 g, tripling the mass and marking the location of the pointer as 3 g, and so on. This device had a response time of about 0.3 s but was overdamped. The desired response (often called "optimum response") is a bit of overshoot and then rapid relaxation to the final reading, so we made additional cuts along the length of the tube in an effort to reduce the damping. This failed because the tube became too weak. In a more successful fabrication, we thinned a tube with a lathe until the desired optimal response was achieved.

In yet another attempt to achieve the desired instrument, we cut rectangles from aluminum sheet and partially encircled the outside of the magnet/mass-spring accelerometer with the aluminum. Varying amounts of damping of the vibration were easily obtained by varying the thickness of the aluminum sheet, the number of sheets wrapped around the plastic tube, and the percentage of circumferential "wrap." The ease of changing the amount of effect of the conducting sheet allows the user to easily compensate for different magnetic field strengths of available neodymium magnets. The combination that yielded optimal response for us used 0.02-in-thick aluminum sheet wrapped approximately three-fifths of the way around the tube. In order to achieve a range of -1 g to $+5$ g, the standard spring was shortened by approximately one-fifth. The unit was calibrated by measuring the weight of the sinker and magnet on a scale, orienting the accelerometer horizontally, and marking the accelerometer tube at the location of the magnet when it was pulled horizontally with a force of zero, one, two, three, four, and five times the weight of the sinker and magnet. The -1 g mark was obtained by extrapolating back one unit from the zero mark. The useful operation of the unit was confirmed via video recording of the unit on the Raptor roller coaster and subsequent playback in slow motion.[7]

Summary

When Physics Day students reported that the popular amusement park physics mass-spring vertical accelerometer was virtually impossible to read in the highly dynamic g-environments of recent roller coasters, we experimented with various means of obtaining damping. The best system achieved the damping via eddy current losses induced by a neodymium magnet that was epoxied to the mass/sinker in aluminum sheet wrapped around the accelerometer.

References

1. Carole Escobar, *Phys. Teach.* **28**, 446 (1990).
2. PASCO scientific, 10101 Foothills Boulevard, Roseville, CA 95678.
3. Charles Reno and Robert Speers, *Phys. Teach.* **33**, 382–384 (1995).
4. Texas Instruments Calculator Division, 7800 Banner Drive, Dallas, TX 75251; Vernier Software, 8565 SW Beaverton Hillsdale Highway, Portland, OR 9722-52429.
5. Arbor Scientific, P.O. Box 2750, Ann Arbor, MI 48106-2750.
6. Ref. 2, catalog #ME-8734.
7. We wish to thank the personnel of Cedar Point for assistance with this measurement.

Simple Corner Reflectors Improve Data from Sonic Motion Detectors

R. A. Morse, St. Albans School, Washington, DC 20016

An annoying problem with real-time graphing of kinematic quantities using ultrasonic motion detectors[1] is the presence of spikes in the graphs. These spikes typically occur when the reflecting surface does not return the pulse to the transducer because it is not normal to the beam or because it is off the center line of the beam. A second problem occurs when trying to use the detector with small, irregularly shaped objects.

I have found that the use of simple corner reflectors makes considerable improvement in the data in both cases. Disposable reflectors can be made simply from index cards and taped onto air track gliders or small electric cars. A larger reflector made from a manila file folder is convenient for students to hold and gives good data even at the extreme ranges of the detector. For experiments using PSSC-style carts, a more durable reflector can be assembled from plywood or insulation board held together with duct tape.

Fig. 1. Corner reflectors mounted on air track glider, toy car, and skate wheel cart. Photo by C. Mannan.

Reference

1. "Motion" by HRM software, available from Queue, Inc., 562 Boston Ave., Bridgeport, CT 06610 and other suppliers.

A Photogate Design for Air Track Experiments

P. F. Hinrichsen, Physics Department, John Abbott College, Ste. Anne de Bellevue, Quebec, Canada H9X 3L9

The standard design of photogates[1,2] for use with air tracks consists of a photoresistor, photodiode, or photodarlington, which detects the light from a 12-V lamp, or an infrared LED. These components are usually mounted about 7 cm apart, on a rectangular frame which clips over the air track, or on a stand. This arrangement suffers from a number of disadvantages.

a) Students sometimes misjudge the clearance, and the gliders then hit and move the gate. The magnetic tape used with the air pulley has to be threaded through the gate, and it usually manages to wrap itself around the phototransistor.

b) The frame of the gate covers the scale on the side of the air track, making it difficult to determine the precise position at which the glider interrupts the beam.

c) The time for which the beam is interrupted is determined by the length of that part of the glider that is at the height of the beam, and this can change when accessories are attached to the glider. This difficulty could be eliminated by attaching a flag to the top of the glider, but this is rarely done.

d) However, the two main disadvantages of the currently used photogates are that they are sensitive to sunlight, and that when the glider is moving with low velocity the output pulse has a slowly rising edge, which does not reliably trigger some "counter-timers." In combination, these effects make it difficult to determine immediately if the photogate, the counter-timer, or neither is at fault when a student complains!

The sensitivity to sunlight can be eliminated and a mechanically more convenient package produced if a photo-reflective sensor is used.[3] All the components are then on the same side of

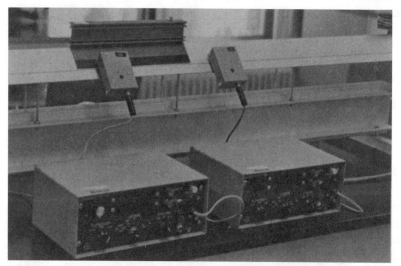

Fig. 1. The setup of two gates, at a spacing equal to the glider length, for acceleration measurements. The black tape on the skirt of the glider triggers the gates.

Fig. 2. The mounting of the photogate on an Ealing air track. The clamp passes under the track, leaving the top of the glider, and the scale on the side of the track unobstructed.

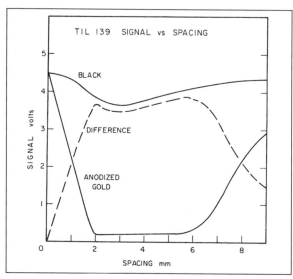

Fig. 3. The output of the TIL 139 as a function of the distance from a gold-anodized glider and from black tape. The useful range is between 1 and 7 mm.

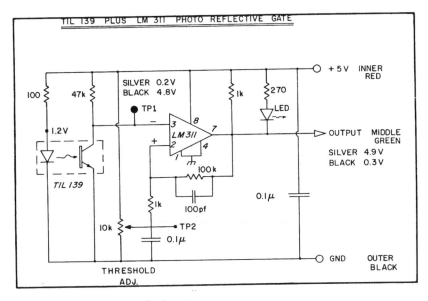

Fig. 4. The circuit of the photo-reflective gate.

the air track and can be mounted together and attached to the air track by means of a clamp that passes under the track, thus leaving free access to the top of the gliders, as shown in Figs. 1 and 2. If the sensor is mounted on the opposite side of the track to the scale, then the position at which the glider triggers the gate can be precisely determined.

The surfaces of the air track and the gliders are good reflectors of infrared, thus black tape attached to the skirt of the glider can be used as a flag. For more sophisticated measurements of velocity and acceleration,[4,5] tapes of alternating black and white bars (available at most stores where drafting supplies are sold) can be used. Although photo-reflective sensors with superior performance are available,[6,7] the TIL 139 was chosen

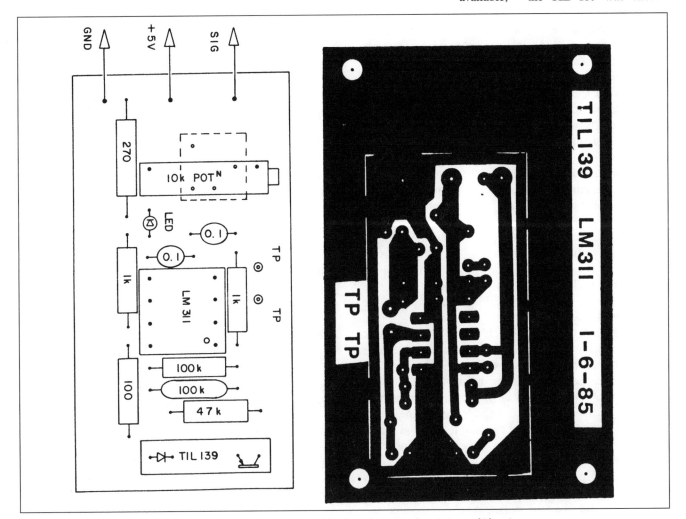

Fig. 5. The foil pattern (full size), and the component layout. Note that provision is made for two alternate types of trimpot.

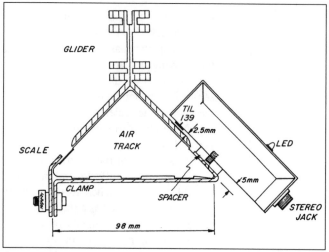

Fig. 6. Dimensions of the mounting on an Ealing air track. The bracket should be strong!

because it is inexpensive and readily available. The signal from a photo-reflecting sensor depends on the reflectivity of the surface and on the distance between the surface and the sensor. A graph of the output of a TIL 139 versus the distance from the surface of a gold-anodized glider is shown in Fig. 3. The thickness of the gliders is 2.4 mm, thus if the sensor is mounted 5 mm from the surface of the air track, both the track and the glider surfaces are within the optimum range. The clearance of 2.6 mm is adequate to avoid any collisions between the gliders and the gate, while being close enough to make the gate completely insensitive to sunlight.

The flag should be at the front of the glider, because the edge can sometimes produce a short unwanted pulse. Different colored gliders give slightly different outputs, and not all the TIL 139s have the same response. For these reasons it was decided to use a trigger circuit with a variable threshold and sufficient hysteresis to avoid multiple triggering on noise. The LM 311 voltage comparator was chosen for low cost, availability, and good documentation.[8,9] The complete circuit, foil pattern, and component layout are shown in Figs. 4 and 5.

The adjustable threshold (~ 2.5 V) can be monitored at the test point. If necessary the hysteresis (140 mV) can be increased by reducing the value of the 100 kΩ resistor. The mounting on an Ealing air track is shown in Fig. 6; however, a considerably smaller package is possible (the minimum size of the circuit is outlined on the foil pattern). The circuit board and stereo phonojack are mounted together on the lid and can be removed for servicing without unclamping the box from the air track.

The LM 311 produces a fast falling edge (from 5.0 V to 0.3 V), and provides sufficient current to drive an LED as well as the output. If a positive output pulse is required, the

inputs (pins 2 and 3) to the LM 311 can be interchanged. The LED has the advantage that one can immediately tell whether the photogate is functioning and allows easy determination of the position at which the glider triggers the gate. It also has the pedagogical advantage of making it clearer to the student exactly how far the glider moves during the measured time interval. The photogates, which cost about $10 for components and box, have proved to be reliable under student use, however, I recommend making the mounting bracket as strong as possible. Some of our students tried to bend the gate away from the air track, to see what makes it work!

The use of two photogates a distance "S" apart, to measure the velocities as V = L/ΔT, and derive the acceleration, can lead to significant systematic errors.[10] This is because L/ΔT is the instantaneous velocity at ΔT/2, not when the middle of the glider is at the gate. The error can be eliminated if two contiguous time intervals are measured, and this can be achieved by adjusting the spacing "S" to be equal to the length of the glider "L." The second gate then starts just as the first stops, and the acceleration is

$$A = (L/\Delta T_2 - L/\Delta T_1)/[(\Delta T_1 + \Delta T_2)/2].$$

This is not only correct, but also simpler to explain, because it is derived from the basic definition of acceleration.

The advent of timers (such as the PASCO model 9215) which have a memory allow both time intervals to be measured with one photogate and timer, thus making the setup both less expensive and more reliable. If the flag has a very small space at its center, i.e., two equal flags with a space just long enough to trigger the gate, then two essentially contiguous time intervals are recorded, and the acceleration can be derived as above.

References

1. The Ealing Corporation, 2225 Massachusetts Ave., Cambridge, MA 02140.
2. PASCO scientific, 1876 Sabre St., Hayward. CA 94545.
3. H.B. Fielding, *Electronics and Wireless World,* Sept. 19 (1984).
4. E.P. Mosco, W.L. Hoffman, and H.H. Tracy, AAPT *Announcer* **12**, (4), 86, JG1 (1982).
5. J. H. Blatt and D.J. Larson, *Am. J. Phys.* **45**, 684 (1977).
6. HP Optoelectronics Division Staff, *Optoelectronics* (McGraw-Hill Publ. Co., NY, 1977).
7. HP 1000 Photo Sensor, Hewlett Packard,1501 Page Mill Road, Palo Alto, CA 94304.
8. P. Horowitz and W. Hill, *The Art of Electronics* (Cambridge University Press, Cambridge, 1980).
9. *Linear Data Book*, (National Semiconductor Corp., 1976).
10. P.F. Hinrichsen, AAPT *Announcer* **13** (4), 101, GG6, (1983).

An Inverted Air Table

Thomas B. Greenslade, Jr., Kenyon College, Gambier, OH 43022

The Daedalon air table[1] has an inverted design in which air is supplied to the pucks from above through flexible hoses. Its advantage is its ability to produce full-scale records of the trajectories of pucks as they travel over the surface; its disadvantage is its cost. Since we had almost all the parts of the table already at hand, Walter Brown, the president of Daedalon, agreed to sell us a pair of pucks, and suggested that we construct the rest of the table ourselves.[2] The resulting table is shown in Fig. 1.

Air from a small compressor flows down the hoses and out holes in the center of the pucks. Flexible conductors running down the tubes are connected to a spark timer. The spark jumps from one puck to a sheet of carbon paper placed under the white paper visible in the photograph, passes through the carbon paper, and back to the second puck. As the spark jumps from the pucks to the carbon paper, black spots of carbon are deposited on the white paper, indicating the positions of the pucks.

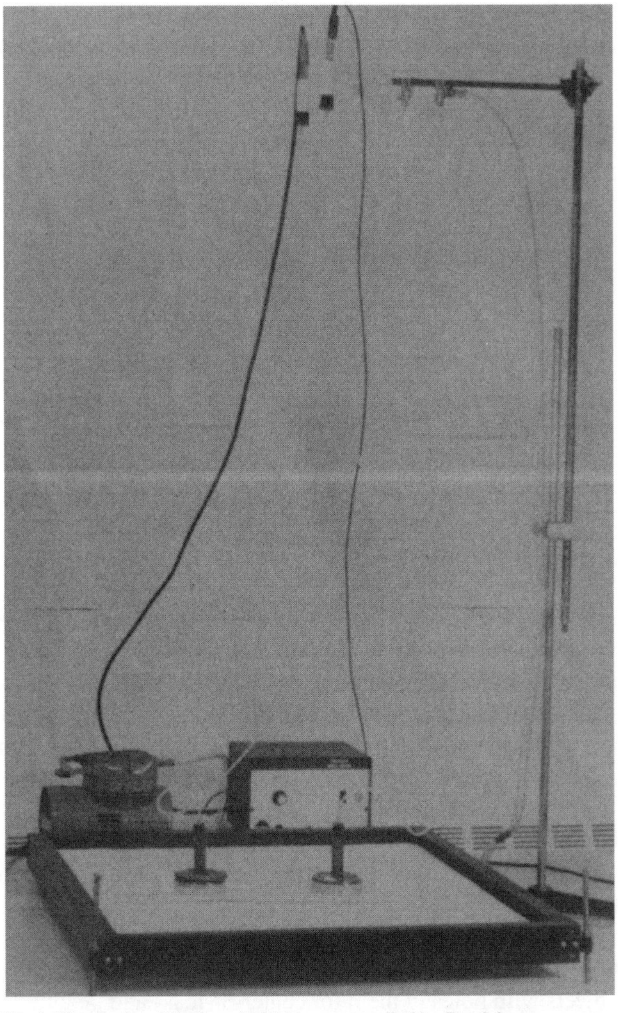

We already had a small air compressor with an output of 0.5 L/s (1 cfm) at a rated pressure of 0.5×10^5 Pa (8 psi). This was originally the air supply for an Ealing air-bearing gyroscope and is described as "the type supplied with small spray outfits." In addition, we had a spark timer which produced 35 kV sparks at rates of 1–60 Hz. Therefore, we had to build the flat surface on which the pucks move and the air-handling manifold shown at the top of the picture. The flat surface is a 60-cm square piece of glass of thickness 0.64 cm (0.25 in) set into a wood frame. One of the three leveling screw assemblies is shown in Fig. 2; a section of door hinge is cut off and the resulting eye is tapped to take the screw.

The air manifold is shown in Fig. 3. The problem here was to get the high potential from the spark timer into the

Fig. 1. The pucks of the inverted table are supplied by Daedalon Corporation; the remainder is locally made or uses commonly available parts. One of the pucks is loaded with lead collars to increase its mass.

Fig. 2. A simple design for a leveling screw.

hoses leading to the pucks. The manifold is made of plastic plumbing pipe of nominal 1/2-in size, and the electrical connections are made through binding posts glued into plugs in the tops of the tees. Daedalon uses and recommends fine gold chain passing down the tubing to the pucks. We experimented with #40 wire with small copper tags soldered to the lower end to make contact with the pucks and have had no problems after one year of use. The tubing is 0.35-cm outside diameter intravenous tubing from the local hospital.

We use this apparatus in a conservation of momentum experiment and in a parabolic motion experiment. In the former, the students study one collision between identical pucks (with one puck initially at rest) and a second collision in which both pucks (one loaded with lead collars to increase its mass) are moving. For the parabolic motion experiment, the table is tilted by a few degrees. One puck is placed in a corner to make a fixed contact to the carbon paper, and the other puck is pushed up at an angle to trace out the parabola. The students are asked to show that the path is a parabola and then analyze the horizontal and vertical components of the motion to see how the velocity varies with time.

Data from the parabolic path can be used to evaluate the magnitude of frictional effects. In a typical experiment, the spark rate was 20 Hz, and forty data points were taken. The horizontal component of the velocity, which can be expected to be constant, started at 24 ± 2 cm/s and ended at 18 ± 2 cm/s, where the uncertainty represents a pessimistic estimate of the error in measuring the horizontal distance

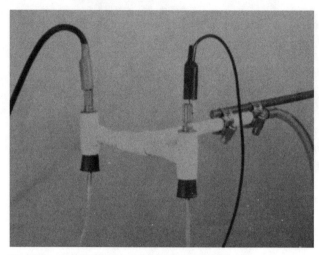

Fig. 3. The air manifold is made of plastic plumbing.

between the dots. The value of the acceleration due to friction effects is thus about 3 cm/s^2; on the way up this acceleration must be subtracted from the component of g down the inclined table, but it is added on the way down.

References
1. The Daedalon air table has been reviewed by Michael Zebarth, *Phys. Teach.* **18,** pp. 681–82 (1980). An improvement in the edge contour of the pucks has been suggested by F.C. Peterson, *Am. J. Phys.* **56**, pp. 473–474 (1988).
2. The cost was $135 for a pair of standard steel pucks.

A Small Air Table

Thomas B. Greenslade, Jr., Department of Physics, Kenyon College, Gambier, OH 43022; greenslade@kenyon.edu

The small, self-contained air table in Fig. 1 was a Christmas present for my two children in about 1975. It was built in an afternoon and evening using only a circular saw and an electric drill, and the cost was quite low. Readers of *The Physics Teacher* may find it useful.

The top is a sheet of Plexiglass™ 36 x 28 cm. Its thickness of 0.1 in (a standard commercial thickness) is enough to keep it from bowing upward due to air pressure, but I would use the 0.2-in thickness if I were to do it again. The holes are drilled with a #50 drill on a 1-cm grid. As I recall, drilling all 945 holes took me less than two hours. Keeping the drill bit cool with water on the surface of the plastic helps to prevent it from grabbing and breaking. The walls of the plenum chamber are 7 cm high, and the top fits into a rabbet around the edges and is secured with small, flathead

screws. The air is supplied by a small blower-fan unit, readily available from surplus dealers. This one is labelled to move 75 cubic feet of air per minute under no load, and its 110-V motor draws 0.30 A. Small screweyes in each corner act as anchor points for a length of thin elastic cord run around the edges; cord from a leftover AAPT meeting badge works well here! Levelling was originally done with shims, but today I would put three levelling screws in the base.

The air pucks are made from thin Plexiglas, and are in the shape of disks of different sizes for collision experiments, a large disk with a small hole in the center for rotation experiments, and various amoebic and rectangular objects with holes in them for center-of-mass and pendulum experiments. A straight pin dropped through a hole in the puck into one of the holes on the table top provides a satisfactory low-friction pivot. The collision disks should be used in pairs, one having a straight edge, and the other having an edge with a "V" profile. This will prevent the disks from digging into the table top when they collide.

If I were to use this air table in the laboratory today, I would videotape various motions, and then analyze them by playing the tape back one frame at a time, marking positions on a piece of acetate taped to the face of the monitor.

For use in projectile motion and pendulum experiments, the table is tilted up with a block of wood through an angle θ. All of the standard experiments can be done, except that g must be replaced by $g \sin θ$.

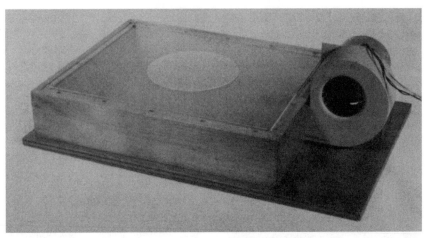

Fig. 1. Homemade air table built in four or five hours with simple tools. Disk to study constant angular velocity pivots on surface by a straight pin.

The center of mass of an irregular body can be determined by hanging the body up by two or more holes drilled in it; "vertical" is indicated by the line of air holes under the body. Once the center of mass is found, a hole is drilled in the body at this point. When the body is pivoted about this hole, it spins freely; alternatively, it is a pendulum with a period of infinity.

Using Magnetic Switches in Motion Experiments

R.C. Nicklin and Robert Miller, Department of Physics and Astronomy, Appalachian State University, Boone, NC 28608

Magnetic switches such as those commonly installed in window security systems are very useful for marking position and time in motion experiments.[1] The switches and their magnets are inexpensive, very reliable, and do not touch the moving object. Typically, in physics experiments the switch is fixed and the magnet moves past it (see Fig. 1). The switch closes when the pole of a magnet gets within about 1 cm and opens when the pole leaves. A computer or other sensing instrument records the times for switch openings and closings. Here are three motion experiments in which we have used magnetic switches.

Inclined Plane

Use silicone caulk to glue a glass tube[2] to a V-groove machined in half-inch square PVC.[3] (The inner diameter of the glass tube must be large enough for a magnet to slide through easily.) As shown in Fig. 2, nylon set screws hold eight magnetic switches next to the glass in holes drilled in the PVC at 1, 4, 9,..., 100 cm. The switches are wired in parallel and each one closes and opens in turn as the magnet slides down the glass tube. The angle of inclination, A, may be varied and is read from a protractor.

The eight switches yield seven time intervals and seven velocities for the sliding magnet. Figure 3 shows

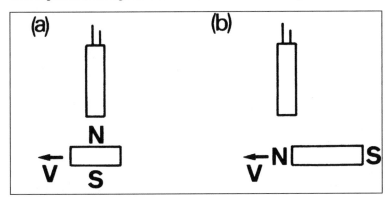

Fig. 1. (a) Disc magnet with poles perpendicular to the disc actuates a switch once; (b) Cylindrical bar magnet actuates a switch twice.

Fig. 2. A cylindrical bar magnet slides through a glass tube past eight switches connected in parallel. Protractor indicates angle of inclination A. The glass tube lies in a V groove along the top edge at the PVC support.

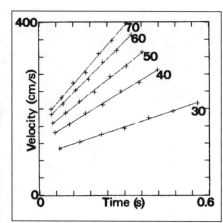

Fig. 3. Data from apparatus in Fig. 2 for angles A of 30° to 70°.

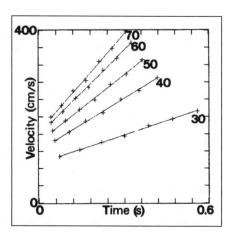

Fig. 4. Relative accelerations a/g from Fig. 3 vs (sin $A - \mu$ cos A) for coefficients of friction μ = 0.25, 0.30, 0.35.

representative velocity-vs-time data for angles A of 30° to 70°. The accelerations are given by the slopes of these lines. Assuming a constant coefficient of friction, μ, the expected acceleration is given by

$$a = g(\sin A - \mu \cos A) \qquad (1)$$

where g is the gravitational acceleration. Although μ, determined from Eq. (1) and data in Fig. 3, varies somewhat with A, Fig. 4 shows how to find a single value ($\mu = 0.30$ here) that represents all the data. The technique is simply to plot experimental values of a/g vs (sin $A - \mu$ cos A) for several values of μ and look for the μ that causes the line to pass through the origin.

Air Track

As shown in Fig. 5, an aluminum glider carries two disk magnets (M) mounted a distance D_1 apart (about 12 cm). A switch rail made from a piece of 3/4-in square PVC has holes drilled 10 cm apart and is attached to the air track. Magnetic switches (S) are placed in the rail a distance D_2 (about 30 cm) apart and are triggered by the magnets as the

glider passes. D_2 should be greater than D_1 in order to make the switching sequence unequivocal.

Average glider velocity at a switch is obtained simply by dividing D_1 by the time interval between switch closings. This arrangement makes it easy to do many traditional experiments with reliable timing, measuring for example: frictional drag along the track (4 switches, 2 magnets, 8 times); momentum loss at end bounce (1 switch, 2 magnets, 4 times); acceleration, and conservation of energy on an elevated track. Studying collisions between gliders is also possible, but it's harder to keep track of the timing sequence.

Sprinting

Apparatus designed to capture position vs time for a sprinter is shown in Fig. 6. The sprinter's feet close switches behind the starting blocks.[4] The first open switch triggers data acquisition. As the sprinter runs, a tape[4] attached to her belt turns an aluminum spool, which carries two disk magnets as diagrammed in Fig. 7. The magnets actuate the magnetic switch. For our setup, the tape interval between switch closings turned out to be 26.5 cm, constant to within about 1% from 0 to 15 m.

Outside diameter for the spool is 20 cm, and 19 cm for the wound-up tape. The spool is mounted on a hardened steel bushing turning on a half-inch shaft. Tape tension is adjusted by squeezing a compression spring, which presses the spool between 1.5-in Teflon thrust bearings. A tension sufficient to keep the spool from freewheeling is not large enough to be felt by the sprinter. The whole spool mechanism may be adjusted vertically on a 3/4-in steel rod attached to a heavy base.

The sprinter's velocity is obtained by dividing the tape interval by successive time intervals. An example is

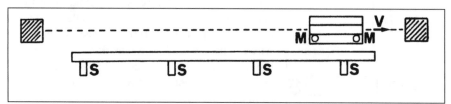

Fig. 5. Top view of air track and gilder. Magnets (M) on glider move past switches (S) mounted on PVC rail attached to track.

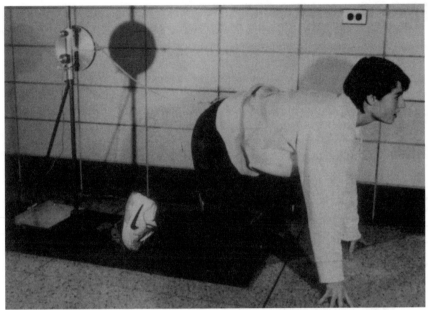

Fig. 6. Measuring tape attached to sprinter turns a spool with two magnets past a switch. Starting blocks also have switches.

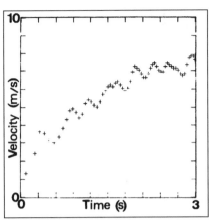

Fig. 8. Typical data from sprint apparatus. Shifting weight from one foot to the other causes the bumps.

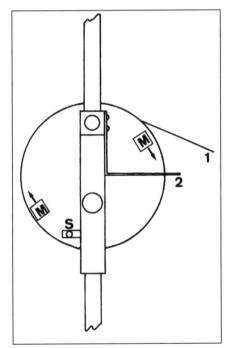

Fig. 7. Spool of Fig. 6 showing magnets (M), switch (S), tape (1), and tape calibration edge (2), which swings out of the way during runs.

given in Fig. 8. The irregularities apparently stem from shifting from one foot to the other. This experiment may be set up in a hallway. Put a "catcher" at the other end to shoo away pedestrians and help the runner stop.

Some Notes

Figure 1(a) shows a disc magnet passing a switch. This is the situation in the air track and

sprinting experiments and results in *one* on/off cycle as the magnet passes. Figure 1(b) shows a cylindrical magnet passing a switch. This arrangement results in *two* on/off cycles as the magnet passes. In this case, use the average of the *first* off and *second* on times to center the magnet on the switch. We routinely use these experiments in our introductory (algebra only) course. Instrumentation consists of MetraByte data-acquisition cards in PC-XT computers (old, but adequate) controlled by programs written in QuickBASIC. The resulting time resolution is about 0.5 ms. For some details on these cards and programs, see Ref. 5.

References

1. Our switches come from Mouser Electronics, 2401 Highway 287 North, Mansfield, TX 76063-4827. Stock #507-AMS-20 I; $2.47 for switch and magnet.
2. We use KIMAX tubing (Kimble) KG-33/80500; 1/2-in o.d., 3/32-in wall.
3. U.S. Plastic Corporation, 1390 Neubrecht Road, Lima, OH 45801; 1/2-in PVC #45069, $0.64/ft; 3/4-in PVC #45071, $1.39/ft.
4. Cannon Sports, Box 11179, Burbank, CA 91510-1179. Official Olympic starting block, $50; 50-m fiberglass measuring tape, RFG165, $17.
5. R.C. Nicklin, *ComputerCraft* **1**, 53 (May/June, 1994).

An Instrument to Show Relative Motion

Stanislaw Bednarek, Department of Physics, University of Lodz, 90-230 Lodz, Poland

One of the basic features of the description of motion is the interdependence of a trajectory and its reference system. The shape of the trajectory in one reference system may be absolutely different in a second reference system. To demonstrate this basic and interesting feature of motion, we have developed a simple instrument that can easily be used during a lecture, with the results immediately visible on the blackboard.

Construction

The basis of the instrument is a rotating wheel (refer to Fig. 1). Make a square hole in the center of a wheel (1), attach a square pivot to the axle (2), and push axle and wheel together with a tight fit to eliminate backlash. Near the edge of the wheel make a round hole into which will go a short pipe (3). Make several such holes along the wheel's radius so that the pipe can be placed at different distances from the axis of rotation. (By this means students can investigate the point trajectories that are not located on the wheel's edge.) Place a weak spring (4) inside the pipe. This spring holds two sharpened pieces of chalk (5) that protrude from either end of the pipe. One piece of chalk will face the blackboard (10), the other faces a transparent (Plexiglas) plate (6) also placed on the axle. Slide a rotating sleeve (8) around the axle, securing it with a nut (7).

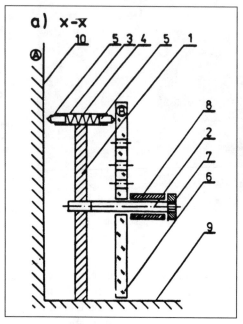

Fig. 1. Construction of reference system instrument. 1—wheel, 2—axle, 3—pipe, 4—spring, 5—chalk, 6—transparent plate, 7—nut, 8—sleeve, 9—blackboard shelf, 10—blackboard plane.

Demonstration

Place the instrument, including the wheel (1) and lower edge of the plate (6) on the chalk ledge (9) of the blackboard. Grasp the sleeve (8) and by hand move the instrument along the ledge; the wheel will roll and the plate will move with the rotating axle. You will see two chalk marks develop—one on the blackboard and one on the transparent plate. (If necessary, you can hold the Plexiglas disk to keep it from turning.)

The vertical plane of the blackboard is the first reference system related to the observer. This system should be marked with the letter A. The moving Plexiglas plate (6), is the second reference system related to the wheel axle, which we mark with the letter B. As you move the instrument, one piece of chalk will draw the trajectory of the point that is located on the wheel edge of system A, the second one on system B. The shape of these trajectories is shown in Figs. 2a and b. In system A the trajectory is a cycloid and in system B a circle. If the pipe (3) is placed in a hole not located near the wheel edge, the trajectory of the point meeting the location of the pipe is an epicycloid in system A and a circle with smaller radius in system B.

Comments

You'll notice that no dimensions for the instrument are given. As a practical matter they depend on what's available. The basic requirement is that there be good visibility by the class, and therefore dimensions should be as large as possible. We made our wheel of Textolite and the see-through plate of Plexiglas. You could use plywood or a bicycle wheel (with a lengthened axle on which to attach the sleeve) for (1). Thanks to the transparency of (6), the chalk drawing of the trajectory is always visible.

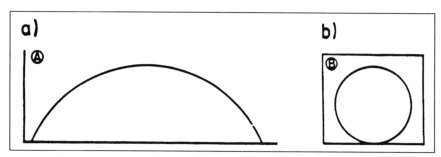

Fig. 2. Trajectory shapes of points on the wheel edge: a) in motionless system, b) in system joined with the wheel axle.

Classroom Foucault Pendulum

John E. Horne, Lecture-Demonstration Facility, Department of Physics, University of Maryland, College Park, MD 20742

Many of us have marveled at the giant pendulum in the Smithsonian Institution in Washington, DC swinging slowly back and forth, precessing clockwise as the Earth turns beneath it, a clear and definitive demonstration that the Earth rotates on its axis. The original such device was demonstrated by Jean Bernard Leon Foucault in 1851.[1–3]

The bobs on some giant Foucault pendulums weigh hundreds of pounds and have supporting wires 200 feet long. These giants give the impression that a Foucault pendulum would be out of reach for a classroom.[4] However, smaller Foucault pendulums have been built for hallway use.[5–9]

The pendulum that I have designed is a nondriver pendulum that can be built in less than an hour, costs very little, and clearly demonstrates Foucault's idea. Best of all, it will work in any classroom during a one-hour class.

Building the Pendulum

You will need:
- One 18-in length of a 2 x 4
- One 4-in length of 5/16-in O.D. copper tubing (3/8-in will also work)
- Eight feet of nylon fishing line
- A bob[10]

Drill a 5/16-in hole centered a half inch from one end of the 2 x 4. Use a drill press in this operation to make sure that the hole is centered and true (Fig. 1A).

Use the copper tubing to make a stabilizing tube. This is simple to make but is a precision device that requires special care and attention during its construction. Remove all burrs from both ends of the tube. Make a mark 3/8 inch from one end of the tube (Fig. 1B). Place a 3-in length of masking tape under the marked-off end (Fig. 1C). Unwind one end of a standard 1-1/4-in paper clip and insert the end into the tube past the 3/8-in mark. Then stick

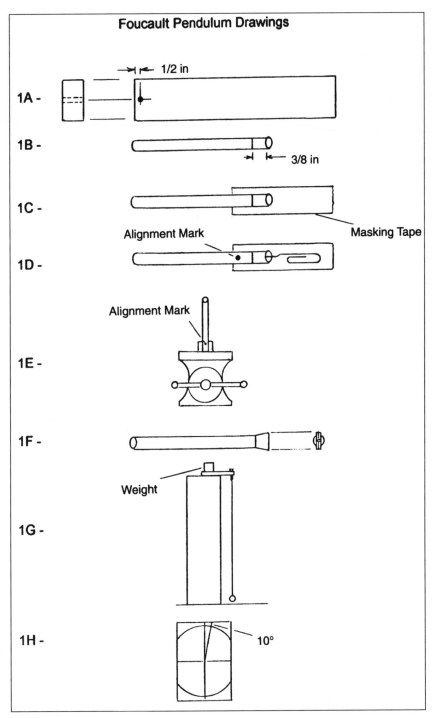

Foucault Pendulum Drawings

1A -
1B -
1C -
1D -
1E -
1F -
1G -
1H -

1/2 in
3/8 in
Alignment Mark
Masking Tape
Alignment Mark
Weight
10°

Fig. 1.

the clip to the masking tape. Make sure that the section of the paper clip inside the tube is lying straight. Put an alignment mark on the tube above the 3/8-in mark and exactly opposite the paper clip (Fig. 1D).

Place the tube assembly vertically in a vise (one that is equipped with "soft jaws") down to the 3/8-in mark. Rotate the tube so that the alignment mark on the tube is toward the front of the vise and the paper clip is toward the back of the vise (Fig. 1E). Tighten the vise and flatten the tube. Don't be stingy with the force.

Take the tube from the vise and pull out the paper clip. The hole should be straight and centered. Straighten the flat end if needed (Fig. 1F). Pay special attention to the opening of the tube on the unflattened end. Make sure that the inside entrance is smooth with absolutely no burrs. A handheld countersink will do a good job to smooth this surface.

Assemble the pendulum by pushing the tube into the hole in the 2 x 4. Thread a length of nylon fishing line into the flattened end of the tube and then tie a knot on this end.

Choose a table, or preferably a tall cabinet, to mount the pendulum. Put the pendulum on the cabinet with 6 or 8 inches of the 2 x 4 hanging over the edge. Place a weight on the 2 x 4 or C-clamp it to the cabinet to keep it from tipping when you attach the bob. Tie the bob to the line keeping the bob an inch or so from the floor. For proper operation, it is very important that the line is hanging centered in the stabilizing tube. Adjust the level of the 2 x 4 if necessary to achieve centering (Fig. 1G).

Using the Pendulum

Draw a cross on a sheet of white 81/2- x 11-in paper. Draw a 10-in diameter circle centered on the cross. The circle will not be continuous. Put a mark at 10° on the circle (Fig. 1H).

Lay the paper on the floor centered under the bob with the long side parallel with the cabinet. Pull the bob 5 or 6 inches outside of the circle and release it so that the bob travels down the center line and parallel with the cabinet. Try to release the bob without exerting any side force since the resultant elliptical path will introduce problems. If the bob does not travel dead center down the line, you can rotate the paper to adjust. However, it may be better to just note where the bob crosses the circle for your starting point.

Use the following method to determine the point that the swinging line crosses the circle. Stand behind the swinging pendulum. Close one eye and observe the line (not the bob) as it crosses the circle. If the line is moving to the right, move your head slightly to the right. If the line is moving to the left, move your head slightly to the left. When you are "right on," the line will cross the circle without movement. That crossing point will be your reading.

Observations

At the latitude of Washington, DC (near the University of Maryland), the pendulum should precess almost 10 degrees in an hour. A 3-in bob on a 6-ft line will easily swing for one hour. A 2-in bob on a 6-ft line will easily swing for a half hour. A precession of 5 degrees (a half hour) is readily apparent. Pay attention when the swing shortens as the bob loses energy. The bob line must touch both sides of the stabilizing tube as it swings, otherwise the pendulum will develop a meaningless elliptical orbit. The single most critical feature of this nondriven Foucault pendulum is the construction and alignment of the stabilizing tube, sometimes called the "Charron ring."

At the Earth's poles, a pendulum's swing will precess 15°/h (360° in 24 h). At the equator, a pendulum will not precess at all. In between the poles and the equator, the swing will precess somewhere between 0°/h and 15°/h, depending on the latitude.[11] The number of degrees of a circle that the Earth will "twist" under a pendulum in 24 h at any given latitude (ϕ) may be determined by the following formula: $n = 360 \sin \phi$ (latitude). Example: At Washington, DC, latitude $\phi = 38°54'$, $\sin \phi = 0.628$, $n = 226°$, or 9.4°/h.[12]

References

1. Emil Fischer and Gottlieb Haberlandt, *Dictionary of Scientific Biography* (Charles Scribner's Sons, New York, 1972), pp. 84–87.
2. *Encyclopedia of Science and Technology* (McGraw-Hill, New York, 1992), Vol. 7, p. 406.
3. H.R. Crane, *Phys. Teach.* **28**, 264–269 (May 1990).
4. Don W. Miller and G. Wayne Caudill, *Am. J. Phys.* **34**, 615–616 (1966).
5. Haym Kruglak et al., *Am. J. Phys.* **46** (4), 438–440 (1978).
6. E.C. Reynhardt, T.A. Van der Walt, and L. Soskolsky, *Am. J. Phys.* **54** (8), 759–761 (1986).
7. Roger W. Sinnot, *Sky Telesc.* 330–332 (October 1980).
8. J.O. Mattila, *Physics Education* **26** (1991).
9. H.R. Crane, *Am. J. Phys.* **49**, 1004 (November 1981).
10. A 3-in bob is available from Sargent Welch, Part # S-4480-30.
11. A. P. French, *Phys. Teach.* **16**, 61–62 (January 1978).
12. *About Foucault Pendulums*, A Scriptographic Booklet by Channing L. Bete Co., Inc. (1972).

Forces, Newton's Laws

Newton's Bathroom Scale

George A. Burman, Tranquillity High School, P.O. Box 457, Tranquillity, CA 93668

I was disappointed, after ordering a "metric" bathroom scale from one of the science supply houses, to find that there was the usual scale in pounds, with only a small additional scale in kilograms. After using the scale for a couple of years, I observed that the metric bathroom scale just reinforced the students' belief that weight was measured in kilograms.

Notwithstanding that in most of Europe and Central/South America the kilogram is used as a measure of weight in the marketplace, I didn't want to perpetuate this practice in my physics classroom. Besides, I had been largely unsuccessful in convincing students that these "Newton things" were anything more than some abstract quantity that was symbolized by an N on spring scales and in diagrams in the book. The students' acceptance of newtons as a unit of weight was to about the same degree as their acceptance of the wisdom of anyone older than nineteen.

So, to try to correct this situation, I constructed a Newton scale to be applied to the existing pound-kilogram scale. After placing a Newton Bathroom Scale in the classroom, the results were dramatic and immediate. Students were heard to say: "I weigh 660 newtons!" or "Hey, newtons are like pounds!" or "How do you change newtons to pounds?" My favorite is, as a student stood on the scale in a doorway, pushing up on the doorjamb: "I can push with a force of 250 newtons!"

Modification of any bathroom scale, either a $35 item from the science catalog or one for $9.95 from the discount store, is fairly easy. Most scales read either 280 pounds or

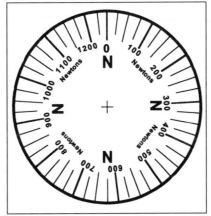

Fig.1a. Dial for 280-pound scales.

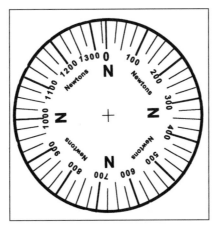

Fig. 1b. Dial for 300-pound scales.

300 pounds full scale. That will determine whether you will use Fig. 1a or 1b. Enlarge the appropriate figure on a copier, cut it out, and paste it on the dial with rubber cement. The only tricky part is taking the bathroom scale apart to get to the dial and putting it back together. Proceed as follows:

1. Turn the scale upside down, find the ends of two springs that hold the top of the scale to the base. Carefully unhook the springs with a pair of long-nose pliers.

2. Without separating the scale, turn it right side up and lift the top away from the base. Now is a good time to examine the inner works of the scale, which is an interesting study of levers in itself Paste the new scale on the dial, cutting away whatever regions are necessary to allow for bumps and rivets.

3. Attach a short piece of thin copper wire to the ends of the springs, thread the wire through the holes where the springs attach to the bottom plate, and carefully put the two halves together. Make sure all the lever fulcrums are resting in their proper places, and turn the scale upside down again.

4. Using the copper wires, pull the ends of the springs up as far as possible. Now, grasp the end of the spring with the longnose pliers, grunt a bit, and rehook the springs. Turn the scale over and all should work well.

Weighing an Accelerating Kilogram-Mass with a Spring Scale

Raymond E. Benenson, Department of Physics, SUNY at Albany, Albany, NY 12222

One hardly expects to find a scale for weighing objects in an elevator, but physics students are often asked to predict the readings when the elevator is accelerating a) upward, b) downward, or c) in free fall. Apparent weight changes in an accelerating frame of reference illustrate both Newton's second law and the use of the free-body diagram. Clyde J. Smith[1] has described an instructive and entertaining demonstration of weightlessness in free fall: washers on elastic cords are pulled into a bucket by virtue of their downward acceleration.

We describe here how to use a large demonstration-type spring scale[2] to weigh a 1-kg mass, first in free fall as a quantitative alternative to Smith's[1] demonstration, and then to show apparent weight increase during upward acceleration provided two ways: the scale-mass combination is 1) part of an Atwood's machine, and 2) serves as the bob of a pendulum. We understand that similar free-fall and pendulum demonstrations are used by other teachers but we are unaware of their having been published.

Fig. 1. Atwood's Machine with ascending kilogram.

Free Fall

The scale and kilogram are dropped together (onto a cushion). Preparation is minimal, and the zero result is quantitative.

Upward Acceleration

A. *Atwood's Machine.* Figure 1 shows a 1-kg mass being weighed by the spring scale as both are accelerated upward by a 19.6-N weight. The approximately 13-cm-diameter aluminum clothesline pulleys shown in the figure have a groove adequate for holding a strong cord, and with light oil applied to their bearings they rotate easily.

The scale weighs approximately 3.2 N; hence, neglecting the effect of the pulleys, the calculated upward acceleration, $a = 2$ m/s^2, leads to an apparent weight $1 \text{ kg} \times (g + a) = 11.8$ N, where $g = 9.8$ m/s^2.

Successive trials gave scale readings of 11.6

Fig. 2. Pendulum with kilogram near lowest position.

$\pm$ 0.2 N, as, for example, in Fig. 1. Scale and kilogram could also be placed in the descending side.

B. *Pendulum.* Conventionally, a simple pendulum is suspended from a stationary scale or (more recently) from a force transducer. However, as shown in Fig. 2, the scale is again part of the accelerating system. To prevent twisting we used an aluminum rod instead of a string.

The apparent weight of the kilogram-mass at its lowest point should be $1 \text{ kg} \times (g + a_c)$, with a_c the centripetal acceleration. The system settles down after the first half of an oscillation, provided care is taken with regard to alignment. The horizontal projection, A, of the amplitude is measured by a meterstick on the floor; the axis of the kilogram-mass is initially held radially.

The easiest way to compare calculation and experiment is to measure the period T of the compound pendulum and assume simple harmonic motion*: $v = 2\pi A/T$ and $a_c = v^2/R$, where $R = 1.6$ m is the distance of the kilogram from its axis of rotation. The observed and calculated weights were, respectively, for $A = 80$ cm, 12.2 ± 0.2 N and 12.5 N. and for $A = 90$ cm, 13.3 ± 0.3 N and 13.3 N. Sources of error include 1) difficulty in reading A from above the meterstick, 2) neglect of damping, 3) the small-angle approximation, and 4) pointer overshoot.

The photographs were taken with ASA 3200 speed film advanced at approximately three frames per second. We thank Joseph Lisoski, Mario Prividera, and June Benenson for help with the photography.

References

1. C.J. Smith, *Phys. Teach.* **27**, 40 (1989).
2. Central Scientific Co., as well as other suppliers.

*Using conservation of energy for the actual compound

pendulum avoids the need to measure T as well as the small-angle approximation. For an initial angular displacement, $\theta_0 = \sin^{-1} A/R$. We can obtain $a_c = \omega^2 R$ by equating the original gravitational potential energy to the maximum kinetic energy: $Mg\, \bar{x}\, (1 - \cos \theta_0) = \frac{1}{2}\, I\omega^2$, where I, ω, and $\bar{x}$ are, respectively, moment of inertia, angular velocity, and distance from fulcrum to center of mass of the compound pendulum. For $I = 3.36$ kg-m^2, $M = 1.74$ kg, and $\bar{x} = 1.32$ m, $A = 80$ and 90 cm gave, respectively, 12.7 and 13.5 N.

Atwood's Machine Using Moment of Inertia Pulley

Edward E. Beasley, Department of Physics, Gallaudet University, Washington, DC 20002

Most experiments with moment of inertia apparatus involve a plotting exercise in the kinematics of linear and/or angular motion to determine the angular acceleration. Then, the net torque is measured, and the moment of inertia, I, is calculated from these data.[1,2]

It is also instructive to determine I using an Atwood's machine. This may be accomplished either as a quick demonstration or as a laboratory exercise by using the heavy wheel of the Central Scientific Company (CENCO), 75290 Rotational Inertia Apparatus as a pulley. Other designs such as the CENCO 30652, or the Welch Scientific Company's 0570J or 0574 also appear to be adaptable as Atwood's machines.

Figure 1 shows the apparatus clamped in place and ready for use, together with the standard laboratory accessories needed for the measurements. The c-clamps, which hold the base of the apparatus to one of the ring stand bases, are backed with wood blocks to prevent crushing the cast metal support base. The bearing surfaces should be wiped clean and lightly oiled. To avoid injury to the user's feet, more than usual care must be exercised when attaching or detaching the heavy pulley from the conical pivot bearings. (A bottom-up, card-

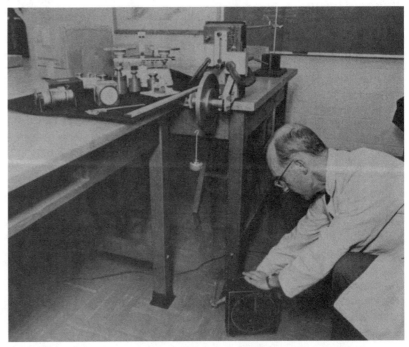

Fig. 1. A moment of inertia wheel shown with the accessories necessary for its adaptation as an Atwood's machine.

board box on the floor beneath the pulley during these steps is suggested.) The 120 cm of 20-lb test monofilament nylon fishline used had a mass of only 0.26 g, so that its effect in causing a change in acceleration is negligible relative to other errors.

With the pulley locked in place and 250 g hanging on each side, an additional 150 g on one side will not cause slippage of the string on the pulley. With the pulley unlocked, and equal masses hanging from each side, the frictional torque in the bearings was determined from the amount of extra mass added to the downward-moving mass to maintain steady motion. With 150 g on each side, this extra mass was 18 g $\pm$ 0.2 g, whereas with 800 g on each side, the extra mass was 21.5 g $\pm$ 0.3 g. About 17 g of these extra masses are needed to compensate for bearing friction from the 5.41-kg inertial pulley. With accelerating masses typically as low as 20 g for convenient times of fall, it is therefore obvious that frictional torques must be determined with reasonable care.

The value calculated for I from the dimensions and pulley mass (0.0220 kg m^2) compares within 15% to the value of I obtained by solving the energy equation (including the energy dissipated as heat in the bearing surfaces). I found that frictional torques and times of fall varied somewhat with the direction of rotation. With a fixed starting position for the pulley, the deviations in times of fall for 5 trials for each of the two directions were 1.3% and 2.5%, yielding I = 0.0193 kg m^2 and 0.0207 kg m^2, respectively.

At the time of this experiment, my students have already seen the Atwood's machine with light pulley and are ready to see the effect of rotational energy on the system. There are many sources of error such as dynamic unbalance in the wheel, nonuniformity of the bearing surfaces, problems in properly adjusting the bearings, systematic errors in timing, etc., which make for fruitful discussion.

References

I. CENCO Selective Experiments in Physics, No. 71991-62.
2. J.G. McCaslin, *Phys. Teach.* **22**, 54 (1984).

A Timing Sensor for the Atwood Machine

William DeBuvitz, Department of Physics, Middlesex County College, 155 Mill Road, P.O. Box 3050, Edison, NJ 08818

Our laboratory schedule for the general physics course has always included an Atwood machine experiment. An Atwood machine consists of two masses m_1 and m_2 connected by a string over a pulley (see Fig. 1). I like this experiment because it gives the students a chance to observe Newton's second law under almost frictionless conditions. The ballbearing pulleys we use have so little mass and so little friction that the students can ignore the effects of the pulley and get good results.

Some laboratory manuals ask the students to calculate the acceleration of the system from Newton's second law:

$$a = \frac{F_{net}}{m} = \frac{(m_2 - m_1)g}{m_2 + m_1} \quad (m_2 > m_1) \qquad (1)$$

then compare it with the measured value. To measure the acceleration, students measure the time t for the mass m_2 to fall a distance d, then substitute into the kinematics formula:

$$a = \frac{2d}{t^2} \qquad (2)$$

I prefer to have my students study the proportional relationships associated with the second law by measuring the acceleration of the system under two different conditions:
(1) To see if the acceleration is proportional to the net force, they vary the net force while keeping the total mass con-

stant. To do this, they start with an equal amount of mass on each hanger and then shift masses from one mass hanger to the other to vary the net force $(m_2 - m_1)g$. They then graph the acceleration versus F_{net} to see if the data suggest a straight line for a direct proportion. I was able to get good results with our pulleys by starting with m_1

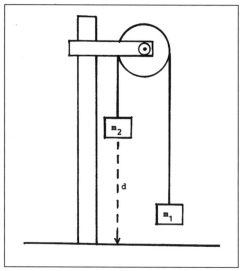

Fig. 1.

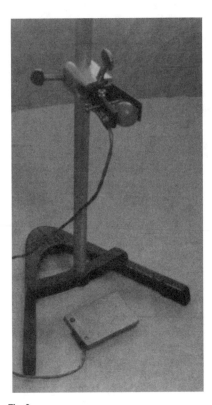

Fig. 2.

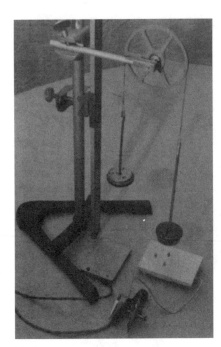

Fig. 3.

Fig. 4.

After some experimentation, I found a simpler way to measure the time using the PASCO timer. Instead of using the photogates, I combine the PASCO Free Fall Adapter #9207 with a homemade sensor. The Free Fall Adapter is designed to measure the time of fall of a steel ball (see Fig. 2). It consists of a clamp and a sensor pad that plug into the timer. When the ball is held in the clamp, it completes an electrical circuit that keeps the timer in the "stopped mode." When the ball is released, the circuit is broken and this starts the timer. When the ball hits the pad, the circuit to the pad is closed and this stops the timer.

Figure 3 shows how I use the Free Fall Adapter with the Atwood machine. (During the experiment, the pulley is placed much higher than in the photo. I had to lower the pulley and use a shorter piece of string in order to get the complete apparatus in the photo.) My homemade sensor is designed to replace the clamp. A close-up view is shown in Fig. 4. The sensor consists of a wooden base with three screws projecting from the top. Two of these screws are wired to the contacts on the clamp. To start a timing, the student presses the hanger with the smaller mass down against the tips of the three screws. The metal hanger completes the circuit to the clamp and this keeps the timer in the stopped mode. The student then releases the hanger, which breaks the circuit and starts the timer. The sensor pad is located directly below the hanger with the larger mass; when this hanger hits the sensor pad, the timer is stopped.

My sensor is easy to build and it has no moving parts, so it is quite durable. The bottom of the sensor is shown in Fig. 5. A list of the materials is given below. The dimensions are given in metric units, but the commercial sizes are in English units.

$= m_2 = 155$ g (including the mass hangers), then shifting 1 g at a time from m_1 to m_2.

(2) To see if the acceleration is inversely proportional to the mass, they vary the total mass while keeping the net force constant. To do this, they start with a certain net force $(m_2 - m_1)g$ and then add equal amounts of mass to both mass hangers. They then graph the acceleration versus $\frac{1}{m}$ (or the acceleration versus m on log-log paper) to see if the data suggest a straight line. I was able to get good results by starting with $m_1 = 50$ g and $m_2 = 54$ g, then adding 50 g at a time to both sides so that the mass difference stayed at 4 g.

The problem with this experiment is the measurement of the time. If the students use a manual timer, their reaction times will be a major source of error. One way to eliminate this problem is to use photogates and an electronic timer. We have the equipment made by PASCO (timer #9215 and photogates #9206) and we have been able to adapt this equipment to the Atwood machine, but the photogates are delicate and difficult to keep in alignment. Another solution is to use the PASCO Smart Pulley, which plugs into a computer interface and graphs the motion on a computer screen. This eliminates all of the problems because it eliminates all of the measurements. The Smart Pulley is an impressive demonstration device, but I prefer that my students have the experience of actually measuring the time, calculating the acceleration, and preparing the graphs.

Fig. 5.

Fig. 6.

- A wooden base. I used a 7- x 10-cm piece of 1/2-in plywood.
- Six 8- x 3/4-in sheet metal screws; three for the contacts and three for the legs.
- Six nuts to act as spacers for the legs.
- About 30 cm of two-conductor wire.
- Two alligator clips.
- A sheet of lead to add weight for stability. I used a 6- x 8.5-cm sheet of 1/16-in thickness. The sheet is held to the bottom of the base by the screws for the legs.
- A piece of electrical tape to insulate the heads of the contact screws from the lead sheet.

I arranged the contact screws in an equilateral triangle with a spacing of 2.5 cm. I felt that this three-point support would make it easier for students to apply steady pressure when holding the mass hanger down on the screws. This is necessary for good electrical contact. I also wanted the base of the sensor to be stable, so I added the lead sheet and used three legs instead of four to prevent wobbling.

The ends of the contact screws are quite sharp and could produce a nasty scratch, so I rounded and polished the tips with a file. Incidentally, the voltages and currents for the timer are quite small, so the exposed metal contacts do not present a shock hazard.

Students should not have much difficulty operating the timing system, providing they exercise reasonable care. What matters the most is how they hold down and release the mass hanger. In particular students should

- *make sure that they hold down the hanger so that the string above it is vertical.* If the string is slanted, the hanger will swing back and forth as it rises and this will affect the operation of the pulley.

- *make sure that the bottom of the hanger is clean so that it makes good electrical contact with the sensor.* If the hanger is not held steady against the contacts (a common occurrence until students get a feel for it), the timer will start by accident. If this happens, the timer can be stopped by simply tapping on the sensor pad.

- *make sure that they release the hanger without jerking it in any way.* I found it difficult to release the hanger smoothly if I held it down with my fingers. Sweat and oils in my skin made my fingers stick to the top mass. I took care of this problem by making a "holding tool" (see Fig. 6). It is simply a metal fork with its inner tines removed.

If students follow these cautions, they should get good results with this timing arrangement. I find that repeated measurements usually agree to the nearest 0.1 s, which is precise enough for my needs. I plan on using this timing system in our Atwood machine laboratories during the next semester.

Demonstrating Normal Forces with an Electronic Balance

Jonathan Mitschele and Matthew Muscato, Saint Joseph's College, Windham, ME 04062-1198

Our first-year physics students usually have great difficulty believing that normal forces actually exist, but last year we convinced them with a novel demonstration that uses a common piece of laboratory equipment, a top-loading electronic balance.

In balances such as the ones in our laboratories (a Fisher Scientific EMD Model 110S and a Mettler BB240), the pan of the balance is mounted on a hollow metal cylinder, surrounded by an attached coil, which fits over the inner pole of a cylindrical permanent magnet. So that the mass of off-center loads will be measured correctly, this cylinder is attached to the balance housing by flexible metal diaphragms fastened at the top and bottom of the cylinder. A null detector-amplifier feedback circuit adjusts an electrical current passing through the coil so that the coil's electromagnetic force balances the downward force of gravity on the pan and its accessories, and maintains them at a fixed no-load position. When an object is placed on the pan, the current in the coil is increased until the loaded pan is again restored to the no-load position. The current necessary to maintain the pan and object in the null position is directly proportional to the weight of the object; this current is readily converted to a mass reading for the object, expressed in gram units.[1]

While the manufacturer surely expects that the balance will be used in the horizontal position—a leveling bubble is provided as an integral part of the balance—it turns out that one *can* break the rules and make weighings while the balance is tipped at various angles. However, because of the way in which the pan cylinder is mounted on diaphragms fixed to the balance housing, only the component of the force of gravity that is normal to the balance pan ($mg \cdot \cos\theta$)

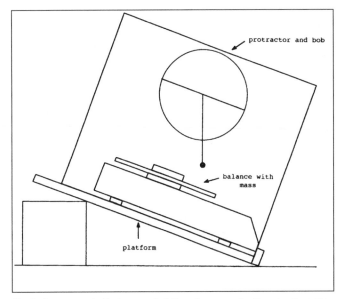

Fig. 1. Arrangement of balance and platform for measuring the normal component of forces.

is measured, so "mass" readings displayed by such balances are actually values of $m \cdot \cos\theta$, where θ is the angle of inclination of the balance, and are proportional to the normal force, N, exerted by the pan on the weight. With a balance that is level (and functioning properly) mass readings will be correct; with a balance that is inclined at an angle θ, mass readings are reduced by a factor of $\cos\theta$.

For an inclined plane to hold the balance at various fixed angles during a demonstration, we use either a PASCO dynamics cart track (PASCO ME-9453) fitted with end stops and attached to a vertical rod with a rod clamp accessory, or a small platform with a raised front edge and sidewall (constructed from three pieces of scrap plywood) that can be elevated at one end with books or boxes (see Fig. 1). The end stops on the dynamics cart track and the raised edge on the homemade platform hold the balance so it cannot slide off when the track or platform is inclined.

Double-sided tape (or a piece of old chewing gum) can be used to prevent the weight from sliding off as the balance is tipped; the weight of this tape

Table I. Observed and predicted masses on an inclined top-loading electronic balance.

Angle of Inclination (degrees)	Balance Reading (grams)	$m \cdot \cos\theta$ (grams)
0.0	51.0	51.0
10.0	50.2	50.2
15.0	49.4	49.2
20.0	47.9	47.9
25.0	46.4	46.2
30.0	44.2	44.1
35.0	41.9	41.8
40.0	39.2	39.0

(or chewing gum) forms a part of the tare when the balance is zeroed.

We measure the angle of inclination (estimated uncertainty ±0.5 degrees) with a protractor that has a plumb bob (a piece of thread and a small weight) hanging from the center hole; the protractor is taped to the edge of the dynamics track or to the side wall of the platform. For each inclination of the balance a mass reading is made by first zeroing the balance and then weighing the mass. Zeroing the balance before weighing is important because the current necessary to bring the pan to the no-load position also varies with inclination.

A typical set of measurements using a Fisher Scientific EMD Model 110S balance and PASCO dynamics track are included in Table I; a Mettler BB240 balance and homemade platform yielded comparable results. As can be seen, experimental results are in excellent agreement with predicted values.

Reference

1. For further details on the construction and operation of electronic compensating balances, see R.M. Schoonover, "A look at the electronic analytical balance," *Anal. Chem.* **54**, 973A (1982); also of interest is U.S. Patent 3,786,884, January 22, 1974, assigned to Mettler Instruments AG, Zurich, Switzerland, which provides a complete description of the construction of such a balance.

Stability and That Pesky Center-of-Mass

Sean M. Cordry, Department of Natural Science, York College, 912 Kiplinger Avenue, York, NE 68467

I designed this simple apparatus in order to demonstrate two concepts regarding the stability of an object: first, that the center-of-mass (CoM) of a system is the sum of the CoM of its components, and second, that the effects of small displacements from an equilibrium position require careful consideration. It comprises three pieces of wood, two "eyes," two hooks, and one latch (Fig. 1).

I begin the demonstration by showing the students all the pieces and trying to balance only the top (curved) piece on the end of my finger, a feat predictably doomed to failure. When I ask my students why the piece will not balance, they respond by pointing out that the CoM of the object is above the pivot point. They are correct in—although misguided by—their observation, for when I ask them how to balance the top piece, they suggest that I hang the two long pieces from the ends. In their minds, they think that a system will be stable if its CoM lies directly below a pivot point.

I oblige them and hang the two long pieces from the ends as directed. To their amazement (and my amusement) the whole assembly goes crashing to the floor when I try to balance the new configuration on the end of my finger. Their paradigm of stability has been appropriately disturbed. I suggest to them that we locate the CoM. To do this, we consider the centers-of-mass of the three individual pieces and conclude that their sum does indeed lie directly below the pivot point. Next, I suggest that they consider the two long pieces to be one system, and the top piece to be another. Naturally, the CoM ends up in the same place, but now we can consider what happens if the apparatus starts to tilt.

As the apparatus tilts, the CoM of the two long pieces remains in the same place. (If the hooks were not at the same level as the pivot, this would not be the case, but the

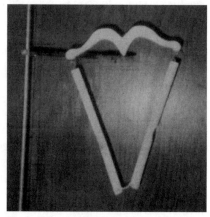

Fig. 2. Fully assembled—and stable—apparatus.

Fig. 1. Disassembled apparatus showing components and various hooks.

educational value of the analysis would still be good.) Therefore, we gained no stability advantage by merely hanging the two long pieces from the ends: the CoM of the top piece is still unstable!

Finally, I latch the ends of the long pieces together, as shown in Fig. 2, and the assembly rests on my fingertip most wonderfully. Connecting the ends changes the way the CoM of the two long pieces behaves when the apparatus starts to tilt: it rises, increasing the gravitational potential energy. The result is an overall stable CoM. (For drama, I usually flip the latch open afterward and send it crashing to the floor

again.)

Note: Although there are many variations of this apparatus, it is the relative motion of the individual pieces that forces students to think about the real stability issue, gravitational potential energy. If the two long pieces were rigidly attached to the top piece, the assembly would balance quite nicely, reinforcing the students' incorrect paradigm! The flexible connections force them to think about small displacements from equilibrium and also about the definition of a "system."

A "Rocket" Cart

Floyd Holt and *George Amann*, F.D. Roosevelt High School, Hyde Park, NY 12538

I n the February 1976 edition of *The Physics Teacher*, a note written by Evan Jones and Peter Urone[1] suggested several demonstrations that could be devised using a carbon dioxide (CO_2) fire extinguisher. Here at F.D. Roosevelt High School, we have taken the authors' suggestions one step further and developed a demonstration of conservation of momentum that we feel our students will never forget.

Using a 6.8-kg (15-lb) CO_2 cylinder as our propulsion source, we mounted the tank on a child's pedal-powered fire truck (Fig. 1) to make the equivalent of a "rocket cart." (If you can obtain an old go-cart, this would be preferable since it has a lower center of mass and consequently is more stable.)

Carbon dioxide has several advantages as a power source over other gases, but its main advantage is that the gas liquifies in the bottle when under pressure. This allows a much larger mass of gas to be included. Thus we are able to maintain the thrust of the gas for 30 seconds or more at full power. Bottled air, on the other hand, cannot contain enough mass to provide thrust for this period of time. In addition, bottled air must be under much higher pressure (on the order of 1×10^7 Pa [1500 lbs/in^2]), making it more dangerous. The thrust is more than sufficient to dramatically accelerate the cart, cylinder, and rider down the hall at an impressive speed. This CO_2 fuel is relatively inexpensive; we pay only $8 to refill the cylinder.

We built a wooden mounting bracket to hold the cylinder and then bolted it onto the back of the cart. This arrangement allows the CO_2 bottle to be easily attached and

Fig. 1. The rocket cart.

removed when depleted. It also holds the cylinder in place during the firing so that the cylinder does not wander or "fishtail." To the side of the cart we added a handle that is attached to the release lever on the cylinder via a cable. This serves as the equivalent of a gas pedal, allowing us to easily control the release of the gas.

When we are ready to do the demonstration, we make sure that the safety devices that keep the cylinder from acci-

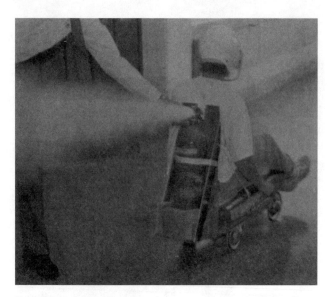

Fig. 2. The rocket cart in motion.

dentally discharging remain in place right up to the final moment. In addition, we always have our driver (usually an athletic student) wear a football helmet as an added safety feature. Obviously, no one should stand behind the cart when the cylinder fires.

Our initial attempts at this demonstration provided several spectacular failures, accompanied by much noise and expelled gas, but very little motion. We discovered that the cylinder has a "diffuser" nozzle in the orifice that ejects the gas in four opposing directions. This prevents the gas from exiting in a focused stream and thus did not provide the thrust we needed. This nozzle behaves much like a spray cap does on a fire hydrant, spreading the gas, thereby cancelling most of its resultant momentum. This nozzle must be removed for successful propulsion of the cart. In addition, for maximum thrust the CO_2 bottle should have as large an orifice as possible. We use ones that have a 0.95-cm (3/8-in) diameter opening, which seem to work well.

As can be seen from Fig. 2, once the gas is released without the diffuser nozzle, this becomes a truly spectacular demonstration. Rather impressive velocities are easily obtainable in relatively short distances. Our students typically reach speeds up to 7 m/s (15 mph) riding the cart in the level school halls. Although we don't recommend using an entire charge of the cylinder for a single run, a test we did under controlled circumstances had the cart and driver reach

14.3 m/s (32 mph) when the entire 6.8 kg of gas was used. With a thrust this large, therefore, we definitely suggest that you do not handhold the cylinder when releasing the gas.

A word of caution: if you perform this demonstration in the school halls, as we do, it would be wise to warn your colleagues of what is going to happen, since it does make a surprisingly loud noise.

When we analyze the motion for our classes, we make several simplifying assumptions. Although the mass of the system is obviously changing, we do not bring this up in the discussion until the end, and then merely as a caveat that the analysis is not 100 percent correct. Since the mass changes by only a few percent during the run, it will not present a significant error. The assumption that the gas is escaping with constant velocity is perhaps a larger problem, since the cylinder cools significantly during the run. An example of our analysis is shown below. First measure the frictional force (f) on the cart and driver by pulling the cart at constant velocity with a Newton scale. Then, during the firing, measure the time the cart accelerates and the distance it travels during this period.

Using

$$s = \left(\frac{1}{2}\right) at^2 \qquad (1)$$

we calculate the cart's acceleration.
Using Newton's second law

$$\mathbf{F}_{net} = \mathbf{F} - f = ma \qquad (2)$$

allows us to calculate the net thrust, F, provided by the gas.

Finally, using the law of impulse momentum

$$\mathbf{F}_{net} \text{ (time)} = \text{mass (change in velocity)} \qquad (3)$$

we are able to calculate the escape velocity of the gas. We weigh the cylinder to determine the mass of gas lost.

Whether you choose to make this demonstration the culmination of your discussion on momentum, as we do, or just choose to use it as a spectacular demonstration of Newton's third law, we feel it is one demonstration your students will talk about for years to come!

Reference

1. Evan Jones and Peter Urone, "Spectacular Rocket Experiment," *Phys. Teach.* **14** (2), 112 (1976).

The Surgical-Hose Rocket

Martin Nicoll, Physics Department, Camosun College, 3100 Foul Bay Road, Victoria, BC, Canada V8P 5J2

Rockets are always an attention-grabber both for your students and anybody else who happens to be walking by. Blasting off water-bottle rockets is great fun and an excellent promo for the department, but any kind of analysis quickly becomes complicated since the exhaust velocity decreases along with the pressure.[1]

A few years ago, after applying the variable-mass analysis of Newton's second law to rockets, a few of our extroverted students started demanding a rocket lab. I quickly outlined the major requirements that would be difficult to fulfill: 1) a very small budget, 2) the exhaust velocity must be constant for ease of analysis and data collection, 3) the ejected mass must be a significant percentage of the total mass, and 4) a very small budget. The students continued to tease me about my failure and I eventually came up with an idea to eject water at a constant velocity. I built "Apollo 1" then renamed it "Appalling 1" since it would not even move! However, it did lead to an "Apollo 2" design that did move but was very difficult to take data from. This design happened to use surgical latex hose to deliver compressed air and when, by mistake, it developed an embolism ("bubble") I was reminded of the surgical-hose water pistols used in my university days. (Who says you don't learn anything useful at university!) On impulse I decided to see how much the exhaust velocity varied as the hose emptied. I was amazed that all the water ended up in one small puddle about 3 m away. The water's velocity did not depend on the size of the embolism! This unique property of surgical latex tubing makes it easy to construct a cheap water-powered rocket that can run along a horizontal wire. Newton's second law with a variable mass can now be verified with just a few simple measurements. The rest of this article fills in the details in case you want to do the lab.

Theory

If we define the exhaust velocity to be $\mathbf{v}_e$, the instantaneous rocket velocity to be $\mathbf{v}_M$, and the instantaneous rocket mass to be M, Newton's second law with no external forces will reduce to

$$\mathbf{v}_e \, dM / dt = M \, d\mathbf{v}_M / dt \qquad (1)$$

(Don't forget that dM/dt is negative for a rocket, so $d\mathbf{v}_M/dt$ is in the opposite direction to $\mathbf{v}_e$ as expected. See any standard text for a derivation.)

If $\mathbf{v}_e$ is constant and the rocket starts from rest, a little

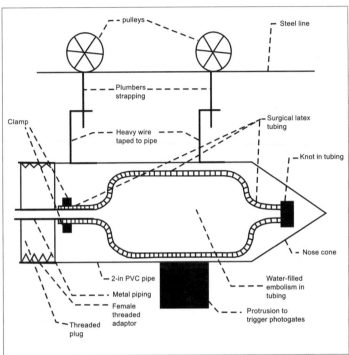

Fig. 1. Cross section of fueled-up water rocket.

integration yields

$$\mathbf{v}_f = \mathbf{v}_e \ln (M_f / M_i) \qquad (2)$$

where $\mathbf{v}_f$ is the final velocity of the rocket. The primary point of the lab is to verify Eq. (2).

A secondary investigation is to verify that the left-hand side of Eq. (1) is, in fact, equal to the thrust of the rocket. Both values, $\mathbf{v}_e$ and dM/dt, can be measured separately and the product compared with the thrust as measured by a spring scale.

Rocket Design

The dimensions given here are nominal, and I see no reason why larger or smaller rockets would not work. In fact it would be interesting to try attaching surgical hose to completely different devices (e.g., a small cart).

Figure 1 may help you follow this design description. Take 23 cm of top-quality surgical latex tubing (9 mm O.D., 4 mm I.D.), and tie a knot in one end. Slip the other end onto a 6-cm length of metal piping that has an appropriate diameter. I used automotive brake-line material with the smooth finish taken off the outside. Clamp the tubing in place with a miniature hose clamp. Now drill a hole in the center of a 2-in PVC threaded plug so that the metal piping can be pushed through and glued into place. Your rocket engine is now complete.

The rocket shell is made of a 50-cm length of 2-in PVC pipe with a female threaded adapter glued on one end. A nose cone can be made out of any suitable material and taped onto the other end. Attach a couple of pulleys to the top of the rocket so it can run along a wire and put a protrusion of some sort on the bottom to trigger photogates.

For a track I used about 20 m of horizontal steel down-rigger line. Attach one end of the wire to a solid object and run the other end through a fixed pulley to a large mass. Adjust the length until the mass is hanging and you have a nice tight wire with the added feature that the tension is adjustable by changing the mass; (or use a come-along). Since water will be spewing out the back, it is easiest to do the lab outdoors, but if the weather does not cooperate I suppose you could do it indoors on sheets of plastic since the volume of water is not that large. How you level the wire will depend on what you have available. I had the class out to my farm and attached one end to the front-end loader of my tractor, so get that tractor onto next year's supplies budget!

Doing the Experiment

The exhaust velocity can be obtained by two methods:

1) Fire the engine in a horizontal, stationary position from a known height and measure the range. The exhaust velocity can then be calculated using projectile motion theory.

2) By applying conservation of mass to fluid flow in a pipe, it can be shown that

$$v_e = \frac{dM/dt}{A\rho}$$

where A is the cross-sectional area of the pipe, ρ is the density of water, and dM/dt is the rate at which mass is being expelled. Area and density are easily obtained, and since dM/dt is constant, you can simply time a known mass being ejected. For accuracy I use a video camera to record the total discharge, then play it back using the frame-by-frame advance feature on the VCR (period = 1/30 s).

I recommend method 2) since you will now have dM/dt to verify the thrust formula.

The final velocity, v_f, is found by using two linked photogates placed a known distance apart. Position the first photogate just past the point on the track where the rocket runs out of water. Equation (2) can now be verified as long as you remembered to measure the initial and final masses.

Some More Details

One difficulty is that the rocket must be easily removable from the wire for fueling up and placing on the scales. I accomplished this by taping wire hooks onto the rocket shell and bolting some plumber's strapping onto the pulleys.

Fueling up is done by connecting to any pressurized water system. The easiest method is to connect a piece of stiff-walled hose (diameter similar to surgical hose) to the tapered taps that are in most labs. If you are doing the lab outside, find the necessary adapters to go from garden-hose fittings to surgical-hose size.

Preignition (i.e., spraying water everywhere before you are ready) is another problem. A miniature valve on the metal tubing would be fancy but would add mass and cost. I drilled two holes in the end of the rocket shell so that a thumb and finger could be inserted to pinch the surgical hose. I also made a cap out of a short piece of clamped-off surgical hose that could slide over the outside end of the metal piping to prevent preignition while on the scale. The engine can be fueled up and put on the scale before threading it into the shell if it is more convenient. Ironically, this caused the biggest problem with my last class; they had no problem with the calculus but could not keep track of all the separate masses to arrive at the correct total (e.g., they would forget the pulleys).

Safety Precautions

The down-rigger line can be very hard to see and is most conveniently located at neck level, so take necessary precautions. When applying the tension for the first time, keep students well back in case the line breaks and whiplashes.

The rocket gets up to surprising speeds (4 m/s), so you will have to design some kind of stopping mechanism or at least give a student a thick pair of gloves.

Remarks

Doing this lab as a class project combined with shooting off a few water-bottle rockets makes for a nice change and is great for class morale. I highly recommend using a video camera, especially with a student in charge, since there always seems to be some extra humorous footage and commentary when you play it back for analysis in class. Besides providing a relatively straightforward verification of the rocket equation, this lab shows students that physics equipment can be constructed from everyday materials. Don't get too wet!

Acknowledgment

I would like to thank Ron Verrall for the help he gave throughout this project.

Reference

1. D. Kagan et al., "Soda-bottle water rockets," *Phys. Teach.* **33**, 150 (1995).

Cavendish Experiment

John E. Carlson, Fox Lane High School, Bedford, NY 10506

Most introductory physics textbooks mention the famous experiment that Henry Cavendish performed in 1798 in which he measured the constant "G" in Newton's Law of Universal Gravitation. In this experiment a long, thin wire is used to support a horizontal rod with masses at the ends.

When two large external masses are brought close to the suspended masses, one to each side, the gravitational forces between them will cause the wire to twist. The angle of twist can be converted to a force and "G" can be determined.

Although the apparatus itself is available commercially,[1] it is possible to build for less than $100 a Cavendish apparatus that gives surprisingly good results. Figure 1 shows a photograph of the apparatus which includes a Plexiglas box to keep out air currents. Within the box a wooden meter stick is supported at the center by a thin wire (#32 single-strand steel). This wire extends through a hole in the top of the box and then through a 1.5-m section of PVC sewer pipe to a circular wooden disk at the top. At the ends of the meter stick 0.50-kg masses hang from screw eyes. A small plane mirror is attached to the middle of the meter stick to reflect a light source, and aluminum window screening covers the inside of the box to allow for grounding of stray electric charge. This is particularly important because stray charges can easily produce a larger electrical force than the gravitational force being measured. Large masses can then be positioned on opposite sides of the ends of the apparatus to create an attracting force that deflects the meter stick. Figure 2 is a closeup view of one end of the apparatus. Approximately 18 kg of lead plates are placed at each end for this purpose.

In the demonstration, a laser beam is reflected by the mirror and projected to a distant screen. Since the torsion pendulum will not likely be at rest, the left and right extremes of motion are marked. The large masses are then switched from one side of the apparatus to the other side. The gravitational forces between the large masses and the masses hanging from the meter stick will deflect the torsion pendulum in the opposite direction, shifting the left and right extremes of motion. Figure 3 shows how the light patterns will appear on a screen. Due to the weakness of the force involved, the angular shift of the light beam will be no more than 0.5 degrees. This is why the laser and mirror are positioned to make the movement more apparent. As a demonstration rather than a laboratory experiment, this apparatus gives students strong visual evidence that even small masses are attracted to each other by gravity.

Fig. 1. Front view of Cavendish apparatus.

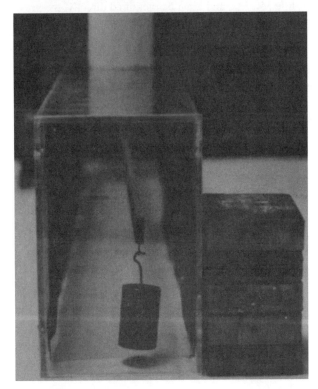

Fig. 2. Side view of Cavendish apparatus.

With a greater amount of time, and when working with students who have studied rotational kinematics, a full mathematical analysis can yield an experimental value for the gravitational constant (G).[2] The gravitational force is represented by:

$$F = \frac{GM_1M_2}{r^2} \qquad (1)$$

By solving for G we get:

$$G = \frac{Fr^2}{M_1M_2} \qquad (2)$$

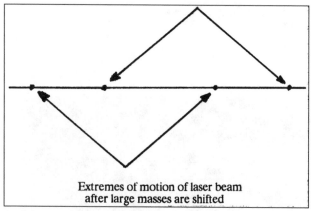

Extremes of motion of laser beam
after large masses are shifted

Fig. 3. Pattern of reflected light of distant screen.

While M_1, M_2, and r can be measured directly, the gravitational force (F) requires an indirect solution. The method relies on the physical properties of a torsional pendulum.[3] First the period of simple harmonic motion is observed. Then the torsional constant (κ) is determined. This allows the calculation of the restoring torque (τ) and finally the force that creates that torque (F). Following is a set of typical data collected for this apparatus:

1) Directly measured quantities:
M_1 = the hanging mass = 0.50 kg
M_2 = the stationary mass = 18 kg
r = distance between M_1 and M_2 = 0.13 m

2) Calculation of the moment of inertia of the meter stick and masses:

$I_{total} = I_{mass} + I_{mass} + I_{meter\ stick}$

$$I_T = MR^2 + MR^2 + ML^2/12 \tag{3}$$

$I_T = (0.5\ kg)(0.5\ m)^2 + (0.5\ kg)(0.5\ m)^2$
$+ (0.144\ kg)(1m)^2/12$
$I_T = 0.125\ kg{\cdot}m^2 + 0.125\ kg{\cdot}m^2 + 0.012\ kg{\cdot}m^2$
$\rightarrow I_T = 0.26\ kg{\cdot}m^2$

3) Determination of the period of the torsional pendulum:
By direct observation of one cycle:
$\rightarrow$ T = 800 seconds

4) Calculation of the torsional constant of the wire (κ): since the period equation is:
$$T = 2\pi\sqrt{I/\kappa} \tag{4}$$

$$\kappa = \frac{4\pi^2 I}{T^2} = \frac{4(3.14)^2(0.26\ kg{\cdot}m^2)}{(800\ s)^2}$$

$\rightarrow \kappa = 1.6 \times 10^{-5}\ kg{\cdot}m^2/s^2$

5) Determination of the angular rotation of the torsional pendulum:
The observed shift of the laser beam on the screen is $0.48°$. The angular shift of the torsional pendulum is one-half that amount, due to the doubling effect created by the mirror as it reflects the light striking it (observed angle = angle of incidence + angle of reflection). In addition, since the large masses twist the torsional pendulum first clockwise then counterclockwise, when their positions are reversed, the angle corresponding to the gravitational pull in just one direction is one-half the previous value. Therefore:

$\rightarrow \theta = (\frac{1}{2})(\frac{1}{2})(0.48°)$
$= 0.12° = 2.1 \times 10^{-3}$ radian

6) Calculation of torque:
$$\tau = \kappa\theta \tag{5}$$
$\rightarrow \tau = (1.6 \times 10^{-5}\ kg{\cdot}m^2/s^2)(2.1 \times 10^{-3}\ rad)$
$= 3.4 \times 10^{-8}\ N{\cdot}m$

7) Calculation of the force on one pair of masses:
$$\tau = R \times 2F \quad \text{(Two equal forces, one at each} \tag{6}$$
end of the meter stick)

$F = \tau/2R = 3.4 \times 10^{-8}N{\cdot}m/(2 \times 0.5\ m)$
$\rightarrow F = 3.4 \times 10^{-8}\ N$

8) Calculation of G:
Since $F = \dfrac{GM_1M_2}{r^2}$ $\tag{7}$

$$G = \frac{Fr^2}{M_1M_2} = \frac{(3.4 \times 10^{-8}N)(0.13m)^2}{(0.50\ kg)(18\ kg)} \tag{8}$$
$\rightarrow G = 6.3 \times 10^{-11}\ N{\cdot}m^2/kg^2$

Sources of error using this equipment:
a) The masses used are not spherical and therefore the distance used for "r" may be off by 10 percent.

b) The torsional pendulum is so sensitive that the angle measured by the laser light beam on the screen is subject to many outside influences such as air currents, floor vibrations, etc.

I will be happy to send detailed plans and a 2.0-m strand of wire free of charge to anyone sending a self-addressed, stamped envelope.

References
1. PASCO scientific, 10101 Foothills Blvd., Roseville, CA 95678.
2. Halliday and Resnick, Fundamentals of Physics (Wiley & Sons, Inc., New York, 1981), p. 244.
3. Ibid., p. 228.

Demonstrating the Brachistochrone and Tautochrone

D. Figueroa, G. Gutierrez, and *C. Fehr,* Physics Department, Universidad Simon Bolivar, Apartado 89000, Caracas, Venezuela; figueroa@usb.ve

The brachistochrone and the tautochrone are among the classic physics demonstrations for which the outcomes are almost always incorrectly predicted by people witnessing them for the first time. These are counterintuitive problems that have no simple analytic solution, but are very powerful in promoting cognitive conflict and revealing student misconceptions.[1] The brachistochrone problem (Which path has the shortest travel time between two points for an object under constant gravitation force?) has played an important role in the history of physics since it challenged the talents of Newton and Leibniz, and is connected with a priority dispute between the two.[2,3] The solution presented by John Bernoulli marked the beginning of the calculus of variations and is the well-known cycloid (the curve traced by a point on the rim of a rolling wheel). The motion on the cycloid is also tautochronous (that is, it has the same descent time to the bottom of the curve for different starting points). This paper reports a simple approach that can help the student analyze both phenomena at the level of introductory college physics without the need for sophisticated mathematics. The situation is modeled by constructing a series of linear paths that join certain points along the track, applying elementary mechanics, and using a spreadsheet.

The Apparatus

We built two large sets of tracks (Figs. 1 and 2) with L-shaped aluminum channels that have been bent after passing between three rollers (see Fig. 3). The channel is rigidly mounted on heavy wooden boards large enough (2.4 m long by 1.0 m high) for easy viewing by a large audience. We use rolling steel balls rather than sliding beads because of the difficulties in eliminating friction. The steel balls are simultaneously released from different places on the tracks by means of electromagnets con-

Fig.1. Apparatus with irregular track and inclined straight track.

Fig. 2. Apparatus with cycloid track and adjustable inclined straight track.

nected to a power supply. [This magazine recently carried a description of another way to produce curved tracks, using Flex Trak™ from toy car racing games.[4]] On our first track set (Fig. 1) we compare travel time for a ball on an inclined straight track with that of a ball on an irregularly shaped track (starting from the same height, but then going downhill, through a deep valley, and then uphill again, finally emerging parallel to the straight-line track).

The second apparatus (Fig. 2) compares a straight track of adjustable slope with a cycloid track (brachistochrone and tautochrone) generated by a circle of radius 37.2 cm.

What Do You Predict?

We start the demo by showing the Fig. 1 apparatus and raising the usual question — Which ball reaches the lower end first? Over several years we have consistently noted two features of the answer from each new group of students. Many of them (20 to 30%) mistakenly state that the shortest travel time is along the straight line because of the shorter length. An even larger fraction (50 to 60%) wrongly believe that the travel times should be equal because the balls descend the same vertical distance, giving up the same gravitational energy, and the conservation of energy requires equal kinetic energies (and speed) at the end.

Of course students are surprised when they observe that the ball on the noticeably longer track always reaches the final point sooner than the ball on the straight track. They feel frustrated and insecure because a law (conservation of energy) that they thought they understood is apparently not true. This draws the class into discussion, exploring possible explanations of the outcome. Then we make an additional observation, and the students discover that they had misunderstood the law. We allow the balls to leave the tracks, falling freely under gravity and describing a parabola. On the tracks, one ball always runs behind the other. When they fall, they hit the floor one after the other—but both land at the same horizontal distance from the

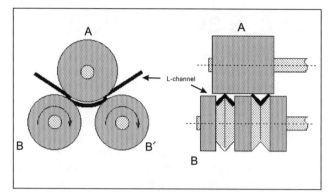

Fig. 3. Rollers used for bending L-shaped channels.

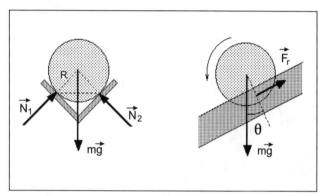

Fig. 4. Forces on rolling ball in L-shaped inclined channel.

end of the tracks!

This clarifies the point, and once students are convinced that conservation of energy really works, we show the other apparatus (cycloid track, Fig. 2). where the brachistochrone (least time) wins the race against the straight track, in a most

dramatic way, for different inclines. Finally, we use the cycloid track to show that the curve of quicker descent happens also to be tautochronous (i.e., two balls released from different points at each side of the cycloid meet at the bottom, independent of the starting point). Our students are again surprised and intrigued by this additional highly counterintuitive result.

The Analysis

To calculate the time needed for the ball to travel between two points on the tracks, we model the situation by approximating the shape of the tracks by a number of straight pieces. Consider the situation where the ball rolls down a single inclined plane at an angle θ with respect to the horizontal. In our experimental setup we use a right-angle channel with the rolling ball touching the channel at two symmetric points (Fig. 4).

The forces on the ball are: its weight $(M\vec{g})$ the two normal forces at each side of the incline $(\vec{N}_1$ and $\vec{N}_2)$, and the frictional forces exerted by the two edges of the incline $(\vec{F}_r)$. The equations of motion for translational and rotational motion, respectively, are:

$$Mg \sin\theta - 2F_r = Ma_{cm}$$

$$2F_r(R/\sqrt{2}) = I\alpha = (\frac{2}{5}MR^2)\alpha$$

where R is the radius of the rolling ball and $R/\sqrt{2}$ is the lever arm for $\vec{F}_r$. If we assume that the ball rolls without slipping, then $a_{cm} = (R/\sqrt{2})\alpha$. Combining the above equations, we obtain the acceleration of the center of mass:

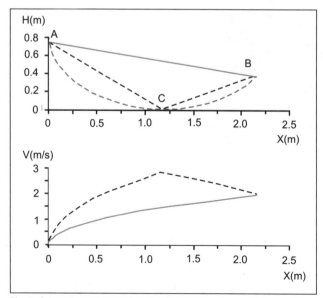

Fig. 5. Comparison of speeds along two straight-paths-model (gray solid line) and single straight path (--- line).

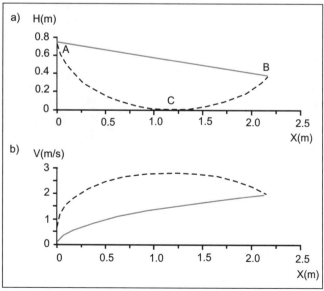

Fig. 6. Comparison of speeds along inclined straight track (solid gray line) and cycloid track (--- line) modeled with 128 straight paths.

Table I. Calculated speeds and times for four straight paths connecting initial and final points along cycloid track.

X (m)	Y (m)	H (m)	L (m)	V_0 (m/s)	V_f (m/s)	T (s)
0.094263	-0.22930	0.229303	0.247922	0	1.580144	0.313797
0.611893	-0.63490	0.405601	0.657611	1.580144	2.629334	0.312443
1.455024	-0.71744	0.082541	0.847162	2.629334	2.452473	0.290074
2.125050	-0.37530	0.342140	0.752326	2.452473	1.512976	0.330122
					TOTAL	
					TIME →	1.246436

$$a_{cm} = \left(\frac{5}{9}\right) g \sin\theta$$

Given the initial speed of the ball, V_0, we can find its final speed after descending (+) or ascending (–) along the incline at a vertical height H:

$$V_f = \sqrt{V_0^2 \pm 2\left(\frac{5}{9}\right) g \sin\theta \left(\frac{H}{\sin\theta}\right)} =$$

$$\sqrt{V_0^2 \pm \left(\frac{10}{9}\right) gH}$$

The total time required for the ball is given by:

$$t = \frac{V_f - V_0}{a_{cm}} = \left(\frac{9}{5}\right)\frac{V_f - V_0}{g\sin\theta} =$$

$$\left(\frac{9L}{5gH}\right)(V_f - V_0)$$

where L is the distance along the plane. Our next step is to choose an intermediate point along the track and consider two inclined straight paths joining this point with the end and final points. The final speed for one path is taken as the initial speed for the following one. We then continue with the process of dividing the tracks into a greater number of straight paths. This is easily accomplished with the help of

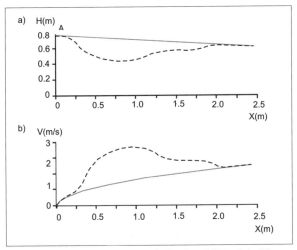

Fig. 7. Comparison of speeds along inclined straight track (solid gray line) and irregular track (---x line) modeled with 128 straight paths.

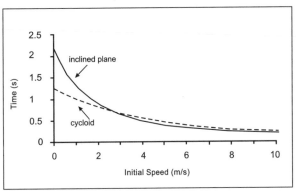

Fig. 8. Comparison of times for traveling along the cycloid track and inclined straight path.

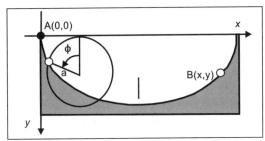

Fig. 9. Inverted cycloid traced by a point located on circle of radius a.

Excel, a very user-friendly spreadsheet. The procedure is illustrated in Table I, for four successive straight paths along the cycloid.

For the two-straight-paths model, results show immediately why the ball on the single incline is always left behind. The calculated time for the two inclines is 1.39 s, compared with 2.13 s for the single incline. Figure 5 shows the instantaneous speed of the ball plotted as a function of the horizontal distance for both tracks. Common sense arguments could be used to explain why the two inclines provide a path of shorter time in spite of the fact that the ball must travel farther. Since the time taken to travel between two points is the distance divided by the average speed, the first incline accelerates the ball rapidly at first and quickly gains a high speed. On the other hand, from conservation of energy, at

Table II. Calculated total times for different numbers of inclines connecting initial and final points along cycloid track.

Number of Inclines	1	2	4	8	16	32	64	128
Total Time (s)	2.1349	1.3946	1.2464	1.2354	1.2318	1.2309	1.2307	1.2303

Table III. Calculated travel times to the bottom, starting from different points on cycloid track.

Starting Point	X (cm)	Y (cm)	Time (s)
A	9.177E-5	74.98878	0.82170
B	22.18388	36.83950	0.821752
C	27.5823	31.914	0.819391
E	49.31402	17.14494	0.821033
F	96.44787	1.929934	0.820884

the end of the two inclines the speed should approach the same value as in the single incline, so the instantaneous speed should be always greater for the model with two inclines.

If we continue the process of dividing the cycloid track in greater number of inclines, 2,4,8,...128, from Table II it is observed that the calculated times approach a constant value. For up to 128 inclines the total time is 1.2303 s, which is within 0.008% of the theoretical value (1.2304 s) calculated analytically for the chosen points along the cycloid (see Appendix). Figures 6 and 7 show the calculated speeds for the two different apparatus, the brachistochrone and the irregular track.

Finally, we used our linear-pieces model to illustrate the tautochronous property of the cycloid, calculating the time taken by the ball to arrive to the bottom of the track after being released from different positions. Calculations were performed by dividing each portion of the cycloid in 128 inclined planes. The resulting travel times for five different initial positions were very close, as can be seen in Table III. The numerically calculated values are very close to the strictly analytical result of 0.822 s, obtained after solving the integral (see Appendix).

Does the Cycloid Always Win the Race?

One advantage of using a spreadsheet to model the track as though composed of linear pieces is that it is easy to change some parameters. Being able to do this is useful in situations where it is hard to see the behavior of equations by just looking at them. For example, we varied the initial speeds of the balls and compared the travel times for the cycloid and the single incline. Numerical calculations were performed in a straightforward way in the spreadsheet for different initial speeds; results are shown in Fig. 8. The two time curves cross at some point ($V_0 \approx 2.8$ m/s), which

means that this cycloid wins the race only for speeds less than this critical value. The analysis predicts that for greater initial speeds the ball on the straight track should arrive first. This result is surprising and shows the difficulty of guessing the outcome of the race when it is presented to the students for the first time. A similar behavior was reported by Zheng et al[5] for circular and parabolic tracks. It would be interesting to see if this behavior could be experimentally verified. However, it is not very easy to make sure that slipping does not occur for these larger initial speeds.

References

1. D.T. Hoffman, "A cycloid race," *Phys. Teach.* **29**, 395 (September 1991).
2. J. Bernoulli, "New problem, to whose solution the mathematicians are invited," *Acta Eruditorum Lipsiae*, 269 (1696).
3. M. de Icaza H, (*Rev. Mexicana de Física* **40**, 459 (1994).
4. W.J. Leonard and William J. Gerace, "The power of simple reasoning," *Phys. Teach.* **34**, 280 (May 1996).
5. T.F. Zheng, et al., "Does bead B always reach d first?" *Phys. Teach.* **33**, 376 (September 1995).

Appendix

The theoretical time required by the ball to go from (0,0) to any point (x,y) along the cycloid is calculated starting from the definition of the speed of the center of mass (CM) along the curve, $V = ds/dt$. Writing the differential of arc in terms of the Cartesian coordinates (x,y)

$$ds = \sqrt{dx^2 + dy^2} = \sqrt{1 + (dy/dx)^2}\, dx$$

Starting from rest, the speed of the CM of the rolling ball at a vertical position y is, from conservation of energy:

$$V = \sqrt{(10/9)gy}$$

The total time required for the ball to go from (0,0) to (X_1, Y_1) is

$$T = \int \frac{ds}{V} = \int_0^{x_1} \sqrt{\frac{1 + (dy/dx)2}{(10/9)gy}}\, dx$$

Using the parametric equation for an inverted cycloid (see Fig. 9):

$$x = a\,(\phi - \sin\phi)$$
$$y = a\,(1 - \cos\phi)$$

The evaluation of the integral gives the total time of the brachistochrone:

$$T_b = \phi_1 \sqrt{\frac{18}{10}} \sqrt{\frac{a}{g}}$$

The factor $\sqrt{18/10}$ does not appear for the case of a sliding bead. Substituting the value of radius $a = 0.373$ m for our cycloid track, $g = 9.80$ m/s^2 and $\phi_1 = 4.70$ rad, corresponding to the chosen final point (x,y), we obtain for the "analytical" travel time $T_b = 1.23$ s, as compared with the "numerical" value of 1.2303 s for the 128 inclines model (see Table II).

In the same way, it is shown that the time required for the ball to roll from the initial position (0,0) or ($\phi_0 = 0$) to the lowest position ($\phi_1 = \pi$) does not depend on the initial position. The tautochronous time for our track is:

$$T_t = \sqrt{\frac{18}{10}} \sqrt{\frac{a}{g}} = 0.822 \text{ s}$$

This is to be compared to the "numerical" values for the 128 inclines model (see Table III).

Rotational Motion, Centripetal Force, Angular Momentum

Apparatus for Rotational Motion

Said Shakerin, Department of Mechanical Engineering, University of the Pacific, Stockton, CA 95211

A simple device for demonstration of rotational motion is shown in Fig. 1. Place a wooden bead on a 20-cm circular loop of copper wire (diameter 0.4 cm) which is brazed to a straight 5-cm handle. Insert the handle in a hand drill. As the drill starts to rotate, while the handle is oriented vertically, the bead moves up from the bottom position. The position of the bead on the loop depends on the angular velocity of the drill. Regardless of this velocity, however, the bead never crosses the horizontal midpoint on the loop. Relevant analysis follows.

Assuming the bead is free to move along the loop (i.e., negligible friction between the loop and the bead), the equa-

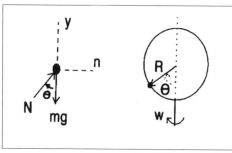

Fig. 2.

tions of motion along the radial and vertical directions are:

$$\Sigma F_n = m a_n \rightarrow N \sin \theta = R\, w^2 \sin \theta$$

$$\Sigma F_y = 0 \rightarrow mg - N \cos \theta = 0$$

Combining the above equations and solving for w, yields

$$w = \left(\frac{g}{(R \cos \theta)} \right)^{\frac{1}{2}}$$

Note: at $\theta = 90°$, $w \rightarrow \infty$

Fig. 1. Teaching tool for rotational motion.

Heavy-Duty Turntable

G. Dewey Beadle, Seneca High School, 3510 Goldsmith Lane, Louisville, KY 40220

Figure 1 shows a heavy-duty turntable suitable for a variety of rotational mechanics experiments. It can be made from a car spindle and wheel—a spindle from a Gremlin or Hornet works well because no modification of the spindle is necessary. The grease seal should be removed, the bearings should be cleaned of grease, and oil should be used as the lubricant. The brake drum is removed by driving the lug bolts out with a large punch. The spindle and hub should be reassembled, and this assembly should be inserted into the "wrong" side of the wheel. The lug nuts are used to secure the wheel to the spindle assembly. The rotating platform shown in Fig. 2 is made from 19-mm (3/4-in) plywood and is 0.45 m in diameter. A rubber mat (stair tread) glued to the top of the plywood platform provides more friction. The total cost for the spindle, the wheel, the plywood disk, and the other hardware is about $40. This turntable is suitable for doing an excellent demonstration illustrating the Coriolis effect.[1]

Reference

1. Lester Evans, *Phys. Teach* **20**, pp. 102–103 (1982).

Fig. 1. A heavy-duty turntable made from a car spindle and wheel.

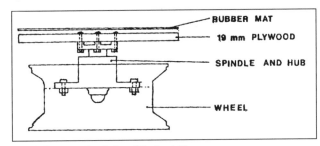

Fig. 2. Cross-sectional view of the turntable.

A Low-Friction Rotator from the Junkyard

Nathaniel R. Greene, Department of Physics, Bloomsburg University, Bloomsburg, PA 17815; ngreene@planetx.bloomu.edu

A low-friction rotating platform can be constructed at a minimal cost using an automotive water pump. These pumps have (see illustration) a heavy-duty ball-bearing race at the top. The body of the water pump is screwed to the stationary horizontal plywood base, and a steel plate is bolted to the rotating flange of the pump (where the pulley ordinarily attaches). In this application the water pump does not pump anything, but simply provides a robust bearing supported by a strong iron housing.

Students can stand on the platform and experience the conservation of angular momentum, for example, the way figure skaters speed up their rotation by pulling in their arms. The device is also sturdy enough for heavy apparatus to be attached to the steel platform.[1] Commercial rotators are available, of course, but those of comparable strength, low friction, and versatility cost hundreds of dollars. The materials described are very cheap and available even in remote corners of the world.[2]

Our device was constructed using the water pump from a 1979 Ford 302 V8 engine, though the make and model are not critical. Upon learning of the educational application, the junkyard owner kindly donated the part. It is important to check that the bearing is still in good condition (it should have no lateral free play). For our steel plate we chose 1/4-in-thick "diamond plate," one side of which is textured for traction. This material is common (and likely free) at a steel scrap yard. Most of the few hours required to assemble the rotator were spent cutting and drilling the steel. A large center hole (~2-cm diameter) is needed for the protruding tip of the pump shaft, as well as smaller holes for the flange bolts. Wood screws attach the pump to the base, which is a piece of 3/4-in plywood approximately 50-cm square. Tested with a load of 180 kg, the rotator spins smoothly and shows no signs of strain.

Acknowledgments

I wish to thank Vincent Hron of the Bloomsburg University Art Department for drawing the figure and Swartz Salvage Inc. of Jerseytown, PA for donating the water pump.

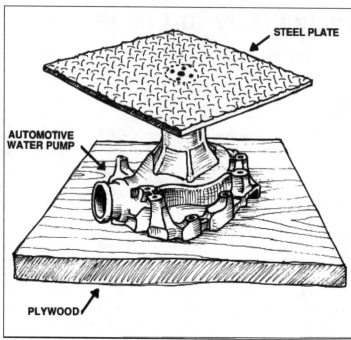

Low-friction rotating platform constructed from an automotive water pump.

References

1. For example, to illustrate the Coriolis effect, have two students toss a ball back and forth while seated on a 2.5-m-long plank that rotates about its midpoint. C-clamps may be used to fasten the plank to the rotator. See W.H.E. Rueckner & S.J. Steel, *The Demonstrative Physicist's Companion* (Harvard Science Center, Cambridge. MA, 1995).
2. The author learned of this device while serving as a Peace Corps physics teacher in Cameroon, West Africa.

A Long and Bumpy Road

Jeffrey R. Regester, McDonogh School, Owings Mills, MD 21117-0380; jrr@erols.com

It is well known that a uniform chain or rope supported at both ends (but otherwise hanging freely) assumes the shape of a catenary. It is less well known that a catenary is also the shape that allows square wheels to roll freely, just as round wheels roll easily on a flat surface. This is because a catenary is just the right shape that, when a square is "rolling" on it, the center of gravity of the wheel maintains a constant height—thus no work is required to lift the center of gravity. See Fig. 1.

While thinking about the upcoming topic of center of gravity for my physics class (during which I always ask the question "Why do wheels work?"), I decided to put this idea to the test by building a catenary road surface, shown in Fig. 2. Students are amazed that anything can roll smoothly on

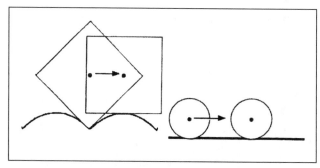

Fig. 1. For a "wheel" of any shape to roll smoothly, its center of gravity (marked with the small black circle) mustn't rise or fall as it rotates about the point of contact with the "ground."

such a bumpy road.

To build your own bumpy road, photocopy Fig. 3 six times. Cut out the road templates using the dotted boxes and use rubber cement to glue them, end to end and in a straight line, on a long narrow piece of nice plywood (at least ½ in thick). You'll need to overlap the segments a little: use the pointed valleys of the catenary to align the strips precisely. Take another piece of the same plywood and glue it to the first, side-by-side, using just two drops of wood glue at opposite ends, so they can easily be separated. This way, you can cut through both pieces and form the two tracks simultaneously. Use a band saw for this, following the catenary line as precisely as possible. Next, glue two of the wheel templates to scraps of the same plywood and cut them out. Drill ¼-in holes through the center of each and glue them to the ends of a ¼-in-diameter dowel five inches long. Finally, glue the two tracks to some scraps of wood, with the same spacing as the square wheels on the dowel. I also made a set of round

Fig. 2. Catenary road and wheels to roll on it.

wheels to demonstrate that, although they work great on a flat surface, they don't on the catenary road.

My classes love this demo, I think partly because it addresses a question so basic that they had never thought of it before: Why do wheels work?

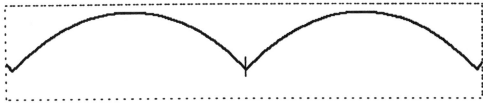

Fig. 3. Templates for the square wheels and catenary road surface.

Moment of Inertia with PVC Pipe and Iron Rebar

David R. Lapp, Tamalpais High School, Mill Valley, CA 94941

A nice introduction to the topic of rotational motion can be made with the moment-of-inertia batons that are available commercially for a little over $100.[1] Students will notice that they appear to be identical (unless, of course, they are painted differently). They have the same length, diameter, center of mass, and total weight (which can be verified with a scale). However, when a student attempts to rotate the batons, one of the batons is noticeably more difficult to rotate. The student is unable to observe that the interior of the batons contains a mass of metal. In the one baton the metal is in one piece and centered. In the other baton, the metal is in two equal pieces and located at the ends. The connection between the amount of torque necessary for a given angular acceleration and the distribution of mass can then be discussed as the inner construction of the two batons is revealed. Students will notice that the baton with the mass in the middle rotates more easily.

The batons I've made are inexpensive (less than $10) and easy to construct. All materials are available at local building-supply stores. Each consists of approximately one-meter sections of 1-in PVC pipe. In the middle of one is a 20-cm piece of 1-in diameter rebar (the kind of iron bar used to reinforce concrete). The other pipe has a 10-cm section of rebar located at each end. I found that the rebar did not quite fit into the PVC pipe. The metal has a ribbed outside that needs to be ground down a bit. Using coarse emery paper is possible but slow; a power grinder is definitely the way to go if one is available. I ground mine down just enough to make a snug fit that actually required hammering into position. This eliminated the necessity of gluing the metal into place. Both pipes have 1-in PVC end caps so that initially students are not able to see the inner construction (see Fig. l). I painted my batons different colors so I could distinguish one from the other without handling them, but this isn't essential.

The difference in moments of inertia is not difficult to determine since the geometry of both batons is rather uncomplicated. The baton with the centered metal piece can be thought of as being two centered slender rods with their axes through the center and, as a first approximation, the other baton can be thought of as one slender rod with its axis at the center together with two point masses rotating at a specific radius (0.45 m) from the axis. The calculations for the moments of inertia for my batons follow.

For the baton with the iron centered:

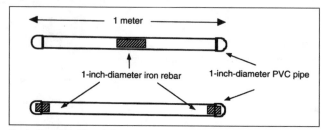

Fig. 1. Moment-of-inertia batons.

$$I_{PVC} + I_{IRON} = \qquad (1)$$

$$\frac{1}{12} M_{PVC} L_{PVC}^2 + \frac{1}{12} M_{IRON} L_{IRON}^2 =$$

$$\frac{1}{12} (0.478 \text{ kg}) (1.0 \text{ m})^2 +$$

$$\frac{1}{12} (0.798 \text{ kg}) (0.20 \text{ m})^2 = 0.042 \text{ kg} \cdot \text{m}^2$$

For the baton with the iron at the ends:

$$I = I_{PVC} + I_{IRON} = \qquad (2)$$

$$\frac{1}{12} M_{PVC} L_{PVC}^2 + 2 (M_{IRON} R_{IRON}^2) =$$

$$\frac{1}{12} (0.478 \text{ kg}) (1.0 \text{ m})^2 +$$

$$2\left(\frac{0.798 \text{ kg}}{2}\right) (0.45 \text{ m})^2 = 0.20 \text{ kg} \cdot \text{m}^2$$

The second calculation shows a moment of inertia almost five times greater than the first, and the subjective test of trying to rotate these at the same time with the same angular acceleration (which is the natural way to rotate these if one is in each hand) bears this out.

This demonstration intrigues and fascinates students. I like it especially because after students understand the geometry of the batons, it is natural for them to predict that distribution of mass is an essential aspect of rotational motion. This early understanding often gives the confidence that so many students seem to need in order to grasp the subtleties of rotational dynamics.

Reference

1. "Mystery Batons," $115.99; Sargent-Welch, P.O. Box 1026, Skokie, IL 60076-8026.

A New Use for an Old Pickle Bucket

Jonathan Mitschele, Saint Joseph's College, Windham, ME 04062-1198

After seeing a picture (much like the illustration in Fig. 1) of a simple apparatus for demonstrating the forces acting on a ball rolling inside and then outside a circular hoop, I wanted such a device for my own classes. As I was casting about the campus for that huge piece of PVC sewer pipe that must be lying around somewhere (or so I thought), my eye fell on one of our more humble trash cans, an old plastic pickle bucket.[1] Just the ticket, I thought, and took it down to our maintenance department for modification. One of the crew cut off the top three or four inches (10 cm) of the bucket, and from this upper piece cut out a vertical notch about 3 inches (7.5 cm) wide. The result is a centripetal force demonstrator (CFD).

This seems to be the perfect design. If you hold the walls of the CFD so that the opening is less than about three inches wide, a one-inch-diameter (2.5-cm) steel ball set in motion along the inside walls will, when it reaches the opening, leave the CFD but continue on to strike the opposite edge. If you put the CFD on a level table with the opening toward the class, everyone can see this happen. I demonstrate this to my class and ask "How can we make the ball leave the CFD without hitting the far side of the opening?" Their intuitive answers—make the ball roll faster or slower—do not work. Students quickly realize that the correct solution is to widen the opening, and with our flexible pickle bucket this is easily done.

We can use elementary geometry to predict the smallest opening through which a ball will pass cleanly. We know that regardless of the speed of the ball, when it reaches the opening and leaves the confines of the walls, it will cease to move in a circular path and begin to travel in a tangential direction. Figure 2 illustrates the geometrical conditions that must be met for the ball to leave the bucket without striking the far edge of the opening. In Fig. 2, s is the size of the minimum opening, measured along the arc, R is the radius of the bucket, and d is the diameter of the ball. Since

$$\cos \theta = \frac{R - d}{R} \qquad (1)$$

and $s = R\theta$,

$$s = R \cos^{-1}\left(\frac{R - d}{R}\right) \qquad (2)$$

For a bucket with inside diameter of 27 cm, the minimum opening for a 2.5-cm-diameter ball is 8.3 cm. This agrees closely with what we have found to be the minimum opening in our experiments, 8.5 cm.

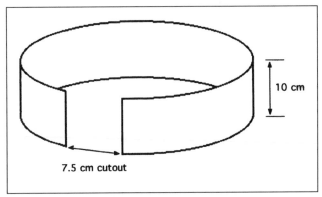

Fig. 1. Centripetal force demonstrator.

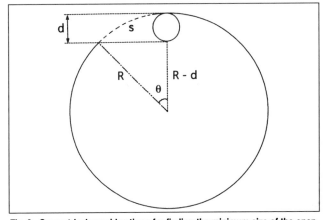

Fig. 2. Geometrical considerations for finding the minimum size of the opening s.

A counterintuitive demonstration such as this can serve as the stimulus for a lively discussion of centripetal forces. Since the materials are so readily available and the making so easy, I recommend this to you as a project worth doing.

Acknowledgment

I would like to express my appreciation to column editor Karl Mamola for suggestions that much improved this column.

Reference

1. Good places to find plastic pickle buckets (approximately 30 cm outside diameter by 40 cm high) are the local cafeteria or pizza parlor. Sheetrock taping compound is supplied in comparable containers, so suitable buckets may also be found at construction sites or obtained from drywall contractors. You can, of course, purchase identical buckets from hardware stores and the like.

Measure Centripetal Force for Under $3

Joe Bunn, Muscatine High School, Muscatine, IA 52761; *and Jay Smith,* Dekalb High School, Dekalb, IL 60115

Many physics teachers are not satisfied with the centripetal force experiments we have to offer our students. Swinging a cork on a string overhead seldom gives good quantitative results, and although there are commercial devices that work well, they are very expensive. As an alternative, we devised the inexpensive centripetal force apparatus shown in Fig. 1, which consists primarily of a cross made from PVC pipe that rotates on a fixed vertical support rod. The apparatus is practical because it makes use of readily available materials and takes only about 10 minutes to construct after the components are gathered. We've found the experiment to be at a good level for high-school students.

Construction

You will need four pieces of PVC pipe: $A = 70$ cm, $B = 30$ cm (two of these), and $C = 17$ cm. We used half-inch PVC because that's what would fit over our support rod, but three-quarter-inch pipe would work over a larger rod. (The suggested lengths make it possible for you to make two pieces of equipment from one 10-ft piece of PVC. Length A is determined by the length of your support rod and the height of the pulley. We have made A as short as 30 cm with no loss in stability.) Following directions on the cans of PVC pipe cleaner and adhesive, connect pipes A, B, and C to the four-way joint and attach end caps as shown in the figure.

For the mass container we used a discarded film canister. With needlenosed pliers, grasp the head of a thumbtack and poke the tack through the center of the bottom of the canister. This tack pointer will serve as a counter when it hits the twist-tie that is taped to the clamp, as shown. Make a hole in one side of the canister for string #2, which goes through the canister and out the top. Referring to Fig. 1, you will see that the length of string #2 determines the amount of rubber-band stretch, which in turn determines the centripetal force. The string length is adjusted by pulling on its free end and closing the canister lid to

hold it in place. On the opposite side of the canister, make another hole and fashion a hook from a paper clip with which to capture string #4. Fill the canister with lead shot, BBs or whatever you have at hand and suspend it from the pipe arm with string #3.

A student pulls string #1 at the correct speed to make the revolving film canister tick the twist-tie each time around while another student measures the period. For a first trial,

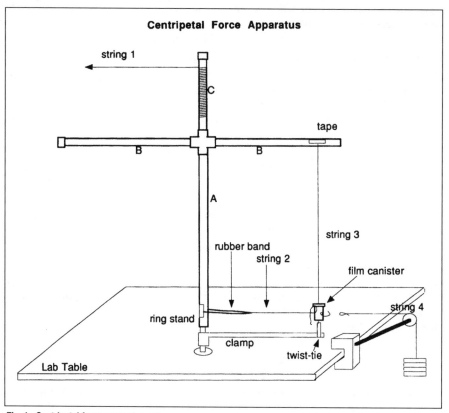

Centripetal Force Apparatus

string 1

C

tape

B
B

A

string 3

rubber band
string 2

film canister

ring stand

string 4

clamp

Lab Table

twist-tie

Fig. 1. Centripetal force apparatus setup.

students should adjust string #2 so the pointer is 1 cm inside the twist-tie when the canister is not moving. Finally, to measure the magnitude of the centripetal force provided by the rubber band, attach string #4 to the film canister and hang a mass over the pulley attached to the lab table. (With this last measurement the system is not rotating!)

Using the Apparatus

Challenge: Determine the mass of the film canister by measuring its speed for different amounts of centripetal force at a particular radius.

As students familiarize themselves with the apparatus by gently pulling string #1 to make the mass revolve and then gradually increasing the speed, they are reminded that when an object is moving in circular motion more centripetal force is needed to make it travel faster or in a smaller circle. As the student pulls on the string, the canister mass moves out from the center until the force provided by the rubber band, the speed of the mass, and the radius of the circle will satisfy $F = mv^2/r$.

Students can vary force, radius, or mass and measure the resulting speed. They should discover that the slope of the F vs v^2 line can be used in the centripetal force formula, along with the radius, to calculate the unknown mass. Errors of less than 5% are obtained with this method.

Acknowledgments

We wish to thank NSF for funding the Physics Teacher Enhancement Program at Northern Illinois University. This grant has allowed 24 teachers to spend three summers studying physics and sharing ideas.

Measuring the Forces Required for Circular Motion

Charles Henderson, Physics Department, Macalester College, St. Paul, MN 55105; Henderson@Macalester.edu

Many students have trouble understanding the forces required for circular motion. They memorize and can recite the equation $F_c = m\omega^2 r$. They often get confused, however, when they are asked to solve problems such as calculating the frictional force necessary to keep a coin on a turntable, the tension in a string necessary to keep a ball swinging in a horizontal or vertical circle, or the apparent weight of a Ferris-wheel rider at the top and bottom. I have been searching for a good laboratory apparatus to allow students to measure these forces. The ideal apparatus would:

- Allow students to directly measure the forces acting on an object moving in uniform circular motion.
- Allow students to study either horizontal or vertical circular motion.
- Allow students to vary the mass and radius.
- Be easy to understand and use.
- Provide good and reliable data.

Most of the available circular-motion setups have students infer the force based on the length of a stretched spring or rubber band. This means it is difficult to measure forces while keeping the radius constant. It also becomes very difficult to measure the forces of vertical circular motion where the forces are constantly changing.

However, while attending a 1997 summer workshop

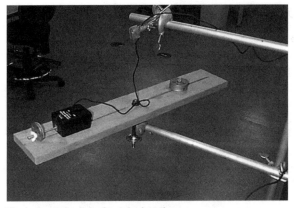

Fig. 1. Apparatus in horizontal orientation.

("Teaching Physics Using Interactive Teaching Methods and Computers" at Dickinson College), participants were given an opportunity to work on a project that they could use in their current teaching situation. I decided to try to design an apparatus that allowed students to examine the forces of circular motion.

It seemed clear to me that a microcomputer-based laboratory (MBL) force probe would be the best measurement tool for this apparatus. A force probe, when used with appropriate software, allows students to measure positive or negative forces along the axis of the force probe. The force probe is ideal for this situation since it can measure forces continu-

Fig. 2. Apparatus in vertical orientation.

ously for a period of time and display a real-time graph of force versus time.

The Apparatus

If you already have an MBL force probe, this apparatus will cost you less than $10 and take less than an hour to construct. The apparatus can also be used, with the addition of a spool and hanging mass, to study other aspects of rotational motion such as moment of inertia, torques, and rotational dynamics.

The apparatus (see Figs. 1 and 2) is essentially a piece of wood mounted on the front hub of a bicycle wheel that rotates with relatively low friction. A force probe is attached to one end of the wood and a counterweight to the other end. A mass is attached to the force probe and the whole thing is given a quick push causing the mass to move in (nearly) uniform circular motion.

All of these components can be taped together as they were in my first version, but the apparatus is easier to use if the force probe and counterweight are bolted to the board so that they can be easily moved. A complete materials list is given in Table I.

Construction

Drill a 5/16-in hole in the center of the piece of wood and two ¼-in holes 1 in from the center as starter holes for a router. With a ¼-in bit, rout out a ¼-in slit from each starter hole to within 1 in from each end of the wood. You should have something that looks like the sketch in Fig. 3.

Bolt the front hub to the wooden piece through the center hole. The ¼-in brass washer should fit snugly into the hole on the top of the Vernier Dual-Range Force Sensor and be supported by the metal rim inside the hole. Secure the force probe to the wooden piece with a 2-in bolt using a split washer and wing nut on the side opposite the force probe. Attach a second 2-in bolt by pushing it through the slit on the other side, securing it with a split washer and wing nut. You can then slip on a slotted mass and secure it by tightening the wing nut. Both the force probe and the slotted masses should move easily upon loosening the wing nut.

Table I. Materials needed to construct and use apparatus.

For Construction:

- Piece of wood   (1 by 4 by 24 in)
- Bicycle front hub   (5½ by 5/16 in)
- 2½-in 6-32 threaded bolt
- Two 6-32 threaded fiberglass wing nuts
- Two 2-in ¼ x 20 threaded bolts
- Two ¼ x 20 wing nuts
- Two ¼-in split washers
- Two ¼-in washers
- ¼-in brass washer

For Use:
- Force probe
- Two lab support rods
- Two double 45° rod clamps
- Table clamp
- Miscellaneous slotted masses

Finally, unscrew the metal weight hook from the force probe. Screw the wing nuts onto a 2½-in threaded bolt and screw the bolt into the force probe. Another slotted mass can then be secured between the two wing nuts.

Using the Apparatus

The apparatus can be used as a student lab exercise, as a

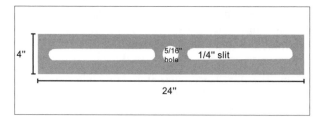

Fig. 3. Wooden portion of apparatus.

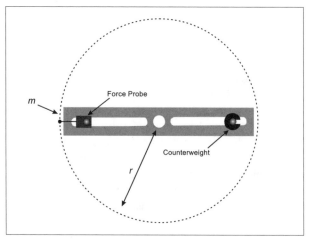

Fig. 4. Sketch of apparatus in horizontal orientation.

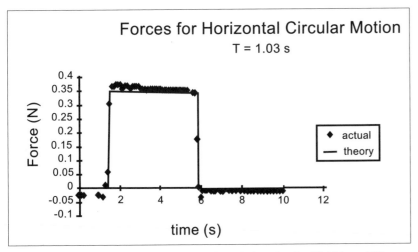

Forces for Horizontal Circular Motion
T = 1.03 s

◆ actual
— theory

Fig. 5. Typical results from the apparatus in its horizontal orientation. For this trial, $m = 25.7$ g, $r = 0.36$ m, and $T = 1.03$ s.

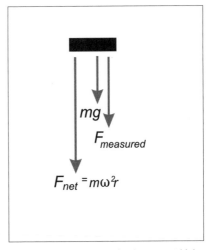

Fig. 6. Free-body diagram for the mass at highest point in its circular path.

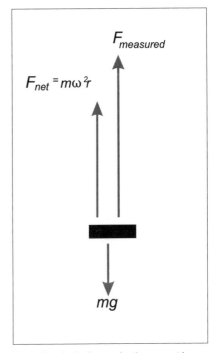

Fig. 7. Free-body diagram for the mass at lowest point in its circular path.

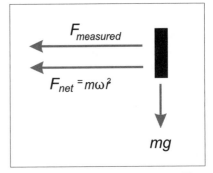

Fig. 8. Free-body diagram for the mass at middle point in its circular path.

traditional demo, or as an interactive lecture demonstration. To use the apparatus, mount a lab support rod vertically on a lab table using the table clamp. Attach another rod horizontally using a double 45° rod clamp. Attach the front hub of the apparatus to the horizontal rod using a second double 45° rod clamp (making sure that the apparatus will not hit anything when it spins).

One of the potential problems with this apparatus is the tangling of the cord connecting the force probe to the computer. To minimize this problem, I find it helpful to mount an additional rod with a hook (or other cord holding device) a short distance in front of the center of rotation. Be sure to leave the cord some slack so that it can wind a bit without pulling on the force probe. For measuring the forces of vertical motion many students find it easy to simply hold the cord loosely in front of the apparatus. Having students alternate the direction of rotation for their data runs also helps limit cord twisting.

There are three things that I tell the students that seem to help preserve the equipment:
 (1) Keep the rotations slow (about a 1-s period);
 (2) Alternate the direction of rotations to minimize cord winding;
 (3) Mount the force probe on the rotating board so that no part of it sticks out past the board.

Once the apparatus is set up, attach a mass (m) to the force probe with the wing nuts (see Fig. 4). Put on an appropriately sized counterweight (the Vernier force probe has a mass of about 130 g) and, by using the apparatus as a balance, find its proper location. Calibrate the force probe. An easy way to do this is by using the apparatus in its vertical position. When the mass is at the highest point, the probe should read $-mg$; and at the lowest point, the probe should read mg. Put the apparatus in either its horizontal or vertical position. Start the data collection program and give the

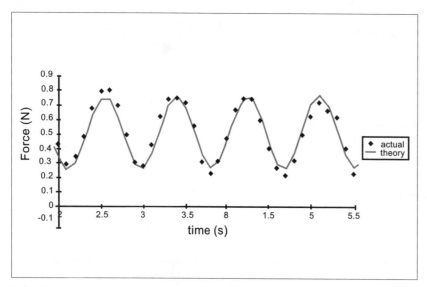

Fig. 9. Typical results from apparatus in its vertical orientation. For this trial, m = 25.7 g, r = 0.36 m, T = 0.85 s, and ϕ = 1.6.

For vertical circular motion, the analysis is a bit more difficult. Let's consider three points on the circular path.

The highest point:
Based on the free-body diagram in Fig. 6, the measured force on the force probe should be

$$F_{measured} = m\omega^2 r - mg \qquad (2)$$

The lowest point:
Based on the free-body diagram in Fig. 7, the measured force on the force probe should be

$$F_{measured} = m\omega^2 r + mg \qquad (3)$$

The middle point:
Based on the free-body diagram in Fig. 8, the measured force on the force probe should be

$$F_{measured} = m\omega^2 r \qquad (4)$$

If we combine these three situations (we would come to the same conclusion if we had considered the location of the mass at a general time t, but the above steps may be useful for students), we would expect the measured force to vary with time as,

$$F_{measured}(t) = m\omega^2 r + mg\sin(\omega t + \phi) \qquad (5)$$

Figure 9 shows a set of typical results for vertical circular motion. The theoretical line is calculated from Eq. (5) where m is the total value of the mass and the holding apparatus (25.7 g), v is calculated from the period of rotation as measured on a stopwatch for four complete rotations, r is the distance from the center of rotation to the center of the mass as measured on a meterstick (36 cm), g is the acceleration due to gravity (9.81 m/s2), t is the time, and f is a phase constant that was adjusted manually to get the best fit. Notice that there is also evidence of friction in this trial.

This apparatus can be used in a wide variety of laboratory situations. To see a copy of the laboratory instructions given to the students in the introductory physics course at Macalester College, visit our web site at www.macalester.edu/~physics — follow the "courses" link, click on "Physics 26 Labs," and look for "Fall lab number 8."

wheel a little push. The apparatus will then cause the mass to move in (nearly) uniform circular motion with the only forces acting on it being the force due to gravity and the force measured on the force probe. Use a stopwatch to measure the time of three or four complete rotations, then stop the apparatus. The apparatus works best with a period of rotation of around 1.0 s. If the period is much shorter than this, a very noticeable amount of friction will be present in the system.

Theory and Results

For horizontal circular motion, we would expect the force probe to read a constant,

$$F_{measured} = m\omega^2 r \qquad (1)$$

when the mass is moving, and zero otherwise. Figure 5 shows a set of typical results for horizontal circular motion. The theoretical line is calculated from Eq. (1) where m is the total value of the mass and the holding apparatus (25.7 g), ω is calculated from the period of rotation as measured on a stopwatch for four complete rotations, and r is the distance from the center of rotation to the center of the mass as measured on a meterstick (36 cm). Notice that the decreasing measured force is an indication of decreasing angular velocity due to friction.

Circular Motion and an Inverse Square Machine

Angus W. Scott, St. Mark's School of Texas, Dallas, TX 75230

Orthodox experiments in rotary motion demonstrate interesting mathematical relationships between velocity and radius, but they tell us nothing about satellite or planetary motion. Using a device that will provide a centripetal force inversely proportional to the square of the radius, it is possible to demonstrate the effects of gravitational forces. There are three experiments which can usefully be performed on the air table and in connection with the first two I have some suggestions that may be new to some readers. The third experiment uses my "inverse square machine" to simulate the motion of a satellite (Fig. 1).

The First Experiment

In this experiment the centripetal force is produced by a weight (Fig. 2). and the motion is analyzed by stroboscopic photography.

To help overcome the problem of small measurements, holes are made in the photograph at each puck position, and the photograph is placed in a paper frame on an overhead projector. The pattern then can be seen on the chalk board, and the path may be drawn.

To create a pattern to scale, a half-meter rule should be photographed on the air table and a hole made in the photograph at each end of the rule. Two dots are drawn on the board 50 cm apart. The photograph is then placed on the projector which is moved until the two dots of light coincide with the two dots on the board. Now distances on the board are full scale for any photograph of the air table taken from the same camera position.

The radius (R) of a circle and also the distance between puck positions now can be measured on the board. If the time between flashes is known then the velocity (V) of the puck can be determined.

Having obtained several values of V and R, a graph of V^2 vs. R can be drawn. The mass of the puck can be determined using the slope of this graph and the weight on the end of the cord.

A Second Experiment

In this experiment the centripetal force is produced in a different way: a spring is used with one end tied to the cord and the other anchored to the floor (Fig. 3). The spring position is arranged so that when the puck radius equals zero, the spring is just unstretched. Thus the centripetal force is proportional to the radius of the puck's path (radius equals spring stretch). It is useful to have an anti-twist device

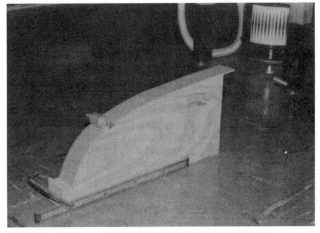

Fig. 1. The inverse square machine used in the third experiment.

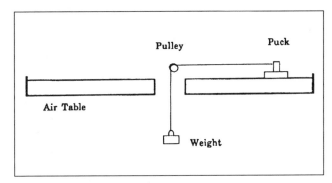

Fig. 2. The centripetal force is constant.

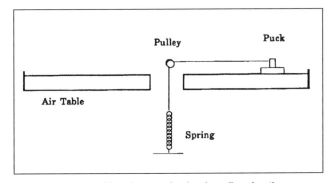

Fig. 3. The centripetal force is proportional to the radius of motion.

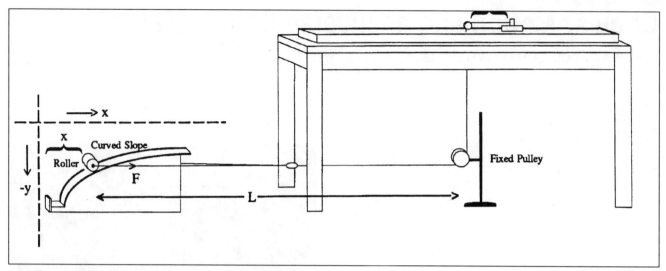

Fig. 4. The centripetal force is inversely proportional to the square of the radius.

between the cord and the spring.

This experiment now can be a repeat of the first with the analysis showing that the velocity is proportional to the radius, and therefore, that both the angular velocity and the period of revolution are constant. There is an alternative way to show that the period is constant for different radii. Rather than projecting the image on the chalkboard, position a laser beam across the table with a photocell and timer on the other side, allowing a vertical rod on the puck to interrupt the beam every half revolution. The time for each revolution remains nearly the same as the puck spirals toward the center.

A Third Experiment—Showing the Motion of Satellites

Figures 1 and 4 show the device that I call my inverse square machine. This device will produce a centripetal force inversely proportional to the square of the radius of the puck's motion, and it will make the puck behave like a satellite.

At one end, the tension in the cord supplies the centripetal force on the puck. At the other end, the tension supplies a force on a roller which can move either up or down a curved slope (Fig. 4). If length L is long enough, the force F is always approximately horizontal. The distance x must be the same as the radius of the puck circle. The forces acting on the roller are shown in Fig. 5 (there is no sliding friction and rolling friction is neglected).

There is equilibrium at a tangent to the slope, so

$$F \cos \theta = mg \sin \theta \qquad (1)$$

or

$$F = mg \tan \theta. \qquad (2)$$

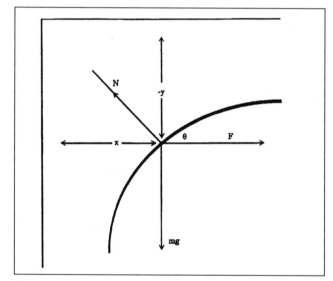

Fig. 5. Equilibrium forces on the roller.

It is required that $F = K/x^2$ and $\tan \theta = dy/dx$. Substituting these values into Eq. (2) yields

$$dy/dx = (K/mg) (1/x^2). \qquad (3)$$

Integrating, we find

$$y = (-K/mg) (1/x) + \text{constant}. \qquad (4)$$

Thus, the required surface is a $(-1/x)$ curve.

I will gladly supply suggestions for the equation of the sloping surface and for suitable masses for the puck and roller.

Angular Momentum Conservation Demonstration

Richard E. Berg and *Robert E. Anders,* University of Maryland, College Park, MD 20742

A simple yet eloquent demonstration of conservation of angular momentum can be constructed using a Lazy Susan, as shown in Fig. 1. A 2-in (5-cm) Lazy Susan is mounted in a horizontal plane on a supporting frame, with a 2-ft (60-cm) arm constructed of extruded aluminum channel mounted on the upper plate of the Lazy Susan. Figure 2 shows the cross section of the aluminum channel. Cylindrical copper weights, mounted onto Teflon blocks, are free to slide inside the channel. A thin nylon cord is attached to each of the Teflon blocks and runs inside the channel and down through the center of the Lazy Susan, where the center of the cord is attached to the end of a metal bead chain. The bead chain allows rotation of the nylon cord with the rotating arms without twisting the cord.

With the weights against limiting blocks at the outer ends of the channel track, the arm may be started in rotation. Pulling the chain pulls in the weights, concomitantly increasing their speed due to conservation of angular momentum. Slowly releasing the chain allows the weights to move back out to their original radius, reducing their speed to its original value.

In addition to showing the law of conservation of angular momentum qualitatively, we can demonstrate both energy and angular momentum conservation semi-quantitatively under the appropriate conditions. Using conservation of angular momentum:

$$mvr = mVR \quad (1)$$

where V is the velocity of the masses at the maximum radius R. When r = R/2, the velocity v is then:

$$v = VR/r = 2V \quad (2)$$

The angular velocity then becomes:

$$\omega = v/r = (2V)/(R/2) = 4V/R = 4\,\omega_0 \quad (3)$$

where $w_0 = V/R$ is the original angular velocity. Thus the arm goes around with four times its original angular velocity, which can be verified approximately by using the demonstration.

The kinetic energy of the masses after they have been pulled in can be determined for the above case:

$$KE = \tfrac{1}{2}mv^2 = \tfrac{1}{2}m\,(VR/r)^2 = 4\,KE_0 \quad (4)$$

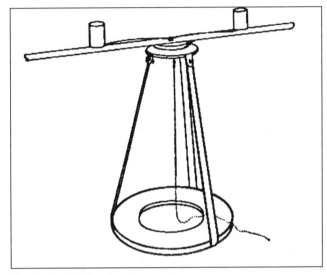

Fig. 1. Angular momentum demonstration.

A student who pulls the mass inward will notice (perhaps with some coaching) that this requires a force somewhat greater than the force required simply to maintain the masses at a fixed radius.

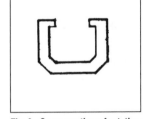

Fig. 2. Cross section of rotating arm.

The work required for the case above can be determined by evaluating the integral W for the work as the masses are pulled inward from radius R to radius r = R/2:

$$W = \int_R^{R/2} F\, dr = -\int_R^{R/2} (mv^2/r)\, dr \quad (5)$$

$$= -mV^2R^2 \int_R^{R/2} (1/r^3)\, dr$$

$$W = 3\left(\frac{1}{2}mV^2\right) = 3KE_0 \quad (6)$$

The total kinetic energy is the sum of the original kinetic energy and the work required to pull the masses inward:

$$KE = KE_0 + W = KE_0 + 3KE_0 = 4KE_0 \quad (7)$$

This is in agreement with the result obtained in Eq. (4) using conservation of angular momentum alone.

For our demonstration, the mass of each sliding cylinder is about 1 kg and its maximum radius is about 28 cm, so the maximum moment of inertia I_R for the two masses is:

$$I_R = 2MR^2 = 2 \times 1.0 \text{ kg} \times (0.28\text{m})^2 \approx 0.16 \text{ kg·m}^2 \tag{8}$$

When the masses are pulled in their combined moment of inertia I_r is:

$$I_r = 2Mr^2 = 2 \times 1.0 \text{ kg} \times (0.14\text{m})^2 \approx 0.04 \text{ kg·m}^2 \tag{9}$$

The moment of inertia of the cross arm of mass m = 97 g and length l = 64 cm is:

$$I_m = ml^2/12 = 0.097 \text{ kg} \times (0.64\text{m})^2/12 \tag{10}$$

$$\approx 0.0033 \text{ kg·m}^2$$

The moment of inertia of the crossbar is less than ten percent of that of the rotating masses in their inward position, so the measurement should be good to about ten percent. Friction in the Lazy Susan degrades it slightly, but the four-to-one ratio is still reasonably clear.

This device has proven to be an effective demonstration. It has been used with different amounts of mathematical analysis, for groups from high-school level through physics majors.

Our angular-motion demonstrator was easy to construct, and has worked for over 20 years with only minor repairs.

The Suitcase Gyroscope — An Angular Momentum Device

John F. Koser, PTRA, Wayzata Senior High School, 305 Vicksburg Lane, Plymouth, MN 55447-3999

Physics teachers often use a rotating stool to illustrate the conservation of angular momentum. As the demonstrator on the rotating stool alters his or her rotational inertia by moving a pair of heavy weights either close to or far from the axis of rotation the demonstrator's rotational velocity changes so as to maintain the angular momentum constant. Another approach to angular momentum conservation can be developed using the idea of what happens when the axis of the rotation is disturbed, thereby producing precession.

I find precession a difficult topic to explain to students because of the spatial understandings that they must develop. To explain why the spinning object actually precesses at a right angle to the direction of the applied force demands the use of a three-dimensional model. The bicycle-wheel gyroscope used in most high school classrooms works well if accompanied with clear explanations and is a demonstration that students will remember if used in conjunction with a turntable or rotating stool. They actually feel the precession force, which is learning firsthand. In an earlier issue of *The Physics Teacher*, J. Higbie nicely sets up a method of graphically explaining gyroscopic precession that could be used with the bicycle-wheel gyroscope. Students seem to be able to visualize the vectors of precession if an explanation of the type Higbie describes is used. I have found that it helps when using this explanation if paper arrows representing vectors are attached to the points of the wheel where illustrated by Higbie when explaining precession. It is also of value to have several other examples to illustrate the phenomenon. One of these is the "suitcase gyroscope" illustrated in this article.

Simple to build and graphic in its action, the device consists of a concealed rotating weighted wheel inside a rigid suitcase which can be carried around corners or rotated by its handle, producing precession that no student who tries it will forget. In their valuable resource for physics teachers, *A Demonstration Handbook for Physics*, George Freier and F.J. Anderson describe one version of a gyroscope in a suitcase but do not supply the details for building it.

The "Suitcase Gyroscope" that I built is shown opened in Fig. 1. Notice that the lining has been removed from the suitcase (an old rigid Samsonite purchased for $.60 at a local garage sale) to make the inner surface more accessible. A slot has been cut in the bottom directly below the rotating

Fig. 1. Interior of "Suitcase Gyroscope" showing bicycle front fork with weighted wheel mounted securely to suitcase wall. Note slot cut in bottom of suitcase just below the wheel.

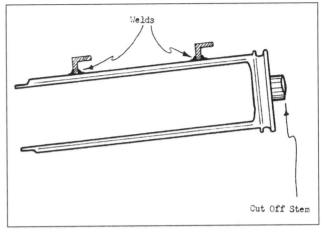

Fig. 2. Bicycle front fork with welded angle iron sections.

Fig. 3. Externally energizing the gyroscope.

wheel (but not on the hinge line) so that the wheel can be started externally using friction drive from a sanding disc on an electric drill. (It is suggested that future builders consider constructing a pedestal in which is hidden a motor with such a disc so that the suitcase can be resting on the pedestal while it is run up to operating angular velocity.)

The wheel is constructed from the front fork of an old 41-cm (16 in.) bicycle. The front fork and wheel were obtained free of cost from a local bicycle shop. First, the tire and tube were removed from the rim as well as the rubber rim liner. Sheets of lead were then cut into uniform strips (the width of the inside of the rim) using a large paper cutter. The strips of lead were then secured to the rim of the wheel with nylon filament tape. Layers were built up until about 26 kg of lead had been applied, securely taped to the inner rim channel with the nylon filament tape. The wheel was then statically balanced with smaller pieces of lead. Multiple layers of duct tape were then applied to build up a durable outside surface.

The bicycle fork was secured to the inside of the suitcase with four 7 mm x 25 mm (1/4 in. x 1 in.) carriage bolts. In order to do this, a bracket was constructed from ordinary 25 mm x 25 mm (1 in. x 1 in.) angle iron. Two pieces of angle iron were cut about 0.20 m long and two holes were drilled in one flange of each piece. Using a small electric arc

welder, the angle irons were welded to one side of the front fork (Fig. 2). The stem of the fork was cut off to allow this assembly to fit into the suitcase. Once the welds were complete, the system was mounted permanently inside the suitcase and tested for operation.

To energize this gyroscope, a small electric drill (2250 rpm) was used (Fig. 3). The ratio of the radius of the friction disc to the radius of the gyroscope wheel is about 0.29, so with the drill running at 2250 rpm, the wheel rotates at just over 650 rpm. With the mass of the wheel as large as it is, this is adequate to provide a momentous (!) demonstration of what happens when the axis of rotation of a spinning object is rotated.

One way of utilizing this device is to energize it, then ask a student to pick up the suitcase, walk briskly (as if to catch a plane when late), and then turn a corner rapidly and continue walking. One of the two things will obviously happen. Either the suitcase will rotate outward about the horizontal axis of its handle pins, or it will rotate inward knocking its carrier's legs out from under him/her. One should be careful to have spotters in the second case to prevent the person from rotating about the point of contact of the suitcase! (In my classroom, one student had her legs knocked from under her as she made a fast turn, the suitcase fell flat side down on the floor, and she landed "spread-eagle" on top of it. From that time on spotters were employed.)

This piece of equipment has been very useful for demonstrating an application of precession vectors. It makes a great "black box" device and is effective because of the interest it generates. The gyroscope will run for several minutes, so once it is energized several students can try its effects and be asked to model what is in the interior of the suitcase. Improvements from the original prototype described in this article could include a bicycle wheel with precision bearings. The idea of using a pedestal as described above would also enhance the device as a piece of demonstration equipment.

References

1. J. Higbie, *Phys. Teach.*, **18**, 210 (1980).
2. G.D. Freier and F.l. Anderson, "Tops and Gyroscopes," *A Demonstration Handbook for Physics*, (American Association of Physics Teachers, 1981), M-49.

Dynamical Balance and the Rotating Rod — A Personal Demonstration

Clifton Bob Clark *and* **Stuart Thompson,** Department of Physics and Astronomy, University of North Carolina at Greensboro, Greensboro, NC 27412-5001

Most texts in analytical mechanics that treat moments and products of inertia also discuss the dynamical balance of rotating rigid bodies.[1,2] The usual treatment specifies that dynamical balance requires the axis of rotation to pass through the center of mass (true for static balance also), and that the axis of rotation be a principal axis of inertia. The first requirement ensures that the net centrifugal force on the body in a system of axes fixed to it will be zero, and the second condition ensures that the sum of the torques due to centrifugal forces is zero. The practical importance is that rotating bodies that are not dynamically balanced cause bearings to wear out quickly and, as in the case of automobile tires that need balancing, cause unwanted "shimmy" or "wobbling" while rotating.

A long, thin rod has symmetry such that the principal axes of inertia at its center are obvious by inspection to the student newly introduced to moments and products of inertia. Most students are surprised that the "out-of-balance" symptoms are produced when the rod is rotated about an axis that is not along a principal axis of inertia. The appara-

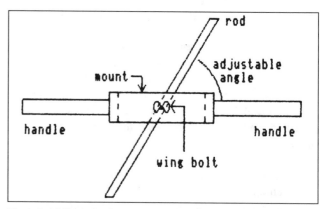

Fig. 1. A schematic drawing of the apparatus.

tus shown in Fig. 1 provides an axle for rotating such a rod either perpendicular to or at an acute angle to the axle. In use, the rod is adjusted to be perpendicular to the axle and is clamped in position. The student then holds the apparatus well in front of him or her with one hand on a handle at each end of the axle, as demonstrated in Fig. 2. The rod is rotated about the axle, and the balanced motion proceeds smoothly. The rod is then clamped at an acute angle and made to rotate again. This time the feel of the changing torque needed to keep the axle fixed is easily discernible.

The apparatus was made from the following materials: a 460-mm (18-in.) solid steel rod, 13 mm (1/2 in.) in diameter; a 100-mm (4-in.) length of aluminum rod, 25 mm (1 in.) in diameter, for the mount; two 230-mm (9-in.) lengths of steel rod, 9.5 mm (3/8 in.) in diameter, for the handles; 2 press fit roller bearings, 7.9 mm (5/16 in.) inside diameter and 16 mm (5/8 in.) outside diameter; and a wing bolt, 6.4 mm (1/4 in.) diameter, 32 mm (1.25 in.) long, with a washer.

The mount required the most machining: a 13-mm (1/2-in.) slot was milled along a 64-mm (2.5 in.) length, to allow the rod to be inserted at the center. A 6.4-mm (1/4-in.) hole was drilled at the center of the mount perpendicular to the slot. Each end of the mount was drilled to permit press fitting a bearing. The rod was drilled at its center and tapped to fit the threads on the wing bolt. The shorter rods (handles) were fitted to the inside of the bearings.

None of the measurements are particularly critical to the functioning of the demonstration apparatus, except that the bearings must fit tightly. A snug fit of the rod in the slot in the mount allows the moderate pressure of the wing bolt to lock the rod at acute angles to the axis for reasonable spin rates. If the rod is set spinning too fast, it will slowly assume the balanced position perpendicular to the axis.

Fig. 2. The apparatus is demonstrated by physics major Laura Keller.

References

1. R.A. Becker, *Introduction to Theoretical Mechanics*, (McGraw-Hill Book Co. Inc., New York, 1954), pp. 280–282.
2. G.R. Fowles, *Analytical Mechanics*, (Saunders College Publishing, New York, 1986), 4th ed., p. 229.

Who Will Win the Race?

Robert H. March, Department of Physics, Dalhousie University, Halifax, Nova Scotia, Canada B3H 3J5

I t is common in texts[1] and in classroom demonstrations to illustrate the geometric nature of the moment of inertia by rolling objects down an inclined plane. Without any timing techniques, it can be observed easily by an entire class that one object gets to the bottom of the inclined plane before another.

Consider a solid cylinder in a race against a cylindrical shell rolling down an inclined plane of angle θ. Measuring torques about the point of contact, then $\tau = I\alpha$ leads to $mgR \sin\theta = [I_{cm} + mR^2] \cdot (a/R)$, or

$$a = (mgR^2\sin\theta / I_{cm} + mR^2$$

$$= [g \sin\theta/(1 + I_{cm}/mR^2)],$$

where a is the linear acceleration down the plane, g is the acceleration of gravity, m is the mass of the cylinder, R is the radius of the cylinder, and I_{cm} is the moment of inertia of the cylinder about the center of mass.

I_{cm} for a solid cylinder = $1/2 \, mR^2$ and I_{cm} for a cylindrical shell = mR^2, giving

$$a_{cyl} = 2/3 \, g \sin\theta$$

or

$$a_{shell} = 1/2 \, g \sin\theta$$

Is there a "dark horse" in the race?

To make the acceleration as large as possible, the geometric factor I_{cm}/mR^2 must be as small as possible. For a sphere the geometric factor is 2/5, but let's try for zero!

A "zero-I" roller will have a finite radius, but all the mass will be on the axis. That is difficult to construct, but with proper choice of materials, you can come close. A roller with a lead axle and two light plastic end pieces works well. The lead cylinder is 7.5 cm long by 2.4 cm in diameter with a plastic Petri dish cover fixed on each end. Each cover has a diameter of 9 cm and a mass just over 7 grams.

Fig. 1. Positions down an inclined plane of the "zero-I" roller, a solid cylinder, and a cylindrical shell—all released from rest at the same time.

For a given end piece and chosen length of lead there is an optimum diameter. If the optimum diameter is too large, the lead cylinder will have a geometric factor of 1/2; if the optimum diameter is too small, the system will be dominated by the dish covers with, again, a geometric factor of 1/2. A computer or a quick bit of calculus will help you determine the best diameter: thus you get a geometric factor of 0.05.

With a geometric factor of 0.05 (nearly zero!) this roller easily wins the race. Fig. 1 shows a solid cylinder, a cylindrical shell, and the "zero-I" roller, all having been released from rest at the top of the inclined plane. If the roller had a geometric factor of zero, the accelerations and hence the displacements at any time would have the ratio 1:2/3:1/2 or 6:4:3 for the roller:cylinder:shell. Friction is not negligible for the small-angled plane shown (approximately 4°), but a quick visual inspection shows that the ratio is approximately correct. It shows unequivocally the order of finish with the roller clearly the winner.

Reference

1. Serway, *Physics for Scientists and Engineers*, (Saunders, 1986).

Apparatus for the Study of Uniform Circular Motion in a Liquid

Erland H. Graf, Department of Physics and Astronomy, SUNY at Stony Brook, NY 11794; egraf@ccmail.sunysb.edu

A few years ago, the cover of *The Physics Teacher* was devoted to a lab experiment that has intrigued, entertained, and (I hope) enlightened Stony Brook students on certain aspects of circular motion.[1] Conceptually, the experiment is quite simple: a vertical laser beam is reflected from the curved surface of a uniformly rotating liquid. Measuring the angle of the reflected beam, the distance of the reflection point from the center of rotation, and the speed of rotation enables the students to determine the profile of the liquid surface and to determine g, the acceleration due to gravity. The apparatus can also be used for quantitative lecture demonstrations.

Theory

When a container of liquid rotates with a uniform angular velocity ω, the liquid will "bank" itself so that at equilibrium the surface of the liquid a distance r from the center of rotation will make an angle θ with the horizontal given by

$$\tan \theta = \omega^2 \, r/g \qquad (1)$$

This can be understood by considering a small mass m of

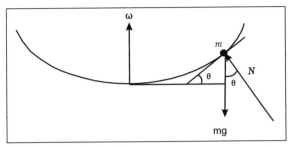

Fig. 1. Free-body diagram of a small mass *m* of liquid at the surface of the rotating system.

liquid at the surface. As shown in Fig. 1, the mass experiences a gravitational force mg and a normal force N from the liquid below, but no net transverse (i.e., parallel to the liquid surface) shear force, since a liquid cannot support shear. At dynamic equilibrium we have:

$$N \cos \theta = mg \qquad (2)$$

$$N \sin \theta = F_{\text{centripetal}} = m\omega^2 r \qquad (3)$$

Dividing Eq. (3) by Eq. (2) gives Eq. (1). This is the same expression obtained for conical pendulums, road banking, etc., discussed in many texts.[2]

Equation (1) can be used to find the profile of the liquid surface. Taking y as the height of the surface a distance r from the center of rotation (with $y = 0$ at $r = 0$), we have

$$\tan \theta = dy/dr \qquad (4)$$

so

$$dy/dr = \omega^2 r/g \qquad (5)$$

and

$$y = \omega^2 r^2 / 2g \qquad (6)$$

which predicts that the shape of the spinning liquid surface should be parabolic, a property used in the fabrication of large mirrors for telescopes.

Apparatus

An overall schematic view of the apparatus is shown in Fig. 2. A cylindrical glass dish (about 18 cm in diameter) containing a viscous liquid (glycerin or mineral oil) sits attached atop a uniformly rotating turntable. The base of the turntable is equipped with leveling screws. (The table used here came from an angular momentum apparatus, but an old phonograph turntable would work also.) The turntable is driven by a small dc electric motor powered by a variable voltage supply, so that the rotational speed is continuously adjustable. A He-Ne laser horizontally mounted on an optical bench is supported about 40 cm above the rotating platform. The laser is equipped with an adjustable 45° mirror to deflect the light beam down onto a point on the surface of the liquid, off which the beam reflects. Moving the laser along the optical bench makes it

possible to position the beam at any point along a diameter of the liquid surface. The incident and reflected beams pass through a transparent plastic ruler horizontally mounted about 25 cm above the liquid. The spots where the beams pass through the ruler are easily visible, especially in a partially darkened room. A tab on the rotating platform passes through a photogate timer once per revolution to measure the period of rotation. The stability of rotation of the apparatus

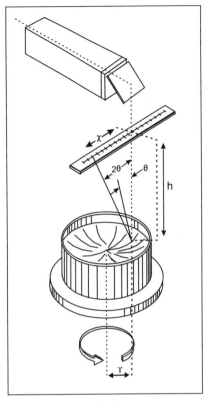

Fig. 2. Overall schematic diagram of apparatus.

described here is better than ~0.5% over several minutes.

Alignment Procedure

For precision (~1%) work, it is necessary to carefully align the apparatus. First, with the table motionless (so that the liquid surface is flat), the distance h between clear plastic ruler and the liquid is checked to be constant (to within 1 mm out of ~25 cm) over the length of the ruler. Second, the laser beam is made strictly vertical: with the liquid still at rest, the 45° mirror is adjusted until the reflected and incident beams coincide. The optical bench and ruler are positioned so that the beam can be scanned over a diameter of the liquid surface, checking for verticality at all points. Finally, the laser beam is spotted directly over the center of the turntable (this point has been marked beforehand), and the power supply is turned up so that the table rotates at moderate speed. If the table is strictly horizontal, the beam will be reflected straight up; if not, the reflected beam will be skewed and the table is adjusted by means of leveling screws on its base until the incident and reflected beams at the center coincide. The apparatus is now ready for taking data.

Measurements

The basic measurements are quite straightforward. With the liquid at rest, the distance h between the surface

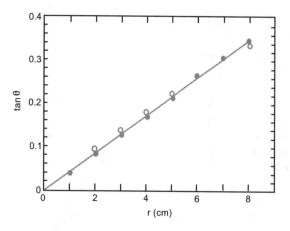

Fig. 3. Tangent of the liquid bank angle θ as a function of distance r from the center of rotation. Angular velocity $\omega = 6.54$ rad/s. Error bars are about the same size as the plotted symbols. Open circles are uncorrected points, filled-in circles are points corrected for liquid height (see text).

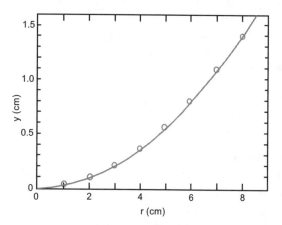

Fig. 4. Height of banked liquid y as a function of distance r from the center of rotation. Conditions are the same as in Fig. 3.

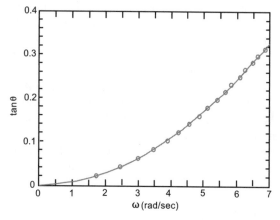

Fig. 5. Tangent of liquid bank angle θ as a function of angular velocity ω. Distance from center of rotation r is fixed at 6.60 ± 0.05 cm, where no height correction is necessary.

of the liquid and the clear plastic ruler is measured. The liquid is set into rotation and the period is measured with the photogate timer. From this, the angular velocity ω of the turntable can be determined. The incident laser beam is set to strike the liquid surface a distance r from the center of rotation, as measured by the ruler. Finally, the banking angle θ at position r is determined by measuring the distance x between the spots where the incident and reflected laser beams pass through the ruler. From the law of reflection, the angle between the incident and reflected beam is 2θ. Since

$$\tan (2\theta) = x/h \qquad (7)$$

θ can be determined from the x and h measurements. Once ω, r, and θ are determined, these experimental variables can be fit to Eq. (1): $\tan \theta = \omega^2 r/g$.

Figure 3 is a plot of $\tan \theta$ vs r for a fixed value of $\omega = 6.54$ rad/s. If Eq. (1) is correct, the plot should be a straight line with slope $a = \omega^2/g$. One difficulty with this plot is that h (the distance between the ruler and the liquid surface) is not constant, but varies by about ± 1 cm at this value of ω, which can lead to systematic errors in $\tan \theta$ of as much as a few percent. This can be compensated, however, by using Eq. (6) for the height of the liquid level and correcting h accordingly. It is an interesting exercise in calculus to show that if the container radius is R, then the rotating liquid at $r = R/\sqrt{2}$ will have the same level as it does when it is not rotating, provided that the liquid at the center has not reached the bottom of the container. The corrected points are also plotted in Fig. 3. A best linear fit to the data yields a value of $g = 9.82 \pm 0.07$ N/kg. Figure 4 shows a plot of the height y of the liquid surface as a function of r, taking $y = 0$ at $r = 0$.

Another approach is to take bank angle data at $r = R/\sqrt{2}$ (= 6.60 ± 0.05 cm in our case) for different values of ω. Here no liquid level correction is necessary. Figure 5 is a plot of $\tan \theta$ vs ω for this value of r. In this case a best-fit parabola yields a value of $g = 9.79 \pm 0.08$ N/kg.

Discussion

The results of careful experimental work with this apparatus are generally quite good, yielding values of g that fall within 1 or 2% of the handbook value. Most students find the experiment fascinating and enjoy exploring the characteristics of the parabolic reflecting surface, often discovering for themselves, for example, the "magic" value of ω for which the reflected beam always passes through the ruler at the center of rotation, no matter what the position of the incident beam.

The experiment also works with water, but a viscous liquid such as glycerin or mineral oil is much superior because it equilibrates much faster (in several seconds) and is not subject to ripples as water is. It is aesthetically pleasing to watch the smoothness and steadiness of the light beam as equilibrium is approached.

Conclusion

The apparatus described here lends itself to experiments and demonstrations that are conceptually accessible and interesting to students. At the same time, it affords ample opportunity for careful measurement technique and includes data analysis that involves making successive approximations, which most students have not encountered before.

Acknowledgments

Many thanks are due to Jose Feliciano of the Stony Brook Instructional Laboratories for constructing the apparatus, to Sid Cahn for his assistance, and to the National Science Foundation for financial support.

References

1. *Phys. Teach.* **32** (No. 4), Front Cover and Table of Contents page (April, 1994).
2. See, for example, H. Young and R. Freedman, *University Physics*, 9th ed. (Addison-Wesley, Reading, MA, 1996), pp. 142–143.

Physics on a Rotating Reference Frame

Robert H. Johns, Manor Junior College, 700 Fox Chase Road, Jenkintown, PA 19046-3399

This note describes some insights into relative motion and the Coriolis force not available from a computer or by watching apparatus on a lab bench. The phenomena are better seen and experienced as a participant. The apparatus is a 5-m-long rotating reference frame made from two 8-ft-long plywood carts, shown in Fig. 1. It can be used in a classroom or lab if the regular furniture is movable, or in a hall or cafeteria.

Newtonian Relativity

Motion is relative; what we see depends on our frame of reference. This can be powerfully illustrated with observers at each end of the rotating cart, passing a ball back and forth. The thrower cannot aim at the person at the other end. If she does, the ball curves away and misses the other person, following the dotted line in Fig. 2. The thrower must anticipate the rotation and throw the ball toward where the catcher will be, much like a quarterback "leading" a receiver by throwing the football ahead of him. The receiver sees the ball travel out in an arc and then curve back in (dashed line in Fig. 2). Both the

Fig. 1. A rotating reference frame. When viewed from the rotating cart, a ball thrown from one end to the other curves in an arc away from the cart and then back in to the receiver. A viewer in the room sees a straight-line path.

thrower and catcher (as well as anyone else in the rotating frame of reference) see this ball motion as a curve.

An observer at rest in the room sees a different motion. If her eye follows the rotating cart she also sees the curving trajectory. But if she watches the ball against the back-the receiver.

The fact that what we see depends on our frame of reference is a new insight to most students, and many will be full of questions. (But what really happens? Which is true?. . .) Don't answer all these; just let the paradox be. Try to avoid the teacher trap of talking too much, and let the experience sink in.

Our observations of motion are not absolute! Both the magnitude and direction of velocity are relative! Students need a gut-level feel for this in order to appreciate the conceptual revolution that special relativity introduced. You may find some students very uncomfortable with two divergent views of the same event, and feel the need to find a unifying explanation, the *real* truth. This can be an upsetting experience for them.

An interesting language insight is the way we use the words *straight* and *curved* to describe the path of the ball from these two reference frames, with no misunderstanding as to meaning. Both trajectories are curved, following the familiar parabola of a thrown ball. But the plane that contains the trajectory seen in the rotating frame must be bent to pass through the ends of the cart and curve out to one side. Even the simplest geometry is messed up when seen from different reference frames. If you draw a line that is straight in the rotating frame (by squirting colored water on the floor along the edge of the rotating cart), the line on the floor is a lovely spiral.

Coriolis Force

Trying to walk from one end of the rotating cart to the other is extraordinarily difficult. An unexpected force is pushing you to the side. The walker must lean against this force, but if he stops moving the strange new sidewards push also stops. Typically the walker is flailing arms and only managing shuffling steps, much like the stagger of an infant just learning to walk. Experiencing this new force is a lot of fun, and the class can pool its experience and give one another lots of advice on survival. After everyone has felt the force, I pose some questions to be answered by trials. Can you escape the side force by jumping or running? Does it change direction as you cross the center of rotation of the cart? Does the force depend on your distance from the center? This sideward force is a welcome discovery: it explains the curvature of the ball thrown from end to end on the rotating cart.

A caution: you may have a harder time with the notion of a fictitious or pseudo force after your students have seen the curved trajectories and felt the Coriolis force. They are quite real in the rotating frame of reference.

Conservation of Angular Momentum

A skater starts a spin and then dramatically increases the

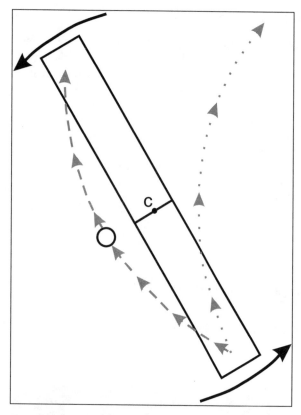

Fig. 2. Top view of trajectories seen by observers in the rotating reference frame. A ball aimed at the opposite end (dotted line) curves away. A successful pass means throwing the ball ahead of the receiver (dashed line). It then curves around to meet the receiver at the other end.

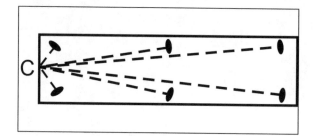

Fig. 3. Location and positioning of wheels on each of the two 2-by-8-ft carts.

ground in the room, she sees a normal path with the ball continuing straight toward some reference point. She sees the receiver move around in his circular path to intercept the ball in its straight path and catch it.

The experience on the rotating cart is surprising: the ball really travels out away from the cart and comes back in. It is not an optical illusion. An interesting task is to try a bounce pass end-to-end on the rotating cart. Does not work. The ball must be bounced on the floor to the side of the cart to get to rate of spin by bringing in her arms and legs. This is usually presented only as an example of the conservation of angular momentum, with no attempt at dynamics. But what force causes her to speed up?

If your students have survived the end-to-end walk on the rotating cart, they will have noticed the cart speeding up as they walked inward, and slowing as they walked outward. Even better, they will have felt the sidewards force that they had to exert on the cart in order to lean and remain upright. Moreover, the sidewards force of their lean as they walked outward exerted a slowing force on the rotating system. The walker supplies the forces that change the angular velocity to conserve angular momentum. Everyone watching the Coriolis dances will observe the changes in rotational speed, but the walker will also feel these accelerating and decelerating forces.

A walker tends to curve off the cart as he walks inward, even as the ball does in Fig. 2. To stay on the rotating cart, he must lean to the left and take steps that seem to aim left as well as forward. The Coriolis force pushes him to the right; he must fight it to stay on the cart. This force will no longer be remote or abstract. Your students will have seen its effects, felt it, and fought it.

Apparatus

Two 2-by-8-ft carts are made from a single 4-by-8 sheet of 3/4-in plywood, which the vendor will probably rip in two for no added charge. Two steel straps bolt the carts together to make the 5-m-long rotating frame. Six non-swivelling 2-in casters are used under each cart. Positioned so that they roll tangent to their radius from the center of rotation, C in Fig. 3, they prevent the long cart from translation motion while it is rotating. The angle of each caster is established by aiming the axle of the caster toward C and then marking the drill holes for bolting the mounting plate to the

plywood. If the cart will be used on wood floors, get casters with rubber wheels; for tile or cement floors the harder plastic wheels will offer a little less friction.

The two poles for pushing the apparatus are permanently attached to the cart by the U-bolts that pass through a hole near one end of the pole and are bolted to the plywood. The poles are made from a length of 3/4-in electrical conduit (electric metallic tubing) cut into two 5-ft pieces; 7/8-in rubber furniture tips are placed over the pushing ends.

Note that there are no side rails or anything else to hold onto while riding the cart. This is not a high-speed apparatus. I like to keep the linear speed at the ends of the cart to no more than a brisk walk. The students need to push rather than pull the cart so that they can see and stop it if someone falls. Constant vigilance is needed.

Solve the storage problem before building the carts, so that you can use them near their storage location. Also give some thought to this as an advertisement. A lab section having a lot of fun with some bizarre physics is a great invitation!

This apparatus was redesigned from an earlier program[1] in an effort to make student involvement easier to accomplish, without going to the gymnasium or parking lot with large-scale equipment. These rotating carts also complement the kinesthesia apparatus developed by Pfister and Laws.[2] A more elaborate mechanism was described in an article by Clifton Bob Clark.[3]

References

1. R.H. Johns, "Gymnasium physics," *Phys. Teach.* **9**, 308 (1971).
2. Hans Pfister and Priscilla Laws, "Kinesthesia-1: Apparatus to experience 1-D motion," *Phys. Teach.* **33**, 214 (1995).
3. C.B. Clark, "Experience in a noninertial lab," *Phys. Teach.* **17**, 526 (1979).

Oscillatory Motion, Elastic Forces

The Variable Gravity Pendulum

José Feliciano, Physics Department, State University of New York, Stony Brook, NY 11794; Jfeliciano@sunysb.edu

Traditionally, the period of the pendulum has been studied experimentally by suspending a bob on a thin, light string, displacing the bob until the string makes an angle Θ with the vertical, and then releasing the bob. In the lab, students use the equation $T = 2\pi \sqrt{L/g}$ to verify the relationship between T, the period in seconds, L, the length of the string in meters, and g, the gravitational field strength. However, gravity, being what it is, cannot be changed unless we perform the experiment on the surface of the Moon, where gravity is one-sixth that of Earth's gravity (an interesting prospect, but not very practical). We can, nonetheless, explore the effects of altering g by letting the pendulum swing in a nonvertical plane. This can be accomplished by suspending an air table on two rods that allow the air table to be tilted to various angles (see Fig. 1), thereby making the effective gravity a function of $g \sin \phi$ (ϕ being the angle of tilt).

The apparatus is made up of:

1. Air table
2. Aluminum disc (diameter 10 cm) as pendulum bob
3. Air supply
4. Ring clamps (to hold air table on vertical rod supports while also allowing air table to be tilted to various angles)
5. Protractor on side of air table to measure tilt angle
6. Protractor on face of air table to measure arc-amplitude of bob
7. Photogate to automatically start and stop timer
8. Timer with photogate input (A computer with a precision timing program, and an interface to the photogate can be used in place of the timer.)

Begin the experiment by aligning the tilt-angle protractor with the horizontal reference line on the air table. Measure and record length of the string from the point of support to the center of the bob. Position photogate in the middle of the air table so it will operate when the bob passes the halfway point of the period. A rod approximately 5 cm long protruding perpendicularly from the surface of the bob acts as the flag that triggers the photogate. (Attaching the string to the bob by means of a small bearing eliminates oscillations of the bob about its center of mass.) The measurement of period as a function of tilt can now be performed at various angles and the results compared with predicted values: $T = 2\pi \sqrt{L/g \sin \phi}$ (see Fig. 2). The apparatus also allows easy measurements of the period as a function of string length and of starting angle Θ.

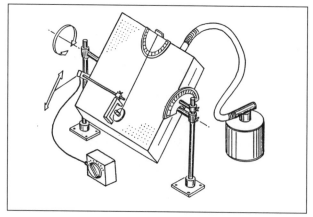

Fig. 1. Apparatus for changing effective *g*.

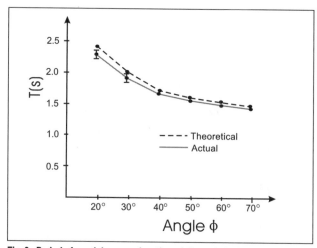

Fig. 2. Period of pendulum as a function of tilt angle (string length 49.4 cm).

An Inexpensive Young's Modulus Apparatus

Thomas B. Greenslade, Jr. and *Richard Wilcox,* Kenyon College, Gambier, OH 43022

Apparatus to measure the value of Young's modulus for a wire has been available for many years from suppliers such as Cenco and Sargent-Welch. This is sturdy equipment, and many pieces fifty years and more old are still in operation. However, the apparatus now costs about $650 a set, and when we needed five more setups (plus two for a secondary school), we built the version described in this note. The cost of each was about $25, plus labor.

A brief description of the experiment is in order. Young's modulus is defined as $Y = $ stress/strain, where the stress is the stretching force F per unit cross-section area A of the wire under test, and the strain is the resulting fractional deformation. If the length of the wire is L and the elongation resulting from the application of force F is δL, then $Y = (F/A)/(\delta L/L)$. Normally δL is too small to measure directly, so an optical lever is used to amplify the stretch of the wire to the point where it can be measured easily. The force F is normally the weight, mg, of masses m hung from the lower end of the wire. The upper end of the wire is securely fastened to a rigid support.

Our version of the classic apparatus is shown in Fig. 1. It is constructed of 3/4-in iron pipe. Since this pipe is normally sold in standard lengths, nonmetric units will be used. The tall uprights are made of 72-in lengths of pipe, which are screwed into floor plates attached to the 3/4-in chipboard base. The base has three 1/4-20 levelling screws that run through corresponding tee-nuts epoxied to the base. At the top, short segments of pipe connect the 90-degree elbows at the top of the uprights to the horizontal arms of a tee-fitting. A square pipe plug fits into the downward-pointing third arm of the tee. The wire under test passes through holes drilled in the top of the tee and in the plug, and is held in place by a set-screw set into the side of the plug.

Figure 2 shows the optical lever, which is freely adapted from the commercial apparatus. A small chipboard platform supports the lever, which pivots on two legs, with its third leg resting on a circular block of metal held to the wire by a set-screw. Our lever measures 10 cm from the pivot line to the third leg, and the base and sides are made of thin plywood. The two pivot legs are made by grinding or turning points on short metal rods, which are epoxied in place. The third leg is a piece of music wire. A small mirror is epoxied to a long bolt that passes through the sides of the lever; this allows the mirror to be tilted at various angles.

Normally a laser beam is reflected from the mirror back onto a piece of paper taped to the wall. As the wire stretch-

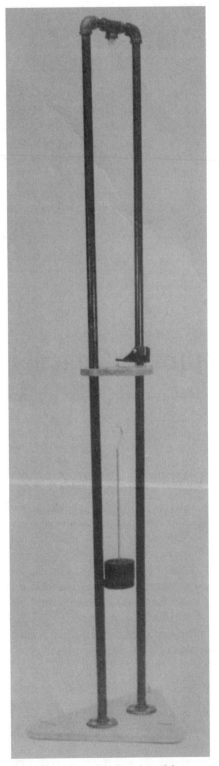

Fig. 1. Overall view of the Young's modulus apparatus.

Fig. 2. Close-up view of the optical lever.

es and the mirror tilts back, the beam moves up the wall. The position of the spot on the paper is marked as a function of the mass hanging on the end of the wire. The laser is not necessary, however. The older technique is to look toward the mirror through a small telescope (such as a spotting scope). On the wall behind is a scale, and different portions of the scale can be seen as the mirror rotates. In principle you can even replace the telescope with a pair of peep sights for ultimate simplicity.

We estimate that after the prototype had been built, the next seven sets of apparatus took about 30 hours to finish. This would make a good project for a Saturday morning teachers' workshop or a science club, since mass production of the parts would rapidly bring down the building time.

An Improved Optical Lever

Zheng Bunker, Foundation Division, Engineering College of Anshan Iron & Steel Company, Anshan, Liaoning, P.R. China

The optical lever is a useful device for measuring small displacements such as those encountered in experiments to determine Young's modulus.[1] A small mirror is mounted on a pivot arrangement so that when a displacement occurs, the mirror rotates slightly. A telescope and a vertical linear scale (meterstick) are mounted at some distance L from the mirror (see Fig. 1). The telescope is aimed at the mirror so that the reflection of a small part of the scale appears against the crosshairs in the field of view. A small angular displacement φ of the mirror results in a substantial change ΔR in the scale reading as seen in the telescope. The angle φ, which is related in a simple way to the small displacement to be measured, may be calculated from the scale readings using $\varphi = \Delta R/2L$.

In the usual optical lever design illustrated in Fig. 1, the telescope and scale are both mounted on one holder.[2] This configuration requires the observer to be several meters from the Young's modulus (or other) apparatus and so it is inconvenient for one individual to both operate the

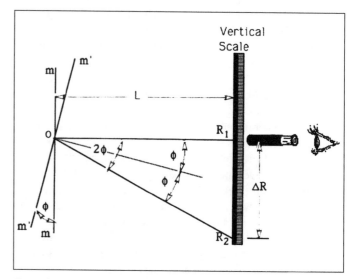

Fig. 1. Geometry of conventional optical lever system.

equipment and make the measurements.

An improved configuration (Fig. 2) has the telescope separated from the scale and placed as close as possible to the mirror. Referring back to Fig. 1, the telescope is simply moved toward the mirror along the line connecting points R_1 and 0. This modified design has a second advantage over the conventional one: by decreasing the distance to the mirror, the field of view in the telescope is increased, which makes the system easier to align. Alternatively, it allows the scale to be placed further away from the mirror while maintaining the same field of view. This increases the optical lever arm and therefore the sensitivity of the system. Of course, the relationship between φ, and ΔR remains the same.

Acknowledgment

I am indebted to the column editor for his editorial aid and constructive suggestions.

References

1. Jerry D. Wilson, *Physics Laboratory Experiments* (Heath, Lexington, MA, 1986), pp. 163–173.
2. Such a telescope and scale may be purchased from Sargent-Welch Company (Catalog Number 2738) for $265.99.

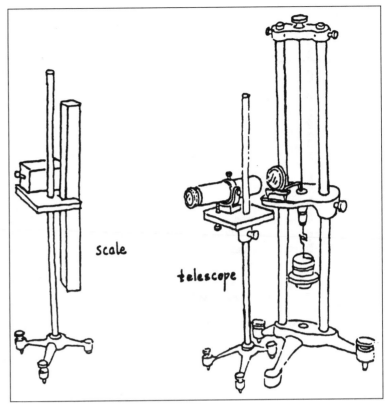

Fig. 2. The improved optical lever.

Linearizing a Nonlinear Spring

Glenn Wagner, Centre Wellington District High School, Fergus, Ontario NIM IY7 Canada

Recently my senior-level physics class completed an experiment to verify Hooke's Law, a standard laboratory exercise in most physics courses. For this exercise the students are asked to determine the force constant, and hence the linear equation, that describes the extension of their spring as a function of the mass placed on it. The springs we used are those found in our local hardware store. A major difficulty the students had in developing this linear equation was the nonlinear behavior produced when small mass loads were placed on the spring.[1] This nonlinearity is not surprising and can be used as a constructive example of how nature sometimes behaves in a nonideal fashion. This nonlinearity, however, might not always be desirable. The following simple procedure outlines how this nonlinearity

can be eliminated from a spring permanently.

Not all springs visibly stretch in response to small masses placed on it. This can be attributed to the "initial tension" that certain springs possess. The initial tension must be eliminated to remove nonlinear behavior. This is achieved when the spring coils are no longer in contact with each other or when a minimum force is applied to the spring. Only then is linear behavior observed.

The coils can be permanently separated from one another by the careful application of a high-temperature heat source, such as an acetylene torch found in a school welding shop or from disposable propane torches found in hardware stores. Acetylene torches can reach temperatures near 5500°F and propane torches near 4500°F.

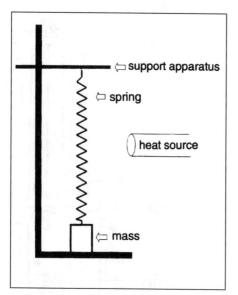

Fig. 1. Experimental apparatus used for removing initial tension in a spring. The extension of the spring has been exaggerated for clarity.

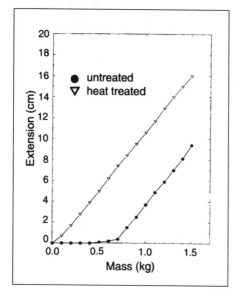

Fig. 2. Extension as a function of mass of a spring before and after heat treatment. The slope remains constant and the initial tension is essentially eliminated.

Begin by suspending a mass on the spring that is great enough to *just* overcome the initial tension. There should be a support surface present so that the spring is not allowed to extend fully with the mass suspended on it (see Fig. 1). Slowly stroke up and down the full length of the spring with the flame from an acetylene torch.

Continued stroking in this manner will cause the spring to reach a critical temperature (this being dependent upon the material composition of the spring) at which point the coils separate permanently when the springs cool down to room temperature while under load. Careful observation of the spring during the heating process will determine whether enough heat is added. Too much heat will result in serious deformities of the spring; too little heat will not remove the initial tension after cooling. With our springs we noticed a distinct permanent discoloration when the correct amount of heat was applied. After approximately 15 minutes of heating, the initial tension was not present once the spring cooled. Figure 2 shows extension of a spring as a function of the mass suspended from the spring before heat treatment and after heat treatment. Note that the spring constant does not change and that the nonlinearity is essentially eliminated after heating.

To try and eliminate variabilities in the heating process, we placed the spring under load in a conventional home oven at 500°F. Unfortunately this did not eliminate the initial tension due to the relatively low temperature of the oven compared with the acetylene torch. Some schools may have access to high-temperature ovens that reach near 2000°F. These ovens have the advantage of uniform heating with better temperature control than possible with acetylene torches.

An unexpected but welcomed class discussion occurred concerning the predicted effects of heat on the force constant of the spring. About half of the students were quick to assume that the force constant would change once the initial tension was removed. This led to a further discussion about what properties determine the force constant of a spring. The tensile strength of the wire, diameter of the wire, and outside diameter of the spring will affect the force constant. A change in the length of two otherwise identical springs will change the force constant as well.

This procedure in which springs are heated to eliminate nonlinearity makes for a nice extension of the Hooke's Law experiment. Students can investigate why the spring may behave nonlinearly to begin with and then integrate some technical studies into their work in order to correct this potential problem.

Reference

1. R.M. Prior, *Phys. Teach.,* **18**, 601 (1980).

Demonstrating the Relationship between Circular and Simple Harmonic Motion

Greg Jakovidis, Department of Physics, Monash University, Clayton, Victoria 3168 Australia; greg.jakovidis@sci.monash.edu.au

The connection between circular and simple harmonic motion (SHM) can be vividly demonstrated using the apparatus shown in Fig. 1. The central piece of equipment is a phonograph turntable, an item that is becoming increasingly available since the advent of the compact disc. You will also need a polystyrene ball that can be mounted via Velcro straps to a vinyl record, which rests on the turntable. The ball is illuminated with an overhead projector. When the ball moves in uniform circular motion, its shadow exhibits SHM, thus demonstrating that SHM is a projection of uniform circular motion on a diameter of the circle. Emphasize to your students that the period (T) of the ball and that of its shadow are equivalent, thus the frequency of SHM can be written as an angular frequency $\omega = \dfrac{2\pi}{T}$.

The link between circular and SHM can be further facilitated by attaching cardboard vectors that describe uniform circular motion of the ball. The shadows of velocity (left side of Fig. 1) and of centripetal force and position vector (right side of Fig. 1) behave in a fashion similar to the corresponding vectors that describe a mass on the end of a spring subject to Hooke's Law. For example, the shadow of

Fig. 1. Apparatus for demonstrating the relationship between circular and simple harmonic motion.

the position vector represents the displacement x in SHM, and the shadow of the centripetal force represents the restoring force in Hooke's Law. Both these vectors vary harmonically with time. Note that in Fig. 1 the magnitude of the force vectors are not to scale.

As an exercise, ask your students to predict and draw the displacement vector along with its corresponding restoring force at the extremities of the SHM and at $x = 0$. It should be evident to the student that the restoring force is proportional to and opposite in direction to the displacement vector; that is, the ball's shadow is subject to Hooke's Law. At the conclusion of this demonstration students should appreciate that angular expressions such as angular frequency and circular (harmonic) functions aptly describe SHM.

Exploring Resonance Phenomena

H. Ric Blacksten, The Sidwell Friends Upper School, 3825 Wisconsin Avenue NW, Washington, DC 20016[1]

You can demonstrate the phenomenon of resonance convincingly using a simple apparatus constructed in minutes from readily available apparatus in the physics classroom/laboratory. The apparatus may be used as an analog to introduce the role of resonance in telecommunications.

Assemble the apparatus shown in Fig. 1 using a ring stand, a flask clamp, a meterstick, four identical laboratory

demonstration springs, two 0.5-kg masses, two 1.0-kg masses, and some office paper clips or binder clips. Clamp the meterstick horizontally with its width vertical. (The clamp should allow movement at one end of the meterstick to be felt at the other, but this should prove no problem.) Using available clips, position springs near each end of the meterstick. Hang a 0.5-kg and 1.0-kg mass at each end of the meterstick. You need not position the springs precisely nor symmetrically along the meterstick.

The springs have identical spring constants, but the 0.5- and 1.0-kg masses differ by a factor of 2. So the resonant frequency of a 0.5-kg mass-spring system will be $\sqrt{2}$ larger than that of a 1.0-kg system. Thus, the natural frequencies of the 0.5- and 1.0-kg spring/mass systems share no harmonics, yet each system is paired in natural frequency with its twin at the other end.

For the simplest demonstration, start one spring/mass oscillating at one end of the stick while you briefly hold the stick at the end. Release the stick. Your students will be surprised to see how quickly the twin spring/mass at the other end undertakes synchronized oscillation, while the other pair remains virtually motionless.

For a broader lesson, begin with a history question posed by Lewis Epstein[2]: Was a limitation of the telegraph an inability to send more than one message at a time over a single wire? This question, which triggered the idea for this apparatus, serves as a fine springboard for introducing the role of resonance in telecommunications. Before your class begins, situate the demonstration apparatus so that one end

of the meterstick faces the class and the other is hidden behind a cloak or partition. Ask your students if they think it is possible to excite one of the two spring/masses they see and not the other. Show them that it is. Before revealing the hidden part of the apparatus, have the students speculate on its workings. Then, having demonstrated that it is possible to use mechanical resonance to "communicate" over a meter distance, launch into a discussion of the key role of resonance in communicating over megameter distances with radio and other telecommunications. In particular, explain that in telegraph communications the "dot" and "dash" are not simple voltage pulses as we might guess, but are oscillating signals, short in duration for the "dot" and long in duration for the "dash." Only a receiving apparatus tuned to the transmission frequency will pick up the sent signal.

If you reconfigure the apparatus with a single spring/mass system at each end of the stick you can demonstrate additional resonance phenomena. In particular you can demonstrate beat-frequency coupling by suspending an identical spring/mass system at each end of the stick. Then modify the frequency of one of the systems by about 2% by attaching a small mass. One or two pennies should work. You will then have coupled oscillators that feed energy back and forth, one spring/mass system slowing to a halt while the other speeds, then vice versa. (This idea is based on a coupled pendulum demonstration described by Robert Ehrlich.[3])

References

1. The author is not currently associated with The Sidwell Friends Upper School. He may be reached at Human Resources Research Organization, 66 Canal Center Plaza, Suite 400, Alexandria, VA 22314.
2. Lewis C. Epstein, *Thinking Physics: Practical Lessons in Critical Thinking*, 2nd ed. (Insight Press, San Francisco, CA 1992), pp. 265–266.
3. Robert Ehrlich, *Turning the World Inside Out and 174 Other Simple Physics Demonstrations* (Princeton University Press, Princeton, NJ, 1990), pp. 94–95.

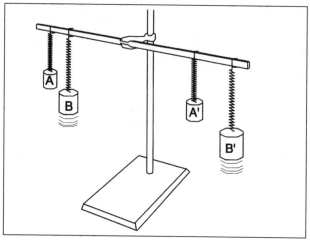

Fig. 1. Apparatus for exploring resonance.

Optoelectronic Detection of String Vibration

Roger J. Hanson, Physics Department, University of Northern Iowa, Cedar Falls, IA 50614-0150

A setup for optoelectronic detection of string vibration using a CdS photoconductive cell has been described in *The Physics Teacher*.[1] We have used a simpler arrangement with an inexpensive, commercially available photon-coupled interrupter module in a research apparatus to study the rate of decay of the different harmonics of a plucked guitar string.[2] This module could be used in the

application described or for any other application where a voltage which is linearly related to the displacement of a vibrating string is required.

The module consists of a gallium arsenide infrared emitting diode coupled to a silicon darlington connected phototransistor in a simple U-shaped plastic housing. The nominal beam diameter is 1 mm, but the effective sensitive region is less. The string is positioned in the light beam so it obstructs varying amounts of the light beam as it vibrates. In our application, in which the string is mounted on rigid supports on a steel beam, it is important to detect a large number of harmonics without the amplitude of motion exceeding the linear response region. Consequently, the detector is mounted as closely as possible to one of the supports where the string motion is small enough to stay in the linear region even for a substantial pluck. Another advantage of this detector location is that it is far from a node of any harmonic other than a very high one.

Fig. 1 shows the arrangement of the module and string, and the circuit used. The relative positioning is such that when the string is not vibrating, its one edge is approximately in the middle of the light beam so that it obstructs about half of the beam. The strings we have studied are large enough in diameter relative to the size of half the light beam so that even when the string is vibrating it does not permit a significant amount of light to get past the other edge of the string.

Fig. 2 shows the output voltage from the circuit as a function of the horizontal displacement of the string (or an opaque card) relative to the module. The data were obtained by moving the module toward the static string or card with a micrometer control. Curves are shown for the H13B1 used in our work and for the currently available H21B1. It can be seen that the responses of the two models are similar. The main difference is that there is a sharper cutoff for the H21 B1 tested, suggesting that the edge of its light beam is more clearly defined. We did not, however, attempt to check on the consistency of different samples of the same model. Either model provides a substantial linear region which can be utilized. The curve in Fig. 2 for the detector moving toward the guitar string is the same as for an opaque card, except in the right region of the curve where some light is apparently getting past the far edge of the string. If it were necessary to use that region, some masking could be provided. An appropriate operating position for the detector relative to the string can be conveniently selected by monitoring the D.C. output voltage of the circuit. It has been found that ordinary room light has little effect on the system, but under some conditions moderate shielding of external light is desirable. The output variation of several tenths of a volt for a vibrating string has been used as an input to an oscilloscope or a frequency analyzer or, with attenuation, to a tape recorder. The setup has been used to make measurements of very high harmonics (100 or more) from a plucked string.

The author thanks Larry Dirkes for calling his attention to the light interrupter module for this application and Trish Kirkpatrick for assistance in taking data.

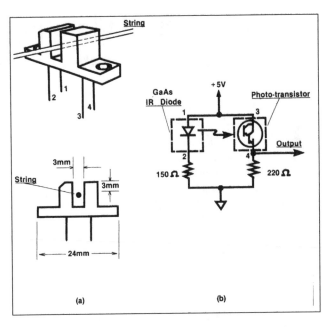

Fig. 1. (a) Photon coupled interrupter module with string position shown. The pictured model is an H21B1 (same dimensions as H21B2 and H21B3). (b) Circuit used for H21B1 and H12B1. The portions enclosed by dashed lines are in the module itself. The other components are external.

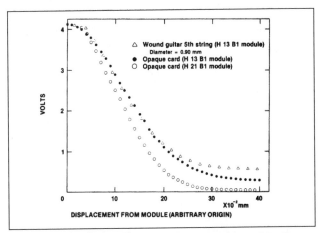

Fig. 2. Output voltage from the circuit of Fig. 1 as a function of the displacement of an opaque card or string from the module. The H13B1 curve for the opaque card slowly approaches zero beyond the right edge of the graph.

References

1. S.K. Chakavarti, *Phys. Teach.*, **24**, 40 (1986). (Note that the relevant Fig. 1 is on p. 42 rather than p. 40.)
2. General Electric Module No. H13B1 has been used. In the current third edition (1984) of the *Optoelectronics Manual* by the General Electric Company, Power Electronics Semiconductor Dept., Auburn, NY 13021, the H13B1 is no longer listed but other modules listed, H21B1, H21B2, H21B3... have similar characteristics. We have recently purchased some H21B1 units at less than $2 each and have found the response curve to be similar to that of the H13B1.

Laser-Enhanced Vibrating String

John Abendschan and **Dick Speakman,** Department of Physics, U.S. Air Force Academy, Colorado Springs, CO 80840

The introductory physics laboratory has traditionally included a vibrating-string apparatus to demonstrate standing-wave behavior and other wave properties. Equipment is available from several companies.[1] By carefully adjusting the tension in the string, a large-amplitude standing wave with distinct nodes and antinodes can be obtained. Although the current apparatus works well, we've discovered a way to make this traditional demonstration significantly more exciting.

To enhance the effect of a vibrating-string demo, use a laser and fiber optic line in lieu of string. A vibrating string can sometimes be difficult to observe, but a laser-illuminated fiber optic line will always display very distinct nodes and antinodes. In a darkened classroom the visual impact can be profound. As the laser light travels down the fiber optic line, it appears to be intensified at the antinodes and minimized at the nodes. In effect, it gives a three-dimensional view of a modulated light beam. In this case the light is being mechanically modulated with standing waves initiated by the vibrator.

The setup is relatively simple and inexpensive. Two to three meters of unjacketed fiber optic line in the commercially available 0.056- or 0.080-in size[2] is all that is needed. Other required hardware is common to most physics labs. When working with fiber optic line, avoid making any sharp bends or the line will break.

For a stable and strong setup, use two #6 ring connectors and one butt connector, as shown in Fig. 1. One ring connector permits the fiber optic line to be linked to the vibrator without tying a knot in the

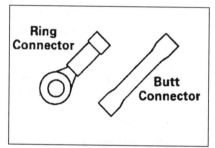

Fig. 1. Most general-purpose hardware kits contain #6 ring connectors and butt connectors.

line. This is done by inserting approximately a half meter of the fiber optic line through the crimping end of the ring connector. Instead of crimping the connector, which will crush the line, mix some epoxy glue and fill the crimp end of the connector and allow it to harden thoroughly. This will make a solid connection, and then a small screw with a nut attaches the line to the vibrator. The excess line, which extends through the crimp, is routed to the laser. The butt connector can then be epoxied near the end of this extension. With this connection, the laser end of the fiber optic line can be firmly held in place with a parallel jaw clamp secured by a double vee clamp. Place the laser on a laser jack and align it with the fiber optic line for maximum conveyance of light.

Epoxy the other #6 ring connector to the far end of the fiber optic line. Weights may be attached to this connection in order to vary the number of nodes and antinodes. Figure 2 shows the location of the three connectors on the setup, and Fig. 3 shows the demonstration apparatus in operation in a semidarkened classroom.

Finally, small nicks or serrations made with a razor blade can be spaced logarithmically along the fiber optic line. By making more serrations at the far end of the line than at the beginning of the line, the escaping light will be more evenly distributed, since the light power decreases along the length of the fiber optic cable. Be sure to exercise caution when handling or aiming the laser. A 2.0-mW laser will nicely illuminate a 2-m cable and can easily be viewed in a semidarkened room. This

Fig. 2. Suggested setup for a laser-enhanced vibrating string.

Fig. 3. A laser-illuminated vibrating line displays a colorful and distinct image of nodes and antinodes.

laser-enhanced vibrating string is guaranteed to keep the students' attention, and its visual impact is certain to enhance learning capabilities and retention.

References

1. PASCO scientific (Roseville, CA 95661-9011) WA-9608 with SF-9324; Sargeant-Welch (Skokie, IL 60077) #3256A.
2. Edmund Scientific (Barrington, NJ 08007) $3 to $6 per meter.

Wilberforce Pendulum, Demonstration Size

*Frank G. Karioris,** Physics Department, Marquette University, Milwaukee, WI 53233

One of the most fascinating of physics demonstrations is the Wilberforce pendulum[1] in which a mass at the end of a spring can vibrate up and down and also rotate about an axis collinear with the spring. When tuned so that the vibrational frequency equals the rotational frequency and the pendulum is set into motion, the energy shifts gradually from one mode to the other so that intervals of pure vibration are interspersed with intervals of pure rotation. This is illustrated in Fig. 1 by calculated curves of the vertical displacement and rotation angle of a Wilberforce pendulum as functions of time. Coupled harmonic oscillations and the equations of motion are covered in intermediate mechanics books[2-4] and articles,[5-11] which include descriptions of demonstrations and corridor displays. Some recent articles deal specifically with the Wilberforce pendulum.[9-11] Although these topics are not normally included in introductory physics courses or in high school, the demonstration may be used there in connection with the usual treatment of oscillatory motion to stimulate interest and pique the curiosity of students.

I have found only one commercial source for this apparatus; its rotor is 3 cm in diameter and the spring about 2 m in length.[12] Many college and university departments have built their own small, table-top models of the Wilberforce apparatus, and over the years each new faculty member learns about them in the lecture-demonstration apparatus storage room.

Floor Model Wilberforce Pendulum

The demonstration-size Wilberforce pendulum shown in Fig. 2 can be seen easily in a large lecture room, illustrates all features of the motions, is surprisingly simple to construct, and costs less than $15 for parts. It can be set into motion by raising (or lowering) the rotor 20 cm or so without rotation and releasing it. The rotor then executes approximately five vibrations without much rotation, begins rotational oscillations while vibrational amplitude decreases, literally stops vibrating, and does approximately five rotation-

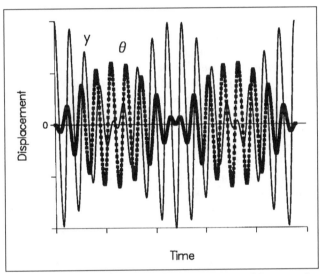

Fig. 1. Calculated displacement versus time for *y*, position of the center of mass of the rotor, and θ, angular position of the rotor, on a Wilberforce pendulum.

al oscillations, begins vibrating again and repeats the process of exchanging energy from vibrational to rotational modes. The period of oscillation is about 1.5 s. The energy is dissipated slowly so that five or six transitions from the vibrational to the rotational mode can be observed during one run. Normal modes with identical frequency for the vibration and rotation can be initiated by twisting the rotor through about 45° (clockwise or counterclockwise) and lifting it about 15 cm. When released, the rotor simultaneously rotates and falls, stops momentarily at its minimum height, then reverses direction, rotating back and rising until it again stops momentarily at its maximum height. The process repeats and is observable for five or six cycles.

Construction Notes

Making the spring turned out to be surprisingly easy. Anticipating some difficult work to make a heavy coil spring, I ordered a 1-lb box of 1/8-in-diameter spring steel wire through a local vendor.[13] The 24 feet of wire comes as a flat coil of 12 turns, with a diameter of about 8 in. When held up by one end, this "spring" oscillates with a period of about 1 s, due to the distributed mass. At each end of the spring, a portion of a turn was bent so as to form a 2-in stub coaxial with the coil. A 3-in section of 3/4-in diameter brass rod with a 1/8-in hole drilled in one end holds the upper end of the spring when two setscrews are tightened. The lower end of the spring fits into a similar brass rod at the rotor (refer to Fig. 2).

The rotor is a 2-lb coffee can, about 6.5 in high and of 5.5-in diameter, with top and bottom removed to reduce air resistance when it bounces up and down at the end of the spring. At the center of the can is a 3-in brass rod of 3/4-in diameter containing six holes drilled and tapped to take 1/4-in drill rod. Two of the holes are at the ends of the rod. The others are spaced 90 degrees apart around the center of the lateral surface. Four drill rods, each 9 in long, are passed through the holes in the can and screwed into the brass rod to support the rotor. Two washers, held between two nuts near the end of each of these rods, provide for tuning the rotational frequency to the vibrational frequency. A short section of drill rod screwed into the bottom of the support rod can be used to add mass to the oscillating system if needed for tuning. Another short section of drill rod is screwed into the top of the support rod and into a drilled and tapped hole in the end of the brass rod at the bottom of the spring.

As shown in Fig. 2, the system is about 1.2 m high and can be supported by conventional laboratory hardware. Tuning is accomplished by first determining the frequency of vibration and then adjusting the positions of the masses on the four rods projecting from the rotor until the rotational frequency is the same as the vibrational frequency.

Fig. 2. Frank G. Karioris with demonstration-size Wilberforce Pendulum.

Frank Karioris died on October 11, 1992, leaving this manuscript. It was edited and submitted to The Physics Teacher by Kenneth Mendelson, Physics Department, Marquette University, Milwaukee, WI 53233. Please address any correspondence to him.

References

1. *Demonstration Experiments in Physics*, edited by Richard M. Sutton (McGraw-Hill, New York, 1938), pp. 134–135.
2. Keith R. Symon, *Mechanics,* 2nd ed. (Addison-Wesley, Reading MA, 1950), pp. 188–198.
3. William F. Osgood, *Mechanics* (Macmillan, New York, 1937), p. 184 describes Blackburn's pendulum, which generates Lissajous figures.
4. *Physics Demonstration Experiments*, edited by Harry F. Meiners (Ronald Press, New York, 1970), p. 365.
5. Paul Chagnon, "Animated displays: Coupled mechanical oscillators," *Phys. Teach.* **30**, 275 (1992).
6. Frank G. Karioris and Kenneth S. Mendelson, "A novel coupled oscillations demonstration," *Am. J. Phys.* **60**, 508 (1992).
7. J. Walker, "Strange things happen when two pendulums interact through a variety of interconnections," *Sci. Am.* **253**, 176 (1985).
8. Robert J. Whitaker, "A note on the Blackburn pendulum," *Am. J. Phys.* **89**, 330 (1991).
9. Robert J. Whitaker, "L.R. Wilberforce and the Wilberforce Pendulum," *Am. J. Phys.* **56**, 37 (1988).
10. Richard E. Berg and Todd S. Marshall, "Wilberforce pendulum oscillations and normal modes," *Am. J. Phys.* **59**, 32 (1991).
11. Ulrich Köpf, "Wilberforce's pendulum revisited," *Am. J. Phys.* **58**, 833 (1990).
12. Central Scientific Co., 1222 Melrose Avenue, Franklin Park, IL 60131-1364, 1991 Catalog No. 34651, Wilberforce Pendulum, $144.
13. Precision Brand Products, Inc., Downers Grove, IL 60515; spring steel music wire, list price $6.54.

The Transient Phenomena of Forced Vibrations

W. Herreman, Fakulteit der Wetenschappen, Katholieke Universiteit Leuven, Campus Kortrijk, B-8500 Kortrijk, Belgium

Forced vibrations of a mass-spring system are described by the equation

$$m\frac{d^2x}{dt^2} + b\frac{dx}{dt} + kx = F_0 \cos \omega t \qquad (1)$$

A resistive force proportional to velocity is supposed. In textbooks of physics for undergraduates and in the December 1990 *TPT* centerfold, the solution of this differential equation is given by

$$x = A \cos (\omega t + \gamma) \qquad (2)$$

Equation (2) contains no adjustable constants of integration; the amplitude, A, and the initial phase, γ, are completely defined by the natural angular frequency, ω_0, of the system, the damping constant, b, the amplitude of the force, F_0, and the angular frequency, ω.

What became of the two constants of integration of this second-order differential equation? The answer is that Eq. (1) with its solution, Eq. (2), only describes the steady-state motion. To describe the

Fig. 1. Experiment for the demonstration of the transient phenomena of forced vibrations.

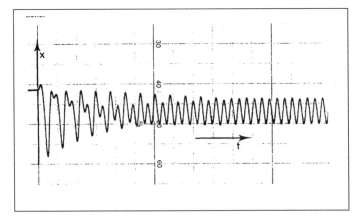

Fig. 2. The transient phenomena and the steady-state motion. The period of the forced vibration is 0.78 ± 0.01 s. The period of the damped system itself equals 1.50 ± 0.01 s.

transient behavior, French[1] suggests a more general solution of Eq. (1):

$$x = Be^{-bt/2m} \cos(\omega_1 t + \beta) + A \cos(\omega t + \gamma) \qquad (3)$$

where B and β are integration constants, and $\omega_1 = (\omega_0^2 - b^2/4m^2)^{1/2}$.

The superposition of these two vibrations gives rise to a transient phenomenon. During the motion the first term vanishes and only the steady-state term is left.

A simple experiment to demonstrate the transient phenomenon is shown in Fig. 1. A spring is attached to each end of a glider on a horizontal linear air track. A cord is tied between one spring and one end of the air track. A cord is also tied between the other spring and an eccentric on the shaft of a variable-speed motor. A mechanical arm is mounted on the glider. At one end of the arm a pen is fixed, which can write on an $x(t)$-recorder placed beside the air track. When the motor is started, the curve representing the transient motion of the glider is drawn on the recorder (Fig. 2). After some time the steady-state motion is achieved.

Reference

1. A.P. French, *Vibrations and Waves* (Thomas Nelson, London, 1971), p. 95.

Mechanical Device to Draw Lissajous Figures

O. Herrera, Instituto de Física, Universidad Católica de Valparaíso, Casilla 4059, Valparaíso, Chile

Here is an easily made mechanical device for drawing Lissajous figures.[1,2]

The proposed device (see Fig. 1) contains four pulleys, all of the same diameter. The pulleys, $A - A'$, form a system connected by a string and acrylic guides so that each pulley has the same angular speed. The same thing applies to system $B - B'$. Both systems are connected by a string between pulley B and an additional pulley D, which is firmly attached to pulley A. Pulley D is easily replaceable, allowing us to modify the angular speed ratio between the $A - A'$ and $B - B'$ systems. Pulleys A and B have been calibrated in order to fix the phase differences. Furthermore, each acrylic guide has a slot so that a bearing with a hole (into which a pen may be inserted) is located in the intersection of these two slots.

In our device, each pulley in the A and B systems has a diameter of 10 cm, whereas the fixed pulley, D, has a 5-cm diameter; the distance between the centers of each pair of pulleys is 40 cm. The whole appliance is set up on a wooden surface measuring approximately 60 x 60 cm.

Figures 2, 3, and 4 show the mechanical device working for $x = A \sin (\omega_2 t)$, and $y = A \sin (\omega_1 t + \delta)$, for given values of ω_2/ω_1 and δ.

References

1. M. Alonso and E.J. Finn, *Physics*, 4th ed. (Addison-Wesley, Reading, MA, 1970), p. 168.
2. M. Wu and W. H. Tsai, *Am. J. Phys.* **52,** 657 (1984).

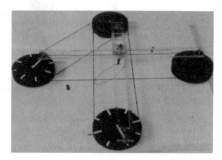

Fig. 2. Lissajous figure for $\omega_2/\omega_1 = 1$ and $\delta = \pi/4$.

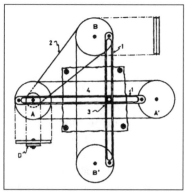

Fig. 1. Diagram of pulley device for drawing Lissajous figures. *A, A', B, B'*—pulleys of wood, *D*—Replaceable pulley, 1—acrylic guides, 2—strings, 3—bearing with pen hole, 4—paper.

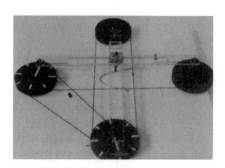

Fig. 3. Lissajous figure for $\omega_2/\omega_1 = 1/2$ and $\delta = \pi/4$.

Fig. 4. Lissajous figure for $\omega_2/\omega_1 = 1/2$ and $\delta = \pi/2$.

Momentum, Energy

An Apparatus for Demonstrating Energy Conservation

R. B. Knollenberg, III, Physics Department, University of Louisville, Louisville, KY 40292

The apparatus described here and shown in Fig. 1 provides a simple classroom demonstration of the principle of the conservation of energy when both linear and rotational motions are involved. The principle is demonstrated by an object that rolls without slipping down an incline at different rates of descent depending upon its rotational inertia while its total mass and rolling diameter remain the same.

The object needed can be easily made from readily available materials. One that works quite well is made from a 4.5 cm diameter x 20 cm long cardboard tube, a 1.0 cm diameter x 30 cm long aluminum rod, and two rubber stoppers that fit in the ends of the cardboard tube and have 1.0-cm diameter holes through them. The object is ready to assemble and use after the addition of a 1.0-cm diameter hole through the center of the cardboard tube perpendicular to its axis. The assembled object consists of the rubber-stoppered cardboard tube with the aluminum rod mounted either along the axis of the cardboard tube by putting it through the holes in the stoppers or perpendicular to the axis of the cardboard tube by inserting it halfway through the hole in the tube's center. The axis of the cardboard tube is the rotational axis of the object.

Roll the object down an incline made of two long parallel rods. (The aluminum rod in the object rotates between the two long inclined rods when it is perpendicular to the rotational axis of the object.) The object rolls down the incline at different rates of descent when its aluminum rod is first along its rotational axis and then perpendicular to it. The difference in the rates of descent is visual evidence of energy conservation. The effect is enhanced if you have two identical objects as described and conduct races between them.

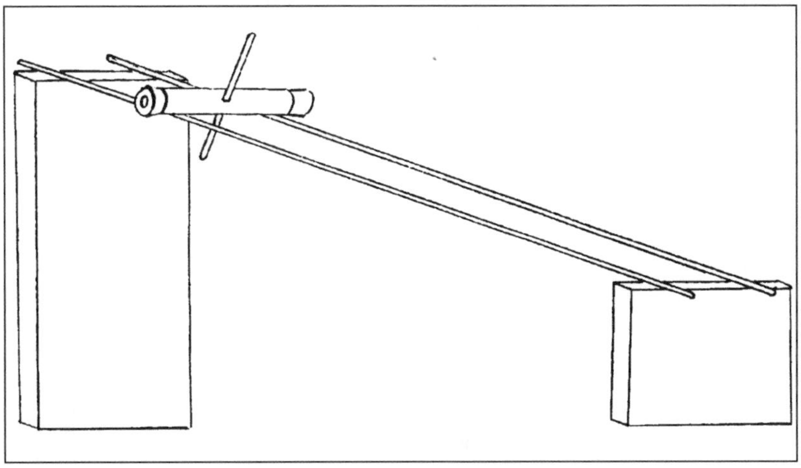

Fig. 1. **The object pictured demonstrates energy conservation.**

A Safe and Inexpensive Ballistic Pendulum

John W. Zwart, Department of Physical Sciences, Dordt College, Sioux Center, IA 51250

The ballistic pendulum provides a classic demonstration of linear momentum conservation; however, if the traditional rifle or pistol is used, student (and instructor) safety may be in jeopardy. Teachers hear many anecdotes about near misses and ricocheting bullets. Even if done as a demonstration, the traditional version of this experiment is rarely performed as a laboratory experiment. Several vendors offer versions for the experiment which replace the firearm with a spring-loaded "gun" or a bow and arrow. These tend to be expensive (about $350 for each setup) and, in my opinion, tend to make the experiment appear more abstract than it is, so that students miss the applicability of physics to an "outside world" phenomenon. To avoid problems of unsafe conditions and high cost, I developed a relatively safe and low-cost alternative.

To review quickly the pertinent physics, consider a projectile of mass m moving with a speed v_m. The projectile strikes a pendulum bob of mass M, becomes embedded in the bob, and the combination swings up to a maximum height h above the point where the collision took place. If the projectile sticks in the bob, the one-dimensional conservation of momentum equation is:

$$m \, v_m = (m + M) \, v_i,$$

where v_i is the speed of the combination of bob and projectile just after the collision but before the combination has risen any appreciable amount. Of course, kinetic energy is not conserved in this completely inelastic collision.

The kinetic energy of the combination is transformed to potential energy as the combination rises. The conservation of energy relation yields:

$$\tfrac{1}{2}(m + M) \, v_i^2 = (m + M) \, g \, h.$$

Using these two equations allows you to calculate the initial speed of the projectile from the rise height of the pendulum.

The apparatus that I used is shown in Fig. 1. The dart gun acts as the firearm, and the projectile is one of the darts with the rubber suction cup removed. While this set-up is far safer than a rifle, students should wear goggles and be cautioned about not firing the modified dart at anyone. The pendulum bob consists of a 35-mm film canister partially filled with modeling clay. The amount of clay should be adjusted to provide a reasonable swing height (roughly one-third to one-half full worked well for me). Capping the film canister

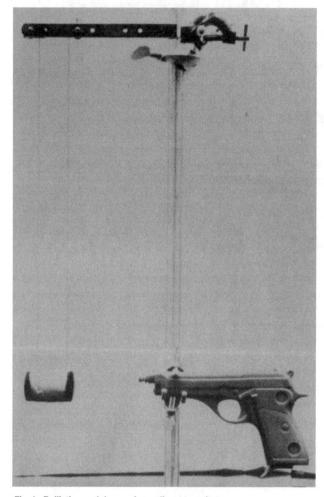

Fig. 1. Ballistic pendulum, using a dime store dart gun.

will prevent the clay from drying out between uses. The bob is suspended by a pair of strings which provides stability and causes the bob to remain horizontal during the swing, making it easier to determine the swing height.

Proper alignment of the dart gun with the bob is important. The gun should be horizontal, and the dart aimed directly at the center of the bob. Misalignment will cause the bob to rotate or the projectile to not stick. If either occurs, the equations above are not valid, and erroneous values for the projectile speed will result. The support strings need to be parallel.

Measurement of the rise height is, of course, the critical measurement after the masses are weighed. Not shown in

Fig. 1 is a sheet of poster board with horizontal lines drawn 2 cm apart. This is placed behind the apparatus. Using different colors for the lines makes it fairly easy to estimate the maximum height of the bob-projectile combination to the nearest centimeter. Students can make a series of measurements and use the average height to calculate the initial speed of the projectile.

A nice conclusion to the experiment is to remove the dart gun from the apparatus and test the calculated value for the initial projectile speed, a test not done easily with the commercial units. Students can calculate the distance the dart should travel when fired horizontally from some appropriate height, such as one meter. Depending on the sophistication of the students, a range of expected travel distances can be calculated from the spread in the pendulum rise heights. There is considerable student interest in this test and satisfaction when the prediction is borne out.

Other experiments or demonstrations can be done with the dart gun once its muzzle velocity is known. One example is a measurement of the coefficient of friction, done by firing the projectile into an object on a horizontal table. Using the distance traveled by the object, the masses of object and projectile, and the velocity of the projectile allows one to calculate the coefficient of friction.

For about $2 worth of new materials and using clamps generally available in the lab, a good ballistic pendulum experiment can be assembled readily. The experiment has proved popular with my students.

Momentum Vectors in a Plane

Kenneth Fox, Smoky Hill High School, Aurora, CO 80111

Momentum is a vector, but how can we show that to our students, especially those who are taking a conceptual level of physics? The collision lab in the PSSC manual is abstract and difficult for many students. As a teacher I found it a real challenge to produce a predictable and repeatable collision in a plane to demonstrate momentum conservation. Here is a solution I discovered.

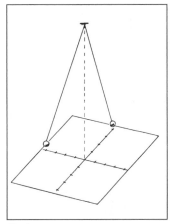

Fig. 1.

Procedure

Attach a string[1] with glue or cup hooks to two tennis balls and hang them from the ceiling at a common point over a grid (Fig. 1). Place a large piece of Velcro on the "equator" of each ball so that they will stick together upon contact. The release points of the balls can be varied, but they arrive at the center of the grid at the same time. Since they are pendulums of the same length, if you release the bobs at the same time, they must arrive at the same time. Because of the Velcro belts, the two balls stick together and swing off in a new plane. (At first I used balls of clay, but

they were small and required too much precision in the moment of release.)

My calculations show that the speed at impact is nearly proportional to the distance the ball is pulled back (up to 20°). Thus, by marking 10-cm increments along two perpendicular axes on the grid, you can manipulate the speed by releasing the balls at known distances. There is some likelihood that the balls will not stick if their speed is too great, so don't choose distances too large. Vector addition of the two momenta will yield a good prediction for the direction of the new plane of swings. Division by the mass of the combined balls gives the amplitude of the resulting swing.

Calculations

Here is a simple calculation from a recent classroom effort. I was using two balls of equal mass (1 b). One ball was pulled to the 40-cm mark, the other to the 20-cm mark.

$$\overrightarrow{momentum_1} + \overrightarrow{momentum_2} =$$

$$\overrightarrow{momentum_{total}} \quad\quad (1)$$

$$(1\ b)\ (40\ speed,\ North)\ +$$

$$(1\ b)\ (20\ speed,\ East)\ =\ (2\ ball)\ (\vec{V}) \quad (2)$$

(45 b-speed, $27°$ E of N) =

$$(2 \text{ b}) (\vec{V}) \qquad (3)$$

$$22 \text{ speed, } 27° E \text{ of } N = \vec{V} \qquad (4)$$

Thus the two balls together should swing out to the 22-cm mark on a line that makes a $27°$ angle with the axis used for the 40-cm pull. Remarkably, they do!

The process works well even when the two velocities are not at right angles or the masses are not equal. I have made a tennis ball in which I put a second cut-up ball, thus $M = 2$ b. It would have been easier to change the mass by adding rocks, but by using the pieces of another ball, it is very clear that I have a mass of 2 b.

I had hoped that this apparatus could be used for collisions that do not have the balls stick. I have not had good luck with the tennis balls since the path each takes after impact is affected by spinning. I suspect that a smaller ball would work better, but the PSSC lab does show elastic interactions quite well. I would appreciate hearing of any improvements that you make in this apparatus.

Reference
1. Since writing this, the author has been using gift ribbon because it does not untwist and change length.

A Momentum Transfer Demonstration with "Happy/Unhappy" Balls

Fred Bucheit, Bald Eagle-Nittany High School, Mill Hall, PA 17751

I finally found a good use for those "happy/unhappy" balls advertised in science catalogs. It involves a very simple setup wherein the balls are suspended on the end of a string, pulled back like a pendulum, and allowed to swing into a board standing on end. With careful placement, the unhappy ball will not topple the board; the happy ball will. This is because the collisions have very different coefficients of restitution. The happy ball, being more elastic, will rebound from the board with greater speed than will the less-elastic, unhappy ball. Since the happy ball suffers a greater change in momentum, it imparts a greater impulse to the board.

Fig. 1.

The setup and procedure are simple. Screw a small hook-eye into each ball. As shown in Fig. 1, bend a wire assembly (or equivalent) in such a way that a string is supported from a point about 24 cm above the desktop. Hang a ball at the end of a 13-cm length of string. Bend the wire near the top in a way that allows you to line up the string at a given angle when the ball is pulled back. The device pictured provides about a 20-degree angle from the vertical when released.

Stand a pine board (about 2 x 8 x 15 cm) on end about 4 cm from the ball when it is hanging vertically. The device pictured supports only one ball but both balls could be supported side by side. With a bit of experimenting before class begins, you can find the best placement of the board so that the unhappy ball will not quite topple the board on impact, but the happy ball will. A cut-off piece of straight pin or a small nail should be inserted into the unhappy ball to give it mass equal to that of the happy ball.

Show your class both balls, which have equal diameters, but do not mention their bouncing properties. After witnessing the collision between the balls and the board, many students will guess that the balls have different mass. This demonstration always leads to an interesting discussion of momentum transfer involving elastic and inelastic collisions.

A Mechanical Glider Launcher for the Air Track

Vassilis Stavrinidis, The Moraitis School, A. Papanastasiou & Ag. Dimitriou, 154 52 Athens, Greece

The air track has long been a very useful system for demonstrating and studying many aspects of mechanics from introductory to college-level physics. An important air-track accessory is the timing system, usually a photogate wired to an electronic timer. Most airtrack experiments require the measurement of at least two time intervals. This may be a problem in instructional environments in which there are only a few timers available. In such situations, a simple device capable of launching a glider with known, highly reproducible speed would be very useful since this would reduce the number of timers required. For example, a collision between two gliders could be repeated a number of times and a single timer used to measure the final glider speeds. This note describes the construction of a glider launching device using a very inexpensive, common hardware item.

Making and Using the Launcher

The apparatus (see Fig. 1) employs a "magnetic touch latch," a common device for convenient opening and closing of small glass doors on indoor closets or stereo cabinets. Such latches are available in U.S. hardware or building supply stores for about $2.50. This type of latch is spring loaded and can be set up to deliver a reproducible impulse of convenient magnitude to an air-track glider. The latch is screwed or glued to a small piece of wood or other light material, which in turn is fastened to a short piece of 90° aluminum stock. This whole assembly is then fastened to the end of the air track with rubber bands (Fig. 2).

With the tongue of the latch in the "out" position, as in Fig. 2, a glider is pushed against the latch until a "click" is heard, indicating that the tongue is locked in the "in" position (Fig. 3). This also compresses the latch spring. Pushing the glider a bit further unlocks the tongue, resulting in a second "click." When you release the glider, it is propelled by the spring, and the initial speed of the glider is remarkably consistent. In 18 measurements on a 0.215-kg glider, the time required to travel 0.200 m was 22 ± 4 ms, which indicates a reproducibility of better than 2%.

A particularly interesting experiment involves the determination of the energy stored in the compressed spring of the latch. Students can easily measure the force required to displace the latch tongue by various distances. This can be done using a calibrated spring scale or by placing the latch in a vertical position and loading it with masses. The force constant of the spring is then found from the displacement-vs-load graph. The calculated potential energy of the compressed spring can then be compared to the kinetic energy imparted to the launched glider. This leads to interesting questions regarding energy transformations, and losses due to friction.

Fig. 1. Magnetic touch latch, the latch holder assembly, and complete launcher system.

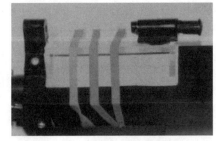

Fig. 2. Launcher fastened to the end of an air track, with latch tongue in the "out" position.

Fig. 3. Magnetic touch latch with tongue in the "in" position.

Impedance Matching on the Air Track

Theodore H. Ansbacher, Museum of Science and Industry, 57th Street and Lake Shore Drive, Chicago, IL 60637

The efficient transfer of energy from one object, or medium, to another—impedance matching—is not usually discussed at the introductory level; yet it is an excellent way to clarify ideas about forces, impulse-momentum, and work-energy relations, as well as being of practical use. A simple device, described here, allows an investigation of impedance matching on the air track appropriate to any introductory course.

In the familiar elastic collision on an air track, when a moving glider hits a glider of equal mass at rest, all energy is transferred, as evidenced by the first glider remaining at rest after the collision. However, if the gliders are of unequal mass then all energy is not transferred, as evidenced by the first glider being still in motion after the collision. The principles of conservation of momentum and energy can be applied to explain these phenomena.

Students may be asked to determine qualitatively what conditions would need to be altered to achieve complete energy transfer between the unequal-mass gliders. The answer is to have a relatively smaller force acting on the glider of less mass than on the glider of greater mass during the collision. This might at first seem to be impossible, as it violates Newton's third law, until it is remembered that this is exactly what a lever (or any other simple machine) accomplishes—unequal forces between two objects, while keeping energy input and output equal.

The problem then becomes how to interpose a lever between two gliders on an air track. A solution is the double-lever device, shown in Fig. 1 and diagrammed in Fig. 2, with a movable fulcrum that allows the ratio of the two forces to be adjusted to achieve impedance matching between any two gliders. This prototype was built from scrap wood, two hinges, and angle irons, with the dimension L = 10 cm.

Referring to Fig. 2, let F_1 be the force exerted by the first glider as it makes contact with the first lever; F_2 be the force that the second lever exerts while in contact with the second glider; and F_3 be the intermediate force that the first lever exerts on the second lever. The distance l of the fulcrum from the midpoint is adjustable. Then for the first lever

$$F_3/F_1 = L/(L + l),$$

while for the second lever

$$F_2/F_3 = (L - l)/L.$$

Combining these two equations gives

$$F_2/F_1 = (L - l)/(L + l). \qquad (1)$$

For any two masses, the ratio of F_2/F_1 necessary to

Fig. 1. Impedance~matching device mounted on an air track. The smaller glider is about to transfer all of its energy to the larger gilder.

achieve complete energy transfer can be calculated. Then, Eq. (1) can be used to determine the correct position for the fulcrum.

For example, take the case where one glider has twice the mass of the other, $M_2 = 2M_1$, and impose the condition of complete energy transfer as shown in Fig. 3. Applying the impulse-momentum relation to each glider gives

$$F_1\Delta T = M_1V_1, \text{ and } F_2\Delta T = M_2V_2{'},$$

where T is the time of interaction. Combining these two equations gives

$$F_1/F_2 \;=\; M_1V_1/M_2V_2. \tag{2}$$

Assuming an elastic collision, the kinetic energy before and after is equal, giving

$$\tfrac{1}{2}M_1V_1^2 \;=\; \tfrac{1}{2}M_2V_2{'}^2. \tag{3}$$

Combining Eqs. (2) and (3) gives the ratio of forces needed to accomplish the complete transfer of energy,

$$F_1/F_2 = 0.707. \tag{4}$$

Going back to Eq. (1) for the double-lever device, a fulcrum position of $l = -0.17L$ produces an impedance match between the two gliders.

The development of this device arose from a rather casual statement in a textbook that the middle ear functioned primarily as an impedance-matching device between air and the fluid of the inner ear. It became necessary to explain to the students (and to myself) just what that statement meant. (Although the bones of the middle ear do function as levers, it turns out that this is not the primary impedance-matching mechanism.) Good classroom discussion may be generated around identifying other situations where good energy transfer is important and by considering simple machines such as impedance-matching devices. This can help clarify ideas about force, work, energy, and conservation of energy. Another good topic for discussion is to explain why momentum, apparently, is not conserved.

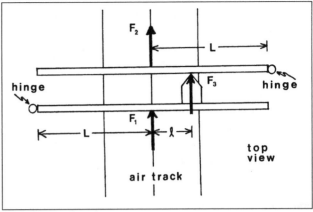

Fig. 2. Top view of impedance-matching device. L is the distance from the hinge to the air track center line: *l* is the distance from the fulcrum to the center line.

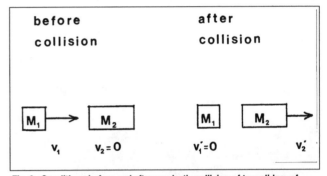

Fig. 3. Conditions before and after an elastic collision of two gliders of unequal mass, assuming complete transfer of energy.

A Measurement Using the Piezoelectric Effect

Judith Bransky, 4123 Indian Run Drive, Dayton, OH 45415

The piezoelectric effect converts mechanical impulses to electrical voltage surges. The piezoelectric effect, characteristic of ferro-electric crystals, is obtained in PZT ceramic materials by annealing them in a DC electric field. This procedure generates preferably oriented dipoles. When the sample is deformed by an external compressive force, a charge displacement occurs that increases the surface charge; a potential difference is built up between the faces. The output voltage can go up to 1 kV for a stress of 200 N/cm^2. In the case of impulse measurements, high-voltage pulses are generated for durations of a few milliseconds. An oscilloscope with a fluorescent memorizing screen or a digital memory can record these pulses.

The ceramic PZT-5A is available for a minimal charge from Vernitron (Thornhill, Southampton, England). Here is an example of how you can use this modern material to measure the coefficient of restitution.

A steel ball of several grams is released from a defined height onto a slab of PZT. The ball is held and released by a small electromagnet. The PZT slab we used was 2 x 2 x 0.5

cm. It comes with a silver coating on the large faces to which thin leads can easily be soldered. The slab is placed on a flat solid surface. A groove allows room for the lower lead. Another plate about 1-cm thick is placed on top of the sample, again allowing for the lead. The upper plate can be made of different materials to measure the coefficient of restitution for different material combinations. It is important to clamp the plates so that no relative motion is possible. The leads of the sample are connected through 1 MΩ to the input of the memorizing oscilloscope. The shunt is necessary to attenuate the input voltage.

The released ball falls on the slab and bounces on it several times. Each of these bounces is represented by a voltage pulse on the screen, and the pulse height is proportional to the impulse delivered by the ball. Several photographs of such recordings are displayed in Figs. 1–5. The ratio of the height of adjacent pulses is exactly the restitution coefficient. This is shown by the following calculation.

By definition the coefficient of restitution is

$$e = -v_f/v_i \qquad (1)$$

where V_f is the velocity after bounce; and v_i is the velocity before bounce.

Since the pulse height is proportional to the impulse

$$U_2/U_1 = I_2/I_1 \qquad (2)$$

where U_1, U_2 are the height of pulses 1 and 2, respectively, and I_1, I_2 are the impulse during first and second bounces, respectively.

Substituting the change of momentum for the impulse

$$I_2/I_1 = \Delta P_2/\Delta P_1$$

$$= m\Delta v_2/m\Delta v_1 = \Delta v_2/\Delta v_1 \qquad (3)$$

where: M is the mass of the ball and ΔP_1, ΔP_2, are the changes of momentum during the first and second bounce, respectively; Δv_1, Δv_2, are the velocity changes during the first and second bounce, respectively. That is

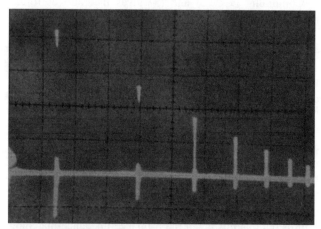

Fig. 2. Steel ball m = 4 g on Plexiglas. Height 17 cm; time base 0.1 s/cm; voltage scale 5 V/cm.

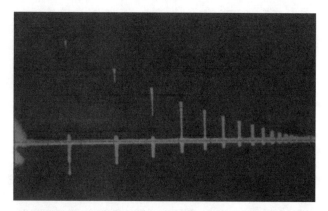

Fig. 1. Steel ball m = 2 g on Plexiglas. Height unknown; time base 0.2 s/cm; voltage scale 5 V/cm.

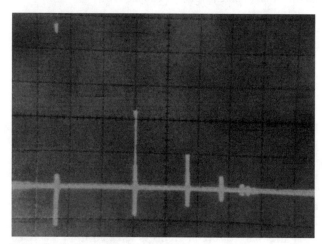

Fig. 4. Steel ball m = 4 g on steel. Height 17 cm; time base 0.1 s/cm; voltage scale 2 V/cm.

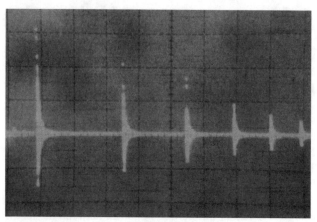

Fig. 3. Glass ball m = 4.8 g on Plexiglas. Height 17 cm; time base 0.1 s/cm; voltage scale 5 V/cm.

$$\Delta v_1 = v_{1f} - v_{1i} \tag{4}$$

$$\Delta v_2 = v_{2f} - v_{2i}$$

$$\Delta v_2 / \Delta v_1 = \frac{v_{2f} - v_{2i}}{v_{1f} - v_{1i}}$$

Since $v_{2i} = -v_{2f}/e$ and $v_{1i} = -v_{if}/e$, Eq. (4) becomes:

$$\frac{v_{2f}(1 + 1/e)}{v_{1f}(1 = 1/e)} = v_{2f}/v_{1f} \tag{5}$$

However, neglecting air resistance

$$v_{1f} = - v_{2i} \tag{6}$$

Thus

$$v_{2f}/v_{1f} = - v_{2f}/v_{2i} = e \tag{7}$$

and

$$U_2/U_1 = e \tag{8}$$

The time intervals between adjacent pulses can also provide the same information. As Eq. (3) shows, each pulse is a measure of the momentum change of the ball. This change in momentum is proportional to the change in velocity and thus is also proportional to the time elapsed between two pulses (or bounces):

$$\Delta t_{21} = 2v_{if}/g \quad ; \quad \Delta t_{32} = 2v_{2f}/g \tag{9}$$

(Δt_{21} and Δt_{32} are the time intervals between pulse 2 and pulse 1, pulse 2 and pulse 3, respectively).

$$\Delta t_{32}/\Delta t_{21} = v_{2f}/v_{1f} \tag{10}$$

$$\text{since } v_{1f} = -v_{2i}$$

$$\Delta t_{32}/\Delta t_{21} = -v_{2f}/v_{2i} = + e \tag{11}$$

The two modes of calculating e, 1) by the ratio of adjacent pulse heights, and 2) by the ratio of adjacent time intervals result in the same value. This can be verified by the various figures presented. Some typical results are:

Steel on Plexiglas	$e = 0.65 \pm 0.02$ (Figs. 1, 2)
Glass on Plexiglas	$e = 0.45 \pm 0.01$ (Fig. 3)
Steel on steel	$e = 0.73 \pm 0.03$ (Fig. 4)
Glass on steel	$e = 0.74 \pm 0.03$
Steel on PZT (directly)	$e = 0.77 + 0.02$ (Fig. 5)

The "impulse-to-voltage" conversion factor (k) can be calculated knowing the height (h) from which the ball was

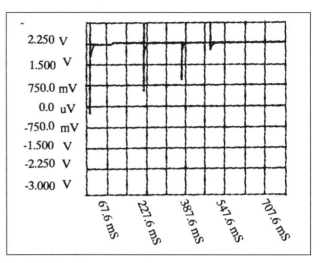

Fig. 5. Digital oscilloscope trace. Steel ball m = 2 g directly on PZT sample. Height 12 cm; time base 0.08 s/cm; voltage scale arbitrary.

initially released, from the value of e, and from the maximum voltage of the first pulse:

$$kU_1 = I_1 = \Delta P_1 = m\Delta v_1 = m(v_{1f} - v_{1i}) \tag{12}$$

$$= - mv_{1i}(e + 1) = m \sqrt{2gh} (1 + e)$$

From the data of Fig. 2:
$$k = I_1/U_1 = 5.7 \times 10^{-4} \text{ kg m/s V}$$

Or, alternatively, if the time intervals are measured in absolute units, the initial and final velocities of any pulse (n) can be computed by equations (9) and by the assumption $v_{nf} = v_{(n+1)}$ i. The change in momentum during the nth pulse is equal to the impulse of the bounce:

$$I_n = P_n = m(v_{nf} - v_{ni}) \tag{13}$$

$$= mg/2 \, [\Delta t_{(n+1)n} - \Delta t_{n(n-1)}]$$

and again from Fig. 2:

$$k = I_2/U_2 = mg/2 \, (\Delta t_{32} - \Delta t_{21}) \tag{14}$$

$$= 6.0 \times 10^{-4} \text{ kg m/s V}$$

in reasonable accordance with the previous result.

The author wishes to thank Achiam Wiener for his technical assistance and fruitful collaboration.

Fluids

A Demonstration to Show the Upthrust Exerted by Air

Zhu E-Qing, Ningho Food College, Zheliang Province, China

Students usually believe that a body that is lighter than air, such as a helium-filled balloon, receives an upthrust exerted by the air. It is more difficult for them to visualize that, for a body heavier than air, a buoyant force also exists. To demonstrate this, pour about 50–60 ml of vinegar into a plastic bag (1–2 l volume) and, after squeezing out the air, tie the bag in the middle by a thread so it is partitioned into two parts. Into the upper part of the bag, put in about 10 cc of baking soda and, again, squeeze out the air and tie the bag closed. Now place the bag on a balance as shown in Fig. 1.

After the balance is adjusted, carefully untie the thread in the center of the bag and allow the baking soda and vinegar to mix. The resultant gas (CO_2) will fill the bag, displacing the air and producing a noticeable buoyant force. (The balance will become unbalanced as shown in Fig. 2.)

By again balancing the scale, the buoyant force can be determined. If the volume of the bag is known, a value for the density of air can be found. Students can see clearly that the total mass, before and after the chemical reaction, is unchanged so that the weight difference of the bag is due to the buoyant force of the air.

A second demonstration to illustrate the buoyancy of air uses a can (0.3–0.5 l volume) of compressed air and a balloon. The apparatus is a paint can with a valve soldered in the lid, the lid soldered to the can, and the lid and bottom of the can connected by a wire soldered to each. The center wire allows greater air pressure (Fig. 3).

Place the pressurized can onto a platform balance, tie an

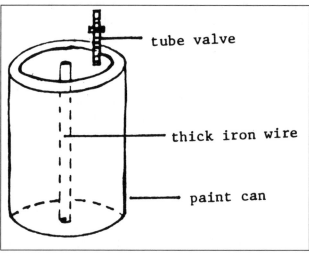

Fig. 2.

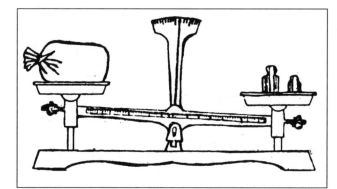

tube valve

thick iron wire

paint can

Fig. 3.

empty balloon over the valve, adjust the balance, and then let the balloon fill with the compressed air. The buoyant force will be noticeable as the balloon inflates. If the volume of the filled balloon can be determined, then the density of air can be calculated.

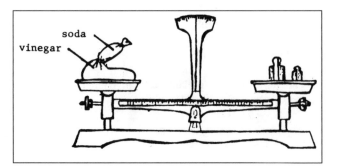

soda

vinegar

Fig. 1.

Archimedes' Principle and Smiley-Faced Balloons

Joseph Miano, Casady School, 9500 N Pennsylvania, Oklahoma City, OK 73156

After noticing smiley-faced Mylar balloons bobbing up and down in a supermarket display, I decided to use one of these balloons in presenting Archimedes' principle of buoyancy to my physics classes. This is my third year using this method, which has met with good success.

Apparatus

All you need is one Mylar helium-filled balloon (from which any weight has been removed), a gondola fashioned from a cut Styrofoam cup and wire, and some tiny masses (I use wire cut into pieces of various sizes). The balloon and gondola must rise when released, demonstrating that the buoyant force is greater than the weight. As wire pieces are added to the gondola, the balloon sinks to the ground, demonstrating that the weight is greater than the buoyancy. After a few minutes of removing and adding pieces of wire, the balloon will neither rise nor fall. Neutral buoyancy has been achieved.

Theory

Archimedes' principle states that the buoyant force is equal to the weight of the fluid displaced:

$$B = \rho_A g V \tag{1}$$

where B = buoyant force, V = volume of the air displaced, and ρ_A = density of air.

At neutral buoyancy

$$B = w \tag{2}$$

where w = weight of all objects being supported.

Therefore

$$w = \rho_A g V \tag{3}$$

Now

$$w = m_{He}g + m_G g + m_B g \tag{4}$$

where m_{He} = mass of helium, m_G = mass of gondola, and m_B = mass of balloon.

Equating (3) and (4),

$$\rho_A g V = (m_{He} + m_G + m_B)g \tag{5}$$

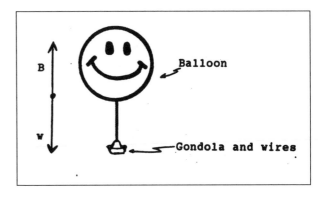

But

$$m_{He} = \rho_{He}V \tag{6}$$

where ρ_{He} = density of helium.

Substituting and simplifying,

$$(\rho_A - \rho_{He})V = m_G + m_B \tag{7}$$

The densities of air and helium can be found in the *Handbook of Chemistry and Physics*[1] and corrected to room temperature and pressure. The mass of the gondola and balloon are easily measured by weighing them on an electronic balance after the experiment is complete and the helium allowed to escape. The volume of the balloon may be found either by displacement of water or by approximating the shape of a disk or an ellipsoid ($V_{ellipsoid} = 4/3 \, \pi \, a^2 b$).

Data

Typical data for this experiment:
$a = 17.5$ cm
$b = 8.5$ cm
$V = 11,000$ cm^3
$\rho_A = 1.20 \times 10^{-3}$ g/cm^3
$\rho_{He} = 0.18 \times 10^{-3}$ g/cm^3

Mass of gondola and balloon = 12.60 g.

Our measurements for the buoyant force agreed with our calculations with a discrepancy of about 10%.

Reference

1. *Handbook of Chemistry and Physics,* 45th edition, edited by R.C. Weast (The Chemical Rubber Company, Cleveland, OH, 1964), pp. B-178 and F-8.

A Density Demonstration

Dick Heckathorn, Midpark High School, 15988 Brinbourne Avenue, Middelburg Hts., OH 44130

Density is a subject with which many high school students have trouble. To aid in helping students understand the increased buoyancy effect of salt-water vs fresh water, fill a container (such as an olive jar) with water. Next, lower a Ban Roll-On[1] ball into the water. It will quickly sink to the bottom. Now, add some rock salt, put the lid on, and shake the jar gently, stopping often to allow the ball to reach an equilibrium position. As the salt dissolves, a density gradient will be established, and the ball will be suspended as shown in Fig. 1. The sphere will remain in this position for many days provided the jar is not disturbed. More shaking will increase the density of the solution, causing the sphere to float higher. If possible, use a plastic container and a plastic lid to prevent salt water corrosion. I have found no other roll-on ball that works. Are there other materials that behave in a similar manner?

Reference

1. Ban Deodorant, Bristol-Myers Products.

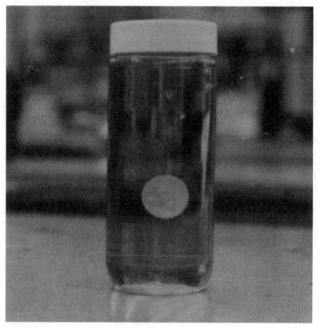

Fig. 1. A deodorant roll-on ball floats in a salt-water solution effectively illustrating the concept of density.

An Alternative Way to Measure Air Density

Robert G. Buschauer, Cerritos College, Norwalk, CA 90650

An article in this journal[1] describes a novel and useful method for determining the density of air. The approach is to measure the mass of a basketball before and after pressurizing it with air. From the mass difference (a few grams) and the volume of air enclosed, one readily computes the density to within 10 percent of the accepted value.

I want to mention that Central Scientific Company[2] makes a device they call the "Weight of Air Cylinder" that can also be used to determine ambient air density. However, instead of inflating the 0.00050 m³ aluminum cylinder, you evacuate it with a mechanical roughing pump (or hand pump). A stop cock allows you to disconnect the evacuated cylinder from the pump before weighing. The air mass difference is nominally 0.0006 kg, which is less than the values ordinarily obtained using the basketball, but still large enough to be measured accurately on an ordinary triple-beam balance.

I have used an earlier model aluminum sphere for the past ten years. It takes about 20 s to evacuate it using a small roughing pump, and measurements to within 10 percent of the accepted value are readily obtained using a standard triple-beam balance and the known volume. Also, the sphere is remarkably robust. I have dropped it several times, and abused it in myriad other ways; yet, it continues to hold vacuum.

References

1. Howard Brody, *Phys. Teach.* **27**, 46 (1989).
2. Central Scientific Company (Franklin Park, IL 60131-1364) #30055, $25.

The Hyphenated Siphon

Raymond E. Benenson, Department of Physics, SUNY, Albany, NY 12222

People who have not had any courses in physics are often fascinated by seeing water run uphill through a siphon (and so is this author). The explanation that is easiest to give is that a partial vacuum is created near, and at, the apex of the siphon, and water is pushed up by atmospheric pressure toward the partial vacuum. A vacuum or compound gauge in a Tee connection (the hyphen of the title), as shown in Fig. 1, will demonstrate that the pressure is less than atmospheric. Assembling and testing the apparatus takes less than ten minutes and, indeed, the particular Bourdon gauge read a gauge pressure, with water flowing, of $-5 \pm 1 \times 10^3$ Pa (-0.7 ± 0.1 psi, gauge). As the author blew into the tube from one end, with the other end sealed, the gauge read $+6.8 \times 10^3$ Pa (he may not be in top condition), which served to illustrate the distinction between positive and negative gauge pressures. Qualitatively, the demonstration is very easy and successful. The quantitative analysis has pitfalls.

At first sight, Bernoulli's equation for an incompressible fluid of density ρ seems to supply the mathematical description:

$$P_a + \rho g h_a + \tfrac{1}{2}\rho v_a^2 = P_b + \rho g h_b + \tfrac{1}{2}\rho v_b^2 \quad (1)$$

where a is one point on a streamline, b another, with p_a and p_b, h_a and h_b, v_a and v_b, respectively, pressures, heights above a reference level, and velocities, and g the acceleration of gravity. Linking points 1 and 3 of Fig. 1, with $v_1 \approx 0$ and $p_1 = p_3 = p_0 =$ atmospheric pressure, then $v_3 = \sqrt{2gh}$. Linking points 2 and 3, the right-most terms in Eq. (1) cancel:

$$p_2 = p_0 - \rho g h_2 - \tfrac{1}{2}\rho v_2^2 \quad (2)$$

showing $p_2 < p_0$. Velocity v_2 can be measured by collecting a water volume, Q, at point 3 for time t and using the equation of continuity:

$$Q/t = Av \quad (3)$$

where A is the cross-sectional area of the hose, assumed uniform.

For the sake of accuracy, the Bourdon gauge was replaced by a water-filled manometer, which read -3.33×10^3 Pa (-34 cm H_2O). A correction for the vapor pressure of water would reduce this to $-3.2 \pm 0.1 \times 10^3$ Pa. The Tee had nearly the same A as the hose, and h_2 can be set at almost zero. For the following measurements: $h_1 = 85$ cm,

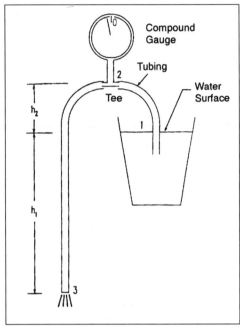

Fig. 1.

hose diam $= 0.6$ cm, $Q/t = 41.7$ cm^3/s, from Eq. (2) $v_3 = 147.5$ cm/s, compared with $\sqrt{2gh} = 408$ cm/s, and calculated $p_2 - p_0 = -1.08 \times 10^3$ Pa. The reason for the poor agreement was thought to be viscosity.

Poiseuille's equation with a gravity term[1] was tried next; for tubing of radius a:

$$Q/t = \frac{\pi a^4}{8\mu}\left[\frac{p_2 - p_0}{\ell} + \rho g\right] \quad (4)$$

where μ is the viscosity of the water and ℓ the length of the hanging hose. For $\ell = 87.5$ cm, $\mu = 7.052 \times 10^{-3}$ poise (water at 36°C), and $p_2 - p_0 = -3.2 \times 10^3$ Pa, as cited above, the calculated Q/t was 280 cm^3/s, again in serious disagreement with experiment.

The estimated Reynolds number, $R > 10^4$, suggested that turbulence is the culprit. Since R varies as μ^{-1}, in order to reduce R and restore laminar flow the experiment was redone with glycerin ($\mu = 9.54$ poise at 25°C) in a specially made glass siphon having a 6 mm inner diameter. A glass U-tube manometer, also filled with glycerin, had one leg connected to the underside of the top of the siphon (below point 2 of Fig. 1) by means of a glass Tee; the other leg was open to air. With suction, the glycerin flow could be started; at the same time, the manometer fluid reached the top of the siphon. For ℓ in Eq. (4) = 25.9 cm, Δp = –6.5 cm glycerin (ρ = 1.26 g/cm^3), then Q (calculated) = 0.31 cm^3/s, which compared very well with Q (measured) = 0.33 $\pm$ 0.02 cm^3/s. Incidentally, an impressive vena contracta appeared below the siphon exit.

An interesting article on combining the Bernoulli and Poiseuille equations has recently appeared.[2] Equation (16) from that article could possibly be adapted to the water case.

Setting up this demonstration is quite easy. However, a sensitive gauge is recommended. The quantitative investigation here was more a matter of resolving a frustration, although Poiseuille's equation could lead to a student experiment on viscosity.[3]

Sincere thanks are due to Earl Nagle for making the glass siphon and attached U-tube manometer.

References

1. *Fundamental Formulas of Physics*, edited by Donald H. Menzel (Prentice-Hall, New York, 1955), Eq.18.6.
2. C.E. Synolakis and H.S. Badeer, *Am. J. Phys.* **57**,1013 (1989).
3. L. Ruby, *Phys. Teach.* **29**, 44 (1991).

Cartesian Diver

Terry Ragsdale, California State University, Los Angeles, CA 90032

T he Cartesian diver as described below will eliminate the terminal problem faced by any open-ended diver. After long periods of submersion, water vaporizes on the inner wall of the container (diver), lowering the buoyancy, and causing it to fall to the bottom of the reservoir.

A closed-off bellows, suitably ballasted, will remain operative for extended periods of time (as long as the bellows' seal remains). Shown (Fig. 1) is the simplest form I tried.

The bellows is 30 mm (diam) x 60 mm, which will just fit through the neck of a transparent plastic floor wax container. I have made them as small as 5 mm x 30 mm.

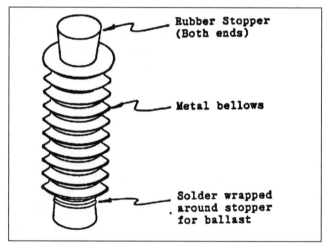

Fig. 1. Metal bellows Cartesian diver.

An Automated Cartesian Diver Apparatus

R.B. Knollenberg, III, University of Louisville, Department of Physics, Louisville, KY 40292

T he automated Cartesian diver apparatus described here and shown in Fig. 1 provides a fascinating, instructive, and dependable display. The diver is made to sink and rise every 15 s by raising and lowering a water reservoir.

The water reservoir consists of a length of water-filled rubber tubing. It is raised and lowered periodically by attaching it to a pipet that passes through a hole in a rotating arm. The pipet turns freely in the hole in the rotating arm so that the water-filled rubber tubing does not twist as the arm with pipet rotates. Thus, as the arm rotates, the water-filled rubber tubing (i.e., the reservoir) rises and falls.

The Cartesian diver is made of a transparent plastic pencil-lead box. It is partially filled with lead shot and water so that it just floats, and it has a small hole in its bottom. The pressure within the water-filled flask containing the Cartesian diver rises and falls as the reservoir rises and falls. When the pressure within the flask is above the air pressure inside the diver, water is forced inside the diver through the small hole in its bottom and it sinks. When the pressure

within the flask falls below the air pressure inside the diver, the process is reversed and the diver rises. The diver can be made to cycle up and down evenly by adjusting the rubber bulb of the pipes back or forth on its glass tubing.

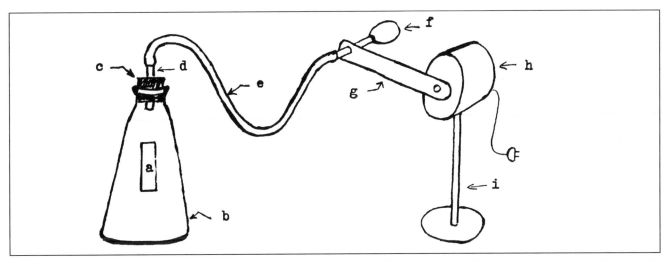

Fig. 1. (a) Cartesian diver (made from a transparent plastic pencil-lead box). (b) 1-liter flask filled with water. (c) Rubber stopper with hole through its center. (d) 5-cm length of 7-mm (outside diameter) glass tubing. (e) 5 mm (inside diameter) x 2.4 mm wall natural latex rubber tubing, 90 cm long. (f) Pipet. (g) Arm, 30 cm long. (h) 4 rpm, 1 20-vac motor. (i) Motor stand.

An Extremely Sensitive Cartesian Diver

Robert M. Graham, Physics Department, University of Nebraska at Omaha, Omaha, NE 68182

At some time in our undergraduate or high-school education most of us have had some experience with a Cartesian diver. The device usually consisted of a commercially purchased diver that was put into a graduated cylinder filled with water and having a rubber membrane stretched over the top. When you pushed down on the membrane, the diver would sink. Another option was to put the diver into a capped two-liter plastic pop bottle filled with water. When the bottle was squeezed, the diver would sink. Yet another option was to use a flat-sided glass bottle as the container. Applying pressure to the flat sides caused the glass to move inward slightly, thereby increasing the internal pressure enough to cause the diver to sink.[1]

The apparatus pictured in Fig. 1 is a bit more sophisticated and mysterious; it is a fairly rigid glass container with an adjustable screw-thread cap that conceals a movable

solid rubber stopper under it. This design makes the diver extremely sensitive not only to external pressure applied to the glass surface, but also to small temperature changes. As in other designs, one of the critical parts of this apparatus is that the glass bottle must have two sides that are flat and also larger than the other two sides.[2] The main difference in this apparatus is that it also has a finely adjustable stopper.

With a minor adjustment, the diver will fall with only a small amount of fingertip pressure applied on the flat sides of the glass bottle. If you pass this apparatus around the class, after three or four squeezes by students the water and the bottle will have been warmed slightly by the students' hands. Because the coefficient of expansion of water at room temperature is nearly eight times that of glass,[3] the warming of the apparatus increases the internal pressure. This causes the bubble in the diver to shrink, decreasing its

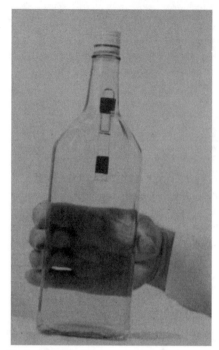

Fig. 1. Cartesian diver.

70mm

47mm

10mm

TAPE

TAPE

TAPE

TEST TUBE

Fig. 2. Test-tube diver.

buoyancy enough to make the diver sink to the bottom and stay there. At this point ask a student to squeeze the bottle on the small sides. This will cause the two large flat sides of the bottle to move outward slightly, decreasing the internal pressure. This makes the bubble in the diver expand in size, thus increasing its buoyancy and making the diver rise. This apparatus can be adjusted so that only moderate (two-finger) pressure is needed for the diver to rise. Previously we had to squeeze "very hard" to cause the diver to rise.[4]

To illustrate the pressure sensitivity of the apparatus, use the following procedure. Exert a gentle squeeze on the larger flat sides of the bottle and the diver will begin to fall. Release the pressure and it will rise. Squeeze it again, but this time for a longer time, and the diver will sink further. If "adjusted properly" the diver will continue to fall even after the pressure is released. The slight increase in water pressure, because of the depth, will cause the bubble to diminish in size enough to send the diver to the bottom. The extreme sensitivity of this Cartesian apparatus can really pique a student's curiosity.

As an additional point of interest, I have observed that small changes in room temperature will cause the diver to either rise or fall depending on the direction of the change. I occasionally hear a "clink" as the diver hits the bottom of the bottle as the room temperature has risen. This "thermometer" is slow to respond just as the *Termometri infingardi* (slow to respond)" reacted to temperature changes in about the year 1641.[5]

Thus, buoyancy as well as elasticity and expansion of

materials with temperature change can be discussed using this apparatus.

The following is a description of the apparatus, the material needed to make it, and directions for assembly and adjustment. The most critical part of the device is a proper bottle. After spending most of an evening in a very large supermarket searching for a proper container, I came upon one that looked ideal and indeed it was (Jose Cuervo Margarita Mix, 1 Liter, UPC code: 82000-16602). Empty the bottle, soak it in warm water for about a half hour, and peel off the labels. Remove the gasket in the cap. The diver I use, which works very well, is an inverted test tube [Sargent-Welch #S-79505-C, 13 mm x 100 mm Kimax (Kimble #45050)]. You also need a #3 solid rubber stopper (such as a Sargent-Welch #S-73305-E), approximately 10 cm of vinyl plastic electrical tape (e.g., Scotch #17-7267), a piece of wire such as a paper clip, and some silicone grease (stopcock lubricant, Sargent-Welch #S-77324-01).

Put three pieces of tape (one very narrow) on the test tube, as shown in Fig. 2. The tape will mark the approximate bubble level and improve visibility of the tube's motion. Using a sharp knife, cut off approximately 8 mm of the top of the stopper. Fill the bottle to the top with water, and do the same with the test tube. Without releasing the test tube, very quickly invert it open side down into the neck of the bottle. The test tube should still be nearly full of water. Gradually lift the tube until a little air enters it. Allow the water level in the tube to reach (approximately) the 47-mm mark (see Fig. 2). Now release the test tube. If it doesn't float, repeat the procedure but this time allow a little more air into the test tube. Lubricate the rubber stopper with the silicone grease. The bottle should be full to the top with water and the test tube floating. Insert the straightened paper clip into the top 2 cm of the neck of the bottle. Now gently insert the rubber stopper alongside the wire in the neck of the bottle. The clip will allow water to escape from the bottle without compressing the air bubble in the test tube. When the rubber stopper extends above the neck of the bottle approximately 3 mm, pull the paper clip out of the neck. At this point the bottle should have absolutely no air in it except for that in the test tube. Install the threaded cap. Turning the cap down a little at a time and alternately squeezing the bottle on the flat sides will result in a very sensitive adjustment of the diver's average density to very nearly that of water. Without the squeeze, the diver's average density will be slightly lower; with a gentle squeeze, it will be slightly higher. The lubricated cork will move freely in and out of the bottle as you adjust the threaded cap. Good luck.

References
1. William Butler, *Am. J. Phys.* **49**, 92 (1981).
2. Butler, p. 92.
3. J. Wilson, *College Physics* (Allyn and Bacon, Needham Heights, MA, 1990), p. 321.
4. Butler, p. 92.
5. W.E. Knowles Middleton, *A History of the Thermometer and Its Use in Meteorology* (The Johns Hopkins Press, Baltimore, MD, 1966), p.29.

Bernoulli Revisited: A Simple Demonstration

A. Sieradzan *and* **W. Chaffee,** Physics Department, Central Michigan University, Mt. Pleasant, MI 48859

A common and popular apparatus used for the demonstration of Bernoulli's principle consists of tubing with narrow and wide sections where the flowing gas, usually air, produces different pressures. These pressures are usually indicated by several liquid manometers made of glass distributed along and connected by side tubes to the main pipe.[1]

The manometers provide a direct and measurable difference in the liquid levels. The actual pressure differences can easily be calculated—if not inferred—from this setup. These pressure differences are not very large, certainly not dramatic, and the system is tedious to set up and is fragile.

One of us (AS), teaching a physics for sports class, wanted a demonstration that would appeal more closely to, and more effectively disturb, the student's intuitive sense that if the flow of a gas is constricted, as by the smaller-diameter

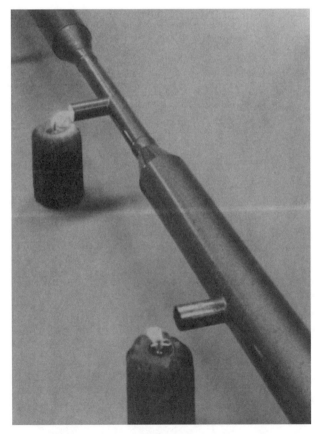

Fig. 2. A close-up view of the first two outlet tubes of the equipment pictured in Fig. 1 with the candles lighted and the air turned on.

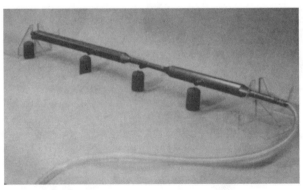

Fig. 1. The Cenco demonstration equipment mounted on low stands with candles next to the side tube outlets.

tubing, then its pressure must increase. Further, if there is a higher pressure, then there must be a higher velocity of air that would flow out of a hole in the side of the smaller-diameter tubing. From this we dreamed up the following demonstration, using the same piece of equipment.

We mounted the tube just above the bench top and used lighted candles to monitor the flow of air in or out of the side tubes (Fig. 1). The demonstration can be conducted in either of two ways:

A) Turn on the air supply before the candles are placed near the side tubes. Then move the candles closer and closer to each side tube, monitoring the effect on the flame. It is almost impossible to bring the candles anywhere near the side tubes connected to the large-diameter main tube without having the flames blow out. On the other hand, the candle near the small-diameter section of the main tube will not only not be blown out but may actually be sucked inward. This effect is seen very dramatically in Fig. 2. (For the purpose of the picture, the side tube from the first large-diameter section of the main tube was throttled using a stopper with a hole in it.)

B) The other way is to place the lighted candles near the side tubes and then turn on the air. Even if you turn on the air slowly, the three candles next to the large-diameter sections of the main tube will very quickly be blown out, and the one near the small-diameter section will either not be blown out at all, or the flame will be sucked into the orifice.

We used a compressor as an air source, but an airtrack air supply or a reversed vacuum cleaner work just fine.

Reference
1. Central Scientific Co., Franklin Park, IL, Item #76462.

Other Mechanics Apparatus

An Inexpensive Acoustic Trigger for Dramatic Flash Photographs

A. B. Western, Rose-Hulman Institute of Technology, Terre Haute, IN 47803, *and J. H. Archibald,* Archibald Scientific, Madison, WI 53705

Few items in physics textbooks arouse as much interest as stop-action photographs of bullets penetrating cards, drops of milk splashing in bowls, or balloons popping. Such photographs make appealing displays, provide motivation in the physics classroom, and draw attention to interesting physical phenomena. It is remarkably easy (and inexpensive) to capture such events on film by using an acoustically triggered electronic rash unit. Photographs as found in Figs. 1–3 make exciting hallway displays and interesting class projects. With little ingenuity, two strobes can be used to allow the timing of extremely fast events.

The flash duration from a typical electronic flash used for home photography is on the order of 50 μs, short enough

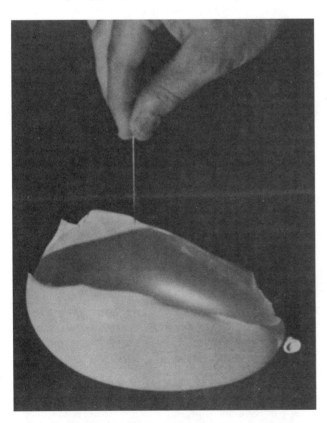

Fig. 1. A balloon is burst with a pin. The balloon splits down the side pricked by the pin. The edges along the tear quickly retract releasing the pressure pulse heard as a "pop." The photograph was taken at f3.8 using Kodak TMAX 400 film.

Fig. 2. A light bulb Is struck by a hammer. The piezoelectric transducer (PZT) sits on the table next to the bulb. The cracks at the bottom of the bulb remind one of the upward normal force of the table on the bulb.

to "freeze" an object traveling at 10 m/s with a blur of only 0.5 mm. The problem, of course, is to synchronize the flash so that it fires while the action is taking place.

Any event generating a sound pulse can be made to trigger an electronic flash to take its own picture. In a darkened room, the camera shutter is opened manually. The event is triggered, firing the flash, after which the shutter is closed.

The circuit shown in Fig. 4 will trigger an electronic flash whenever a suitably large acoustic pulse hits the piezoelectric transducer (PZT). The transducer is inexpensive and commonly sold as a buzzer in electronics stores.[1] Remarkably little signal conditioning is necessary. The PZT output is amplified by a gain of 1000 amplifier[2] and fed directly to the gate of a silicon-controlled rectifier (SCR).[3] When the small current from the amplifier enters the gate of the SCR, a much larger current flows between the terminals of the electronic flash causing it to fire. Total component cost, exclusive of the flash unit[4] and camera, is under $5.

Figs. 1–3 show some of the interesting physics that can be captured in such photographs. Fig. 1 shows a balloon popping after being stuck with a pin. Interestingly, a long

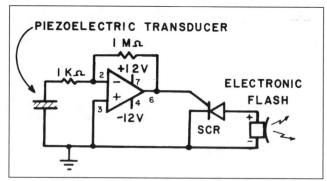

Fig. 4. Electronic circuit for acoustically triggering an electronic flash. Op-Amp and SCR choices are not critical.

tear develops along the pricked half of the balloon, the edges of the balloon quickly retract about half way, releasing the pressure pulse which is the pop. The other half of the balloon is nearly unchanged. A rather dramatic demonstration of inertia! In Fig. 2, a light bulb is broken with a hammer. It is striking (no pun intended) because the bulb first breaks at the table, an excellent reminder of Newton's third law. (Show this to students who have difficulty believing in the normal force.) Fig. 3 shows a balloon filled with water being pricked with a pin. The surface of the water is disturbed by the rapidly contracting balloon, but the bulk of the water retains its shape. The inertia of the water is quite evident.

We would be grateful to receive copies of other pictures illustrating physical principles that were taken using the circuit described.

References

1. One possibility is Radio Shack part no. 273-064 ($1.99). Remove the back of the plastic mount.
2. The amplifier design is the classic inverting amplifier configuration based on an operational amplifier (OP-Amp). The 741 OP-Amp works fine: it can be powered from two 9 V transistor batteries rather than the ± 12 V shown in Fig. 5. Since the capacity coupled Op-Amp must draw its input bias current through the I MΩ feedback resistor, the amplifier is partially turned on even in the quiescent state. This makes the device quite sensitive; a finger snap across the room will activate it. An amplifier with lower input bias current (e.g., 3140) will be less sensitive. Alternatively the feedback resistor can be made smaller to reduce sensitivity.
3. We used Radio Shack part no. 276-1020 ($1.19), a 400 V, 6 amp SCR.
4. Virtually any electronic strobe will work. Costs for bottom-of-the-line units are around $20–$25. It is necessary that the positive and negative terminals of the flash unit be attached with the polarity shown. It is easy to identify the polarity by connecting an ordinary voltmeter to the pins on the base of the flash unit.

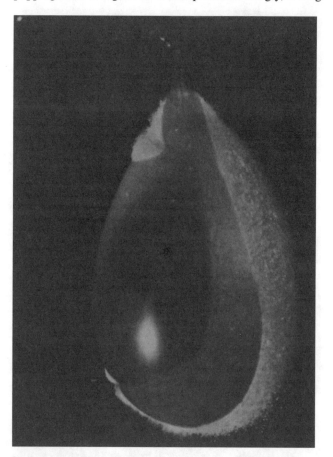

Fig. 3. A balloon filled with water bursts as it is pricked with a pin. The water surface is agitated by the motion of the balloon. The bulk of the water retains its shape due to inertia.

Add Flash to Your Class with an LED Student Strobe

Robert F. Dorner, Mathematics, Computer Science, and Physics Department, Montclair State University, Upper Montclair, NJ 07043; dornerr@saturn.montclair.edu

The widely used and inexpensive light-emitting diode (LED), a device that converts electrical energy into light, has been improved. Now it can be used as a source of illumination. A high-brightness LED produces 12,000 micro-candles focused at 4° radiance.[1] Typically, it operates at 2 V and requires 20 to 50 mA for continuous operation, or may be pulsed up to 100 mA. Unlike the incandescent lamp with its thermal mass, the high-brightness LED may be turned on and off very rapidly. You may have seen this improved LED in use for upper brake lights on new cars. It could replace an ordinary LED in many applications. Its ability to flash rapidly makes it ideal for physics projects, and the remarkable brightness brings a physics class to prompt attention.

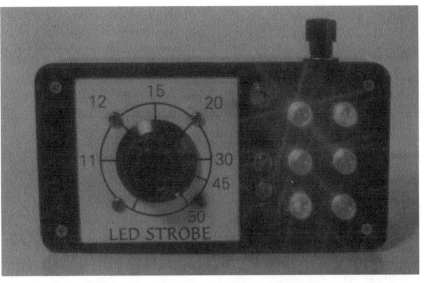

Fig. 1. Strobe is housed in a small project box. Large knob controls flashing frequency; push button turns strobe on; terminals, enabled by DPDT switch, are for remote LED's.

This column describes one application for high-brightness LED's—a portable and rugged apparatus that can be constructed for less than $50. It can be attached to moving objects to study motion or used to demonstrate free fall. The device won a first-place prize in competition at the AAPT 1996 Summer Meeting. Figure 1 shows the apparatus (we refer to it as a student strobe) that within its range of operation (10 to 50 Hz) may be used much like an ordinary strobe to freeze motion. However, since it is portable it is easily attached to moving objects to show changes in velocity. Furthermore, it can be used as a pendulum, or, if cushioned, dropped for free-fall demonstrations. It's a durable item; our students have a free hand to develop applications and projects, some of which have turned out to be real attention-getters!

How the Strobe Works

As Fig. 2 shows, the circuit uses batteries as a source of power for both the timing electronics and LED's. The potential between upper and lower wires whenever the switch is closed is 18 V. Three circuit stages are connected to the common power supply. The 555 chip produces timing pulses, the 2N222 transistor inverts the polarity of the pulses, and the power MOSFET (Metal Oxide Semiconductor Field-Effect Transistor) uses these

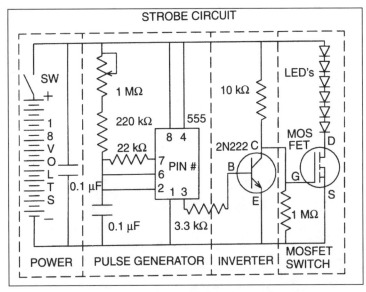

Fig. 2. Strobe circuit may be constructed and tested in stages. Wire lengths and assembly methods are not critical. Use ordinary LED's to test operation.

feeble pulses to control the larger current required by the six high-brightness LED's.

The 18-V supply can be two 9-V transistor radio batteries for lightweight, intermittent-use applications.

Longer battery life, an hour or more depending on flash

rate, would be provided by twelve AA, C, or D cells in series. The 0.1-μF capacitor connected across the power supply charges between flashes and improves battery life. The pulse generator is a common 555 timer chip, which bases its rate on an RC time constant.[2] When the strobe is on, current flows through the 1-MΩ potentiometer and 220-kΩ resistor charging the 0.1-μF capacitor. This establishes the off period of the strobe, which can be adjusted with the potentiometer. Once the capacitor reaches two-thirds of the power-supply voltage, pins 6 and 2 change the state (flip the flip-flop) of the 555 timer. At this point in the cycle the capacitor is rapidly discharged through the 22-kΩ resistor. This results in a negative pulse at pin 3 of the 555 and the strobe flash time. The 22-kΩ resistor may be changed to vary duration of the flash.

While the capacitor is charging, output pin 3 of the 555 timer chip is positive, which turns on the 2N222 NPN transistor switch.[3] Since resistance between emitter (E) and collector (C) of the 2N222 is low when it is on, the collector is close to battery negative potential. In this way a positive input at the base (B) of the 2N222 produces a negative output at the collector of the transistor. When the timer provides a negative pulse, the transistor is turned off and the collector is "pulled up" to the positive battery potential by the 10-kΩ resistor. In simple terms the transistor inverts (changes polarity of) the timer pulse.

The MOSFET is a very useful and easy-to-use component.[4,5] It uses a low voltage and requires practically no current between gate (G) and source (S) to control a large cur-

Parts List

Quantity	Item	Radio Shack #
1	555 IC	276-1718
1	2N222 transistor	276-2009
1	IRF-510 MOSFET	276-2072
1	1-MΩ potentiometer	271-211
2	0.1-μF capacitors	272-1069
6	bright LED's	276-206
5	assorted resistors	
1	PC board	276-159
1	project box	270-223
3	AA battery holders	270-319
12	AA batteries	23-582

rent between source and drain (D). Since the gate is sensitive to electric fields and may be damaged by static charges, a 1-MΩ resistor is connected between gate and source as a precaution. The source-to-drain route of the MOSFET acts as a switch to turn on and off the series string of high-brightness LED's. Though this string of LED's draws only 100 mA, the MOSFET can handle 3-A continuous or 8-A pulsed current. This circuit may be used to provide high-current pulses for other experiments.

Constructing the Strobe

Many approaches may be taken to constructing the strobe light.[6,7] We suggest keeping initial costs low by using a power supply and conventional LED's until the circuit is "debugged" on a standard bread board. The next step is to transfer and solder the components in their exact relative position to a universal printed circuit board that has the same pattern of connections as the bread board. Both bread board and universal printed circuit board are available from Radio Shack™. You can miniaturize even further by building the circuit on the still smaller universal circuit board indicated in the parts list.

If the strobe does not function correctly, check all circuit connections carefully. It is easy to connect a component incorrectly, so reference should be made to the pin identification located on the components packaging. Calibration can be achieved with a frequency counter or oscilloscope, or compare the flashes to a calibrated lab strobe. If you encounter difficulty in achieving the desired range of operation, try several capacitors since they are commonly accurate to only 10%.

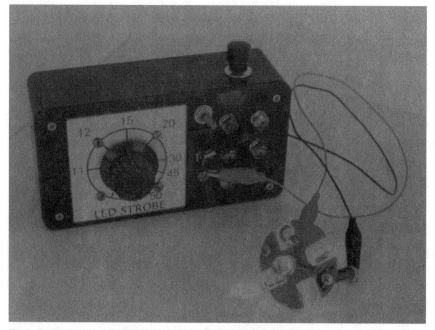

Fig. 3. Remotely operated LED's are housed in pill bottles. These "tethered strobes" may be dropped to illustrate free fall or attached to other apparatus.

Variations and Applications

We put our strobe in a small project box; however, variations include remotely located LED's that are tethered to the circuit by thin wire. These LED's can be swung in circles by their wire or used as a pendulum bob (Fig. 3). The LED's can be spaced a greater distance from one another and used to illuminate linear or circular tracks for carts or other moving objects. We are in the process of developing a ball to play "strobe catch," an evening game we believe will be great fun. Physicists and their students will have to learn to follow the flashes in the dark sky.

References

1. Available from Radio Shack (catalog #276-206) for $3.99.
2. Forest M. Mims III, *Engineer's Mini-Notebook 555 Timer IC Circuits* (Radio Shack, 1984), p. 7.
3. Eugene Hecht, *Physics* (Wadsworth, Belmont, CA, 1994), pp. 822–824.
4. Arthur Beiser, *Modern Technical Physics* (Addison-Wesley, Reading, MA, 1992), pp. 824–825.
5. *Semiconductor Reference Guide* (Radio Shack, 1992), pp. 7–8.
6. Forest M. Mims III, *Getting Started in Electronics* (Radio Shack, 1988).
7. Forest M. Mims III, *Engineer's Mini-Notebook Schematic Symbols, Device Packages, Design and Testing* (Radio Shack, 1988).

Bridge Crusher for Physics Olympics

Richard E. Berg, Lecture-Demonstration Facility, Physics Department, University of Maryland, College Park, MD 20742

For many years a perennial problem in our physics olympics competitions has been crushing balsa or popsicle stick bridges. This event always consumed the greatest effort and the most time, and even then there were a few bridges that never got crushed due to lack of weights or time. Then a few years ago we made a relatively simple bridge crushing device that uses a standard hydraulic jack similar to those sold commercially for, among other things, a wooden 2 x 4 breaking demonstration. With this bridge crusher all of the bridges were successfully crushed—about forty bridges in less than four hours, and the event was the first one completed! While our device uses a rather large hydraulic jack, smaller versions can be made, which are easier to move and use jacks that many high school or college physics departments already possess.

Figure 1 shows the basic features of our bridge crusher. A bridge deck loading block, 5.08 cm x 5.08 cm x 10.16 cm (2 in x 2 in x 4 in) with a 2.54-cm (1 in) diam pinhole machined through the middle of one of the long sides, is placed on the center of the bridge deck.[1] The bridge is positioned on the base, in which indents have been machined to accept the bridge pilings. The base is attached to the hydraulic jack and moves upward when the jack is pumped. The deck loading block support is mounted to an adjustable upper plate by a single screw. The length of the threaded rods, by which the upper plate is mounted to the jack mounting plate, is chosen to accommodate the size range of bridges to be crushed. Connecting the loading block support to the upper plate by a single screw allows the bridge to be

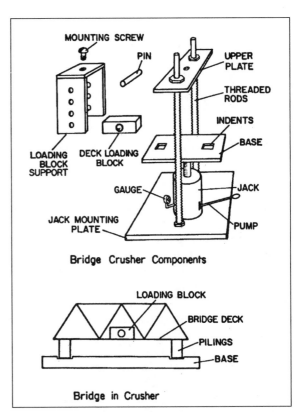

Bridge Crusher Components

Bridge in Crusher

Fig. 1. The top part of the figure shows the components that make up the bridge crusher; the bottom half features a bridge placed in the crusher.

inserted into the crusher with the deck loading block in place on the bridge deck and the loading block support rotated slightly so the deck loading block can be pinned while avoiding interference with the threaded rods. After pinning the loading block, the loading block support is rotated and the bridge pilings positioned in the base indents. The jack may then be pumped slightly so the bridge is held in place firmly between the base and the loading block. Having several pairs of holes in the loading block support allows positioning of the block to accommodate a range of bridge sizes without any adjustment of the nuts holding the upper plate in place on the threaded rods.

Our pressure gauge uses a slave needle[2] that remains at the highest reading to which the pressure has risen until it is reset between bridges.

Before the competition, specifications must be set for the maximum size and separation of the pilings to fit the indents on the base plate. Also, the allowable range of distances from the baseplate to the bridge deck must be specified so that it can be covered by adjusting the nuts holding the upper plate or, preferably, by pinning the loading block to the appropriate holes. The size, mass, and geometry of the bridges can be adjusted yearly to keep the competition fresh.

For actual olympics competition, the procedure is as follows:

1. Each bridge is checked for size, geometry, and weight according to the olympics rules.
2. The competing students then mount their bridges onto the crusher and call the judge.
3. Each group then pumps its own bridge until the bridge collapses.
4. The maximum load for scoring is the reading of the gauge slave needle as read by the judge.
5. The judge then resets the slave needle to zero for the next competitor.

Acknowledgment

I should like to thank Jack Touart for his suggestions and his help in constructing the bridge crushers.

References

1. For the next physics olympics, we plan to increase the length of the loading block to provide uniform loading over the entire bridge platform.
2. Our gauges were made by Ametek U.S. Gauge Division, and distributed by Tate Engineering in Baltimore, MD. The slave indicator, called a "lazy hand," was installed by the distributor.

Converting a Hand Calculator into an Event Counter

John Kwasnoski, Western New England College, Springfield, MA 01119

One experiment we do in our Energy Physics course is to measure the rotation of a bicycle wheel on a stationary bicycle to determine the energy and horsepower developed by the rider. To facilitate making these measurements we have converted a simple four-function hand calculator into an event counter. The counter is operated as follows:

1. Open the hand calculator and identify the switch connections for the memory plus (M+) key.
2. In parallel with the M + contacts in the calculator, solder a two-conductor output jack, and mount the jack in the calculator case.
3. Externally connect a normally open magnetic reed switch to the M+ wired parallel jack so that this switch can trigger the M+ key.
4. Mount the magnetic reed switch near the bicycle wheel and tape a small magnet onto the wheel so that it will close the switch when it passes—once each revolution of the wheel.
5. To activate the counter enter the number 1; as the wheel spins one is added to the previous total in memory each time the magnet passes the reed switch.

To read the event counter, simply press the memory recall button on the calculator. The total number of times the switch has been activated will be displayed thus indicating the number of wheel revolutions made in the elapsed time period.

The speed of the reed switch introduces some limitations at very high counting rates, but for our experiment this has not been a problem. To overcome the high-speed counting problem we presently are adapting a phototransistor gate to substitute for the reed switch. Using the high-speed switching characteristics of the phototransistor, we expect to increase the frequency capabilities of the counter.

A Laboratory Air-Supply System

Chuck Crawford, Science Support Technician, St. Lawrence University, Canton, NY 13167; crawford@bbs.tsf.com

Commercial air-supply systems for apparatus such as air tracks and tables are inherently troublesome for several reasons. *First*, since they are quite expensive and can drive only one or two air tracks, they represent a substantial investment. *Second*, all but the most expensive are quite noisy, particularly the "glorified" shop vacuum types. This can be a real problem in a lab with multiple air-track setups. *Third*, the "universal" motors commonly used are generally not well suited to continuous duty applications due to the high speed at which they operate, brush and commutator wear, etc. *Finally*, the air they supply can be quite warm, which in some instances can cause problems in gathering accurate data due to thermal expansion.

I was seeking an alternative to these types of blowers for use in our physics labs, where often there are four 8-ft air tracks in use simultaneously. Commercial shop vacuums, though relatively inexpensive, have many of the undesirable characteristics of the commercial blowers. Air compressors and other positive displacement machines are very noisy and require frequent maintenance; more-over, the air produced may contain oil and water, which can be harmful to an air track, eventually clogging the tiny air holes, and posing a possible environmental hazard.

An Alternative System

Regenerative blowers (also known as "ring compressors") are industrial-grade air suppliers used for aeration, oxygenation, pneumatic transport, sparging, drying, and so on. They are available in a wide range of sizes and can supply pressure or vacuum.[1] Compared with conventional blower systems, the regenerative blower has many advantages in the physics lab, including being much quieter than blowers generally in use. As a bonus for the lab technician, the regenerative blower has only one moving part, and is powered by a highly reliable induction motor equipped with sealed ball bearings. Rated for continuous duty within specific operating conditions, the regenerative blower requires almost no maintenance. An occasional cleaning of the intake filter is all it needs.

The Regenerative Principle

Impeller blades passing the inlet port draw air into the blower (see Fig. 1). The impeller blades then accelerate the air outward and forward (arrow 1). Here the "regenerative" principle takes effect as the air is turned back by the annular-shaped housing (arrow 2) to the base of the following blades (arrow 3), where it is again hurled outward (arrow 4). Each "regeneration" imparts more pressure to the air. When it reaches the stripper section at the outlet (the stripper is the part of the blower located between the inlet and the outlet in which the annulus is reduced in size to fit closely to the sides and tips of the impeller blades), the air is "stripped" from the impeller and diverted out of the blower. The pressures or vacuums generated by one or two spinning, non-contacting, oil-free impellers are equal to those obtained by many larger multistage positive displacement blowers.[2] Another way to visualize this cycle is to think of the air as being "rolled up" into ever tighter packets (much as one might roll up a piece of paper into a smaller, tighter tube) until it reaches the stripper and can go no farther.

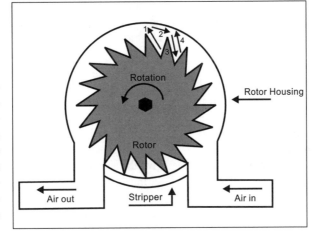

Fig 1. A simplified regenerative blower.

Installing a Regenerative Blower System

I determined that the air consumption of a standard 8-ft air track is approximately 18 cubic feet per minute at 3.38 inches of water. The published airflow performance graph (Fig. 2) for one model indicates that it can supply 95 cubic feet per minute at 3.38 in of water, clearly enough to drive four air tracks and probably five. Next, I consulted with the faculty members who would be using the system about their ideal air-supply system. I was surprised to learn that noise level was of primary importance, followed closely by reliability and ease of setup and use. To further enhance the already acceptable noise level of the unit, I decided to install the blower in a stockroom adjacent to the lab, and pipe the air in via 1½-in PVC pipe. This required punching a 2-in-diameter hole through the cinder-block wall separating the two rooms. To make the system easy to set up and use, and to insure future flexibility, I piped the air through a four-way

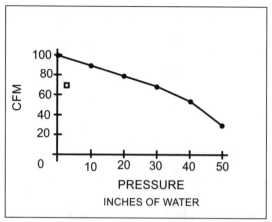

Fig. 2. Airflow performance for Fuji VFC 404P-5T regenerative blower.

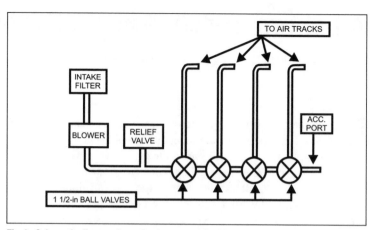

Fig. 3. Schematic diagram for author's regenerative blower system.

valve manifold, easily constructed of 1½-in PVC pipe and 1½-in PVC ball valves. I also left a capped port for future or temporary use (see Fig. 3).

I continued the piping up the wall and into the space above the drop ceiling. The pipes were terminated above each air-track station with a 1½-in PVC by 1½-in compression drain-type fitting. I mounted the fitting into a piece of 1-by-6-by-24-in wood, cut a 5½ by 24-in piece off the ceiling tile, and screwed the wood to the metal ceiling grid in place of the 5½ by 24-in piece of tile. I installed the drop through the wood with a 1½-in PVC coupling on either side, with a short PVC nipple connecting them. (see Fig. 4).

Using a street el in the upper coupling simplifies construction. (A street fitting is any fitting with one side male, the other female.) This provides a very strong and stable air-drop. I also discovered that inexpensive 1½-in water hose (such as would be found on a swimming-pool filter) fits nicely into the compression fitting using the 1½-in compression ring provided with the fitting. This provides a flexible drop to the tracks; moreover, when not in use, this type of hose easily coils up and out of the way near the ceiling.

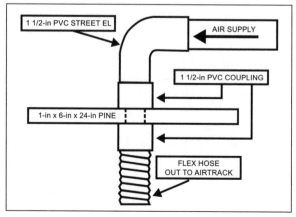

Fig. 4. Air drop construction details.

Constructing a Pressure Relief Valve

It is necessary to provide a way to vent the air supply back to atmosphere in the event that the airflow is blocked (for example, if all the manifold valves are closed). The suppliers of the blowers sell relief valves, but they are quite expensive because of the way they must be constructed to withstand industrial conditions. A simple spring-loaded flapper-type of arrangement is adequate and easily constructed (see Fig. 5). I began by installing a 1½-in PVC tee near the outlet of the blower; into this I glued a 6-in piece of 1½-in PVC pipe fitted with a hinged flapper (I used ¼-in Plexiglas), a spring, and simple adjusting mechanism. I adjusted the spring tension to give the specified minimum flow rate for the blower by measuring the temperature of the airflow (with the manifold valves closed) as close to the outlet as possible through a small hole in the PVC pipe, which I later plugged. A graph of airflow versus air temperature is included with the blower. (Note that Fig. 5 is shown in the relieving position.)

Intake Air Filter

An intake air filter is required to filter dust and other airborne particles, which could over time degrade air-track performance by clogging the tiny air holes on the tracks. I constructed a filter from a commonly available PVC adapter (1½ by 3 in). I chose this fitting to provide a larger surface area for the filter media. As shown in Fig. 6, I put a small piece of hardware cloth in the bottom of the fitting (which is somewhat funnel shaped) to prevent the blower from ingesting the filter media, then covered that with several layers of furnace-filter media, and then added another piece of hardware cloth cut slightly oversize. When pushed into the fitting, this acts as a retainer.

Comments

Since our system was installed in a remote location, a switch was necessary to control the blower from the lab. This should be done by a qualified electrician, working to

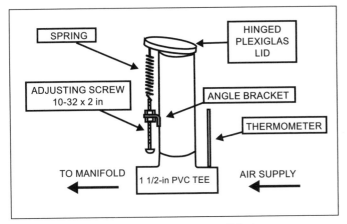

Fig. 5. Construction details for simple flapper-type relief valve.

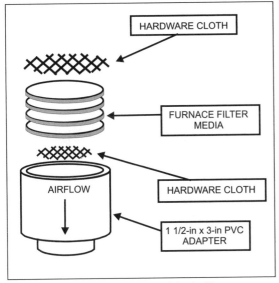

Fig. 6. Construction details for simple air-intake filter.

local code. Our whole system cost around $700 to install. While this is a substantial investment, it must be weighed against the fact that this regenerative system will far outlast any commercial blowers, which typically cost $290 to $325 for two tracks and cannot supply vacuum if required.

The system I describe in this note is highly reliable, quiet, and elegant in its simplicity. Feedback received since its installation has been overwhelmingly positive. Instructors using the system claim that the data collected has never been so accurate, resulting in less frustration for both instructors and students, and thereby providing a better overall lab experience. I'm fairly sure this is due in no small part to the fact that the lab environment is much more conducive to learning without four "shop" vacuums running for three hours at a stretch.

References

1. W.W. Grainger Industrial Supply, 6285 E. Molloy Road, Syracuse, NY 13057-1070; 1-800-323-0620.
2. Publication # 5M-6/93, p. 2, available from EG&G RO-TRON, Industrial Division, North Street, Saugerties, NY 12477; 914-246-3401.

WAVES & SOUND

Longitudinal and Transverse Waves in a Spring

P.J. Ouseph and Thomas Poothackanal, Physics Department, University of Louisville, Louisville, KY 40292

In the September 1992 "How Things Work" section of *The Physics Teacher*, H. Richard Crane described the usefulness of 2-in diameter loudspeakers for classroom demonstration.[1] A variety of demonstration instruments using these loudspeakers are discussed in the literature.[2,3] We describe here an apparatus that displays longitudinal and transverse waves in a spring to large classes with the help of an overhead projector. Both types of waves can be produced in a spring attached to a loudspeaker by exciting the loudspeaker. In a 1987 article[4] we discussed electromagnetic excitation of longitudinal waves in a spring. In that system a magnet was attached to the free end of a spring and the other end of the magnet was symmetrically positioned along the axis of a coil connected to a variable-frequency ac source. The waves were generated by the electromagnetic interaction between the hanging magnet and the coil. Clearly, a system in which the spring is excited by a loudspeaker is simpler and easier to construct. The magnet-coil system, however, did enable us to study forced oscillations of a simple harmonic oscillator.[5]

Our wave generator for demonstrating longitudinal and transverse standing waves is shown in Fig. 1. The spring has a length of 10 cm, a diameter of 7 mm, and a force constant of 10 N/m. One end of this spring is fixed to a 5-mm-long Teflon rod that slips into a hole in an aluminum piece glued to the loudspeaker. Since the Teflon piece is free to rotate, the loudspeaker can be rotated to desired orientations without twisting the spring. The other end of the spring is fixed to an aluminum rod that goes through a piece of

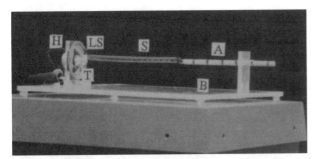

Fig. 1. Wave generator to demonstrate longitudinal and transverse waves. *S* is the spring; *A*, aluminum rod with inch marks holding one end of the spring; *LS*, loudspeaker; *T*. Teflon rod holding one end of the spring; *B*, Plexiglas base; *H*, L-shaped Plexiglas speaker hold.

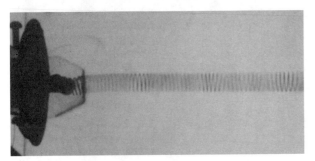

Fig. 2. Longitudinal waves as seen on the overhead projector screen. Sections of the spring clearly seen are the nodes; between the nodes the spring appears funny because of the vibration of these sections. The loudspeaker is perpendicular to the spring.

Plexiglas (2 x 5 cm). The tension in the spring is varied by moving the rod in and out through the Plexiglas. There are centimeter marks on the aluminum rod starting from the position where the length of the spring is 10 cm (unstretched length) to a position where the length of the spring is 20 cm long. With the help of these markings the tension in the spring can be calculated. The loudspeaker is fixed to an L-shaped Plexiglas holder that can be rotated so that the speaker plane is perpendicular or parallel to the spring. Note that the loudspeaker holder is pivoted to rotate about an axis that passes through the Teflon rod so that the end of the spring attached to the rod is stationary during rotation of the loudspeaker. The loudspeaker holder and the aluminum rod holder are fixed to a 25 x 25-cm Plexiglas base. This means that when the system is placed on an overhead projector the speaker and the spring are clearly seen on the screen. The loudspeaker is connected to the output of a variable-frequency function generator (Hewlett-Packard model HP 331 DA).

Longitudinal waves are produced in the spring when the plane of the loudspeaker is perpendicular to the spring. In this position, movement of the loudspeaker cone in and out produces elongation and compression of the spring producing longitudinal waves. At resonant frequencies, nodes of the standing waves are clearly visible on the screen (Fig. 2). A node will appear as a sharp image of a single turn of the spring. Between the nodes, the spring is seen as fuzzy

because of the oscillation. For longitudinal waves in a spring, the resonant frequencies are given by the equation

$$f_{1n} = \frac{n}{2} \sqrt{\frac{k}{m}} \qquad (1)$$

where k is the force constant of the spring and m its mass. The resonant frequencies are independent of the length of the spring as well as the tension in the spring. This can be demonstrated dramatically by first obtaining a standing wave and then stretching the spring. The fact that the resonant frequency does not change with tension is contrary to the expectation of most students.

To observe *transverse waves*, rotate the loudspeaker through 90° so that its plane is parallel to the spring. The resonant frequencies for transverse waves are given by the equation

$$f_{tn} = \frac{n}{2l} \sqrt{\frac{T}{\mu}} \qquad (2)$$

In this equation the length l, tension T, and mass per unit length μ vary as the spring is stretched. If the unstretched length is L_o and the spring is stretched through x, the length is $L_o + x$, tension is kx and μ is $M/(L_o + x)$, where M is the total mass of the spring. Equation (2) can now be written in the form

$$f_{tn} = \frac{n}{2} \sqrt{\frac{k}{M} \left(\frac{1}{1 + \frac{L_0}{x}} \right)} \qquad (3)$$

The stretching length x is the only variable in the equation, from which we see that the resonant frequencies increase with stretching. This dependence can be demonstrated by pulling the aluminum rod in and out. For small applied tensions, the amplitude of oscillation is about 1 cm, one-and-a-half times the diameter of the spring. Note that if the loudspeaker is fixed with an orientation at 45° with the spring, both longitudinal and transverse waves can be excited but with smaller amplitudes.

We've discovered that with this system data can be collected and analyzed even during a one-hour lecture period.

References

1. H. Richard Crane, "Never throw a 2-in speaker away: It has many uses," *Phys. Teach.* **30**, 375 (1992).
2. H. Richard Crane, "The noises your muscles make," *Phys. Teach.* **27**, 687 (1989).
3. P.J. Ouseph, "Chladni plates for overhead projectors," *Am. J. Phys.* **59**, 665 (1991).
4. P.J. Ouseph, "Standing longitudinal waves," *Am. J. Phys.* **55**, 666 (1987).
5. P. J. Ouseph, "Electro-magnetically driven resonance apparatus," *Am. J. Phys.* **55**, 1126 (1987).

Transverse Wave Machine

Thomas B. Greenslade, Jr., Kenyon College, Gambier, OH 43022

In an article on nineteenth-century wave machines published about ten years ago in *The Physics Teacher*,[1] I noted that many of the demonstrations of waves are not available today and expressed the hope that they might be made once more. This note describes an easily made replica of a 1900-vintage machine designed to demonstrate transverse waves.

The prototype is shown in Fig. 1. This wave machine was made by the German firm of Max Kohl and originally cost $12.50. Because of its small size (only 17 cm high), it was intended to be used for shadow projection of the waves. I have examined two machines, one at the Smithsonian Institution and the other at the University of Notre Dame, and noted that apart from the crank handle, the construction is all metal. The base is solid cast iron to give it stability, and the sliders are aluminum.

The reproduction (Fig. 2) is constructed primarily of wood. The tricky part is the production of the camshaft on which the lower ends of the sliders rest. This is composed of 25 disks, each about 7 mm thick, which are sliced from a hardwood broom handle with a circular saw. Each disk has an eccentric hole drilled in it (see the examples in the foreground of Fig. 2), and the disks are then assembled on a 1/4 in x 20 tpi (threads per inch) threaded rod. A simple jig is used to hold the disks in position for drilling to ensure that each has the same eccentricity. Each disk is rotated 22.5° relative to its neighbor so that 16 disks are needed to produce one cycle or wavelength. Glue and a small brad fix the disks in position along the rod. A set of wooden checkers would provide ready-made disks. Unfortunately, all the checkers I found in the local stores were made of molded plastic with deeply indented faces, which would make them more difficult to assemble on the rod.

The sliders are 8 cm long and made from stout coat-hanger wire. The ends are rounded on a grindstone so that they slip easily on the eccentric disks. Note that the block that holds the sliders is tilted slightly so that the sliders point somewhat away from the support rod. This makes the system turn quite well in one direction, although it stalls in the other direction.

The total construction time for this apparatus was about five hours. No attempt was made to optimize the design, which was dictated primarily by the availability of parts.

A wave machine of this type is ideal for showing the relationship between simple harmonic motion and wave motion. Start out by cutting a narrow slit toward one end of a file card, and tack this card to the slider block so that one slider

Fig. 1. Transverse wave machine produced by Max Kohl about 1900. Smithsonian catalog number 325,957. Smithsonian photograph. This picture appears as Fig. 9 of Ref. 1.

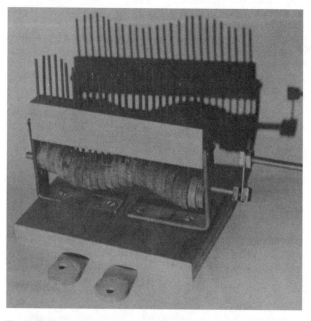

Fig. 2. Modern transverse wave machine made from readily available materials. This machine is best used for shadow projection because of its small size (16 cm high). Examples of the eccentric disks that make up the camshaft are in the foreground.

is visible. Turning the crank moves the slider up and down in simple harmonic motion. Now cut a second, parallel slit one wavelength distant so that two sliders can be seen; they will move in phase. Cutting a third slit midway between these two slits will show a slider that moves 180° out of phase with the two end ones.

Reference

1. T. B. Greenslade, Jr., "Apparatus for natural philosophy: Nineteenth-century wave machines," *Phys. Teach* **18**, 510 (1980).

Harmonic Sliders

Thomas B. Greenslade, Jr., Kenyon College, Gambier, OH 43022

In 1802 Thomas Young published a description of a wave addition device[1] that has doubtless formed the basis for a number of demonstrations on constructive and destructive interference and beats. This note gives the particulars of a simply built piece of apparatus, which is based directly on Young's design.

The device is shown in Fig. 1. Thirty-two thin wooden sliders are free to move up in a wooden frame independently of each other. A notch in the individual sliders and a strip of wood across the bottom of the frame holds them in their rest position in the frame, as shown in Fig. 1(a). The shape of the slider can be seen in the slider in front of the device in Fig. 1(b). The tops of the sliders are cut in the form of a sine wave about 2.5 wavelengths long.

A sinusoidal template made of thin wood moves in a slot cut in the base. The top of the template is cut into a sine wave of the same amplitude and wavelength as the sliders. In Fig. 1(b) the template is adjusted so that its peaks and those of the sliders are in phase. The frame holding the sliders runs on a pair of parallel steel rods and is slid down so that the bottom of each slider is in contact with the template; chamfering the ends of the sliders allows the center of each slider to touch the template. The top of the sliders now displays a sine wave of twice the original amplitude.

Moving the template a half wavelength to the left gives destructive interference, and the top of the sliders forms a horizontal surface. Young also used a template with a different wavelength so that beats could be displayed by the shape of the top of the sliders.

This instrument was built small for ease of storage and use in shadow projection. The base is 22 cm long, and the sliders range in length from 5.4 to 7.2 cm, thereby giving an amplitude of 0.9 cm to the waves. The sliders are about 0.5 cm thick. Total building time was about four hours.

A similar, though larger, wave addition device was made by the firm of E.S. Ritchie of Boston in the years following 1860; a picture of it was published a few years ago in this journal.[2]

I have chosen to use Young's title for this note. The use

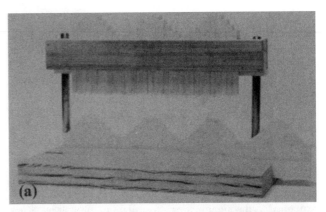

Fig 1. (a) The sliders and the template both have the same wavelength and are in phase. (b) The frame holding the sliders has been lowered, allowing the two waves to interfere constructively.

of the word "harmonic" in the title refers to the harmonic, or sinusoidal, shape of the sliders. Young motivated his device by reference to tides and to musical acoustics. His two illustrations show the addition of two waves of the same spatial frequency and two waves of different frequencies. Were Thomas Young to write his article today, he might very well have it published in *The Physics Teacher*.

References

1. Thomas Young, *Journals of the Royal Institution of Great Britain* **I**, 261(1802).
2. Thomas B. Greenslade, Jr., *Phys. Teach* **18**, 510, (1980).

Melde's Experiment with an Aquarium Aerator
Rich Dynamics with Inexpensive Apparatus

Mark Graham, Department of Physics and Astronomy, University of Alabama, P.O. Box 870324, Tuscaloosa, AL 35487-0324; mark@voicemall.com

Education majors taught by Dean Stan Jones explore standing waves at University of Alabama. Left to right: Anna Craft, Lucie Klingler, and Jaime Ludack.

Melde's experiment consists of a taut string with a periodic driving force applied to it.[1-3] With the proper conditions for resonance, the string will vibrate with great amplitude. A typical standing-wave pattern has large-amplitude vibration throughout the string between points of no motion called nodes, which surprise students so much that they often must touch them to believe they are there! Standing waves are usually explained as interference between transmitted and reflected waves,[4] but especially for those uncomfortable with the oxymoron "standing wave," the pattern can also be explained as the eigenmodes of oscillation of a continuous system.[5] The distance between adjacent nodes in the string has a length corresponding to one-half wavelength of the wave traveling through the string.

Sometimes Melde's experiment is done with signal generators passing current through a wire in a magnetic field, allowing the student to tune to resonance by tuning the frequency (our former method).[6] At constant frequency, it is also possible to tune to resonance by adjusting the speed of the transverse wave, accomplished by adjusting the tension on a string. Less expensive commercial vibrators are available that oscillate a metal plate under an electromagnet driven by line current.[7]

Noncommercial vibrators have been made from loudspeakers,[8] doorbell-clappers,[9] buzzers,[10] motors,[11] hair cutters,[3] jigsaws,[3] and ac-dc converters,[12] but the method I describe here came from a childhood memory of when my older brother Bob showed me the inside of an aquarium aerator. An aerator consists of an electromagnet driven by line current that shakes a magnet glued to the end of an armature. This in turn drives the bellows that pump the air. The frequency of the vibration is the line frequency of the current, which is 60 Hz in the United States, and is the source of the obnoxious drone you hear in a pet store. [*Note:* Commercial vibrators produce a frequency of twice the line frequency because the electromagnet drives a steel plate (no permanent magnet) that is attracted to the electromagnet twice each cycle.]

Apparatus Setup

To use the aerator to drive a string, unscrew the bottom of the pump (unplugged of course) and tie a string to the end of the armature (see Fig. 1). It is prudent to wrap tape around the transformer end to prevent maverick fingers from touching electrical connections. You can immediately

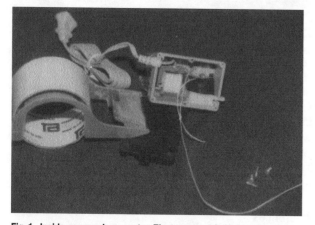

Fig. 1. Inside an aquarium aerator. Electromagnet (left) drives permanent magnet (middle) on one end of armature. This drives bellows (right) that pump air through spout (right). String tied to end of armature as shown used to create standing waves.

Fig. 2. Left: standing wave in homogeneous string for which each swell has the same length, even though they appear smaller in the distance. Right: tapered fly line grows thicker with distance. Swells in foreground are longer than neighbor to left, but swells in distance become smaller, implying that wave is slower in thicker end of fly line.

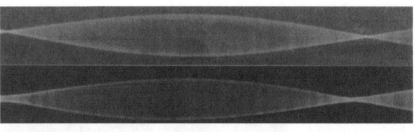

Fig. 3. Standing waves in a string appear colored when viewed in fluorescent light, which emits different intensities of color throughout cycle. Viewed from above, standing wave appears blue on the edges; viewed sideways, edges appear orange.

show standing waves by just holding the pump in one hand and tugging on the string with the other. For a more controlled demonstration, secure the aerator to the table with a C clamp and run the string over a pulley. Hang a cup containing gunshot, sand, or even water on the end and adjust the weight to create the standing wave. The speed of the waves, c, is found by weighing the cup for the tension T, weighing a long piece of string of known length for the linear density μ, and computing $c = \sqrt{T/\mu}$. The standard formula $\lambda = 2L/n$, which includes the assumption that the length of the string corresponds to an integral number of "swells," should not be used because the vibrator position is neither a node nor an antinode.[13] If you look closely at one of the standing waves made by this device, the swell nearest the vibrator is shorter than the others. The wavelength is measured as twice the distance between two nodes.[13] Many modes may be obtained, and we have gotten as few as two antinodes for a length of string greater than a meter. Upon graphing wavelength versus speed, students measured a line frequency with no more than 5% error.

A few techniques will maximize the amplitude of the standing waves. First, the tension can be carefully tuned by using a spoon to deliver sand slowly into the bucket when the system is near resonance. Second, the great tension required to achieve small numbers of antinodes will eventually tug the vibrating arm so far away from the electromagnet that it is no longer driven. You can prevent this by clamping the aerator at an angle so the arm is as much parallel to the direction of the string tension as possible. Finally (as teachers at our 1997 summer workshop discovered), if the pump is prevented from pumping air, the standing wave amplitude will be greatly enhanced. You can glue the aera-

tor's spout closed or insert one of the backing screws into the spout. When all of these techniques were applied, we got antinode widths sometimes of an inch and a half!

Phenomena with Standing Waves in a String

The criterion for the formation of a standing wave is that after transmission, the reflected wave returns to antinodes an odd number of half-periods later. This means that a standing wave can form even if the wave speed is not constant throughout the string. With the additional piscine resource of a tapered fly line, you can make standing waves with varying wavelength, showing that the wavelength shortens as the string gets thicker, proving that the speed decreases with the linear density of the string[14] (see Fig. 2).

Students are mesmerized when the device is shown with a strobe light at the line frequency. (But, stroboscopic light can induce epileptic seizures, so epileptics should be warned not to watch.) Observers can distinctly see the pump arm "slowly" oscillating back and forth. The strobe light reveals that the string vibration is usually circular motion, just as when children play jump rope, and the rope appears as a rigid structure just rotating, not oscillating. Rotation is natural for a system being driven only along one direction.[15] The twirling string may be thought of as two transverse waves in orthogonal planes a quarter cycle apart, just as two modes of polarization describe circularly polarized light.

The twirling string may be literally viewed this way if it is lit by fluorescent lighting. You may notice reddish and bluish tints to the standing wave (see Fig. 3), especially if the string is white and viewed against a black background[16] Fluorescent lights do not emit all colors simultaneously with equal intensity along the phase of their line cycle, which is the same frequency as the vibration of the string.[17] When viewed from above, the wave appears one way, perhaps red in the middle and blue on the edges, but when viewed sideways, the colors are swapped because of the quarter-cycle difference in phase. When you tune past maximum resonance of the standing waves, the color scheme will switch because of the change in phase of the string's vibration with respect to the driving force.[18] The direction of the rotation also switches, as a stroboscope reveals.

The picture on the cover was taken by first photographing the vibrating string under stroboscopic light at five times its vibrational frequency. A side-by-side pair of red and green laser beams were then sliced perpendicularly through the vibrating string. The resulting picture reveals that when this is repeated at intervals along the length of the string, the motion of a string particle is indeed circular.

A more sophisticated trajectory occurs (see Fig. 4) when an additional mode at half-line frequency develops in

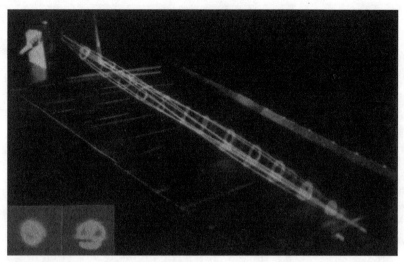

Fig. 4. Mode created when typical twirling string sways at half the vibrator frequency. Close-ups of string's cross section in lower left shows two typical Lissajous trajectories of an element of string, photographed by sweeping a laser though the standing wave.

beats, slow swaying and rotation of vibrational planes, switching from planar to rotational motion, and jumps in amplitude.

In about an hour and with a total cost of about ten dollars per apparatus, teachers at our Advanced Placement Physics Teachers Workshop[24] constructed a standing-wave generator from an aquarium aerator, took the data, and deduced the vibra-

one plane while the string is being tuned to an even number of swells. Half-frequency vibrations occur when a string is being driven longitudinally rather than transversely. If you were holding a planar standing wave in a rope, from its stretching you would feel the tension increase above default twice each period. You might try to excite the wave by just varying the tension, one example of parametric excitation.[19] However, by driving your hand longitudinally back and forth at the same frequency of the existing standing wave, you would only increase the tension above default once each period, producing a standing wave at half frequency. The tendency for the string to jump into this mixed subharmonic mode can be annoying when you're taking data for Melde's experiment itself, but can be quelled by pinching the string at one of the swaying would-be nodes of the expected pattern.

The ability to pinch a node while leaving the pattern beyond unaffected makes transverse waves difficult to believe in. Although planar waves in a string are presented as the archetype of transverse waves[20] and are even modeled this way in advanced mechanics books,[21] the motion of an element of string in a planar vibration cannot in general be just strictly transverse. To vibrate, the string must stretch, and the stretching of an element of string is a maximum where the slope is greatest. "Transverse" waves might better be referred to as planar waves, because the stretching of an element of string means a point on the string undergoes both transverse and longitudinal motion. This means energy can be transmitted longitudinally through the node.[22]

The stretching of the string makes the equations of motion nonlinear. This effect results in exceedingly rich dynamics when driven sufficiently hard.[23] When the tension is slowly changed, you can observe such diverse behavior as

tion frequency. I hope that other teachers will find this an exciting and easy laboratory as well.

Acknowledgments

Great thanks are due Jerry Busenitz, Gene Byrd, Ronald Edge, Stan Jones, J. W. Harrell, our graduate students, and the participants of the Advanced Placement Physics Teachers Workshop for their suggestions. Our Educational Media department was invaluable in advising me how to take the photographs appearing in this article. I also thank The Fin Inn, John's Photo, and The Worm Shack of Tuscaloosa, Alabama, for their assistance in the production of this demonstration. David Burba of Vanderbilt University was essential in pointing out some of the references used in this article.

References

1. Richard Manliffe Sutton, *Demonstrations Experiments in Physics* (McGraw-Hill, New York, 1938), p. 143.
2. George D. Freir and Frances J. Anderson, *A Demonstration Handbook for Physics* (American Association of Physics Teachers, 1996), p. S-6.
3. Philip Johnson, Karl Trappe et al., *PIRA Demonstration Bibliograph* (Physics Instructional Resource Association, 1997), 3B22.10–11.
4. Paul G. Hewitt, *Conceptual Physics* (Little, Brown, & Company, 1985), p. 285.
5. J. Rekveld, *Am. J. Phys.* **26**, 159–163 (1958).
6. PASCO scientific, P.O. Box 619011, 10101 Foothills Blvd., Roseville, CA 95678-9011.
7. Central Scientific Company, 3300 CENCO Parkway, Franklin Park, IL 60131.

8. F.P. Clay, Jr. and R.L. Kernell, *Am. J. Phys.* **50**, 910–912 (1982).

9. David D. Lockhart, *Phys. Teach.* **9**, 283 (1971).

10. Alan H. Cromer and David Garelick, *Am. J. Phys.* **43**, 926 (1975).

11. Wallace A. Hilton, *Am. J. Phys.* **20**, 310 (1952).

12. Daniel Nashol, *Am. J. Phys.* **33**, 856 (1965).

13. David Halliday and Robert Resnick, *Physics for Students of Science and Engineering* (Wiley, 1960), p. 417.

14. Richard B. Minnix and D. Rae Carpenter, Jr., *Phys. Teach.* **21**, 53–54 (1983).

15. Robert W. Leonard, *Am. Phys. Teach.* **5,** 175–176 (1937).

16. Sue Gray AlSalam and Ronald D. Edge, *Phys. Teach.* **18**, 518 (1980).

17. Salvatore Ganci, *Am J. Phys.* **52**, 250–251 (1984).

18. A.S. McWilliams, *Am. J. Phys.* **43,** 1112 (1975).

19. A.B. Pippard, *The Physics of Vibration* (Cambridge, 1978) Chap. 10.

20. David Halliday, Robert Resnick and Jearl Walker, *Fundamentals of Physics* (Wiley, 1997), p. 401.

21. Alexander L. Fetter and John Dirk Walecka, *Theoretical Mechanics of Particles and Continua* (McGraw-Hill, 1980), p. 221.

22. Reuben Benumof, *Am. J. Phys.* **48,** 387–392 (1980).

23. John A. Elliot, *Am. J. Phys.* **50,** 1148–1150 (1982).

24. For information on participating in our summer Advanced Placement Teachers Workshop, contact Rebecca Pow at rpow@ccs.ua.edu, 205-348-3021 (University of Alabama, College of Continuing Studies, P.O. Box 870388, Tuscaloosa, AL 35487) or A.K. Smith, Chapel Hill High School, 1709 High School Road, Chapel Hill, NC 27516.

Wave Speed on a String Revisited

Ray Scott Wakeland and Bennet Brabson, Indiana University, Bloomington, IN 47405

Two excellent articles in *The Physics Teacher* addressed the need for "time-of-flight" measurements of wave velocity in the air and in strings.[1,2] Michael Edmiston's strain-gauge apparatus allows measurements of wave speed in strings to one to two percent accuracy. The development of a new acoustics laboratory at Indiana University has resulted in a technique for making such a measurements that, although it is less elegant, requires equipment that is considerably less novel and expensive than strain-gauges and fast strip-chart recorders. Also, this method can be used as a simple extension of a study of standing waves on a string, thereby providing quick confirmation of the relationship between wave speed and standing-wave frequencies.

We use our normal standing-wave apparatus[3] but change from nylon line to steel wire 2.29 x 10^{-4} m in diameter (1/0 gauge =.009-in diameter piano wire). A tension of 14.7 N provides sharp pulses and a convenient fundamental frequency of 105 Hz for the 1-m wire.[4] The ends of this wire are connected by alligator-clip leads to an oscilloscope. Two horseshoe magnets[5] are placed on the standing-wave apparatus straddling the wire so that mechanical pulses in the wire passing by the magnets induce voltages that are picked up by the scope. Our setup is shown in Fig. 1. Plucking the wire manually very close to one end sends a short pulse down the wire, and attaching a 10-cm piece of masking tape along the wire at the opposite end reduces excessive reflections. The scope is triggered when the pulse passes the first magnet. The sweep rate can be adjusted so that the voltage pulse from the second magnet also appears on the screen (Fig. 2).

At this point, students can readily see that moving the magnets closer together also moves the voltage peaks closer together. A related bit of physics easily observed with this arrangement is the inverted voltage pulse produced by the reflected pulse traveling back down the wire. Since reversing a magnet also reverses the sign of the observed voltage, it is necessary to orient both magnets in the same direction across the scope and in the direction that produces positive voltages. The measurement of wave speed is made by plucking repeatedly to obtain accurately the time between the two voltage peaks and by noting the distance between the magnets. Varying in conjunction the sweep rate and the distance between the magnets will allow optimum use of the scope screen for more exact time measurements. The velocity is the distance over the time.

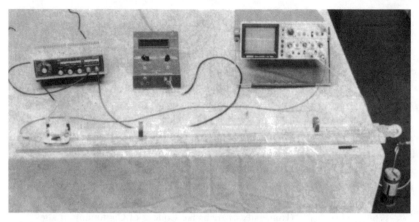

Fig. 1. By wiring a standing-wave apparatus with a thin conducting wire attached to an oscillo-scope, direct measurement of wave velocity can be added to the standing-wave lab. The two small horseshoe magnets, shown in the photo straddling the wire, induce voltages in the wire in response to pulses traveling along the string. The 10-cm piece of masking tape on the wire damps out excessive reflections. A frequency counter is used to facilitate the standing-wave section of the lab.

Students should be discouraged from plucking too vigorously. A violent pluck seems to disrupt the tension long enough to change the wave speed significantly during the first traversal of the wire—the harder the pluck, the slower the speed. As the plucking is repeated, the *shortest* observed time should be accepted as correct since this will correspond to the least disruptive pluck. A ballpoint pen cap makes a useful string pick and gives more uniform voltage pulses than does plucking with fingers. The trigger level should be as low as possible without causing unwanted traces.

The magnets can now be removed for an immediate verification of wave speed using the standing-wave method on the same apparatus with the same wire and tension.[6] This measurement is almost certainly more accurate but is less direct. With careful measurement, accuracy of better than three percent discrepancy between the two measurements is not hard to achieve.

References

1. Brian W. Holmes and Mario L. Capitolo, "Acoustics demonstration tube," *Phys. Teach.* **24**, 297 (1986).
2. Michael D. Edmiston, "Wave speed on a string," *Phys. Teach.* **25**, 510 (1987).
3. Standing-wave systems (often called sonometers) are available from several of the large physics lab suppliers. Central Scientific's most advanced system is magnetically driven so it is already wired with steel. PASCO has a new "variable frequency mechanical drive" for this and other purposes. The system used at Indiana University is driven by a small loudspeaker with the cone removed. For more information on this system contact its developer, William Krejci, Director of Undergraduate Laboratories, Physics Department, Indiana University, Bloomington, IN 47405.
4. Piano wire is available at piano stores or can be ordered from McMaster-Carr, P.O. Box 4355, Chicago, IL 60680. We obtained similar results with thin nichrome wire. Large wire gives less satisfactory standing waves; copper wire tends to break under tensions suitable for standing-wave measurement.
5. We use the Alnico 5 magnet (#78328) from Central Scientific Company. It has a very strong field between the poles (1.2 T), but not much lifting power, and is therefore quite safe. With this magnet, voltage pulses of 40 mV are common. Weaker magnets will work but are less appropriate for other acoustics lab experiments such as ribbon microphone construction.
6. Some sonometers have fixed-frequency drivers (usually driven tuning forks). With such setups, it might be appropriate to do the standing-wave part of the experiment first since tension adjustment is the only way to get the desired standing wave.

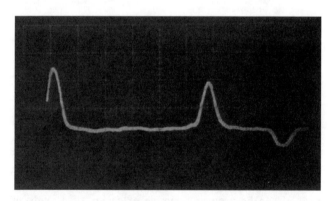

Fig. 2. The oscilloscope is triggered by the voltage induced as the pulse passes the first magnet. The time between the two pulses allows a direct measurement of the wave speed since the distance between the magnets is known. The small, inverted signal on the far right is the pulse reflecting from the masking tape.

Measurements of Sound Velocity by Means of PZT

Judith Bransky, 4123 Indian Run Drive, Dayton, OH 45415

Piezoelectric ceramic can be used as an impact-to-voltage transducer. The advantage of using this device for various experiments in the student laboratory lies in its accuracy and simplicity. In a previous paper[1], we described an application of the piezoelectric effect for the determination of mechanical parameters (in particular, the coefficient of restitution). We have also used this device for the determination of the velocity of sound in metals, plastics, glass, and liquids. A somewhat similar experiment, using the recoil of a rod from an impacting hammer,[2] is generally used in the student laboratory.

We use a small plate (20 x 20 x 2 mm) of PZT-5A ceramics[3] coated with silver electrodes on both sides.

The speed of sound is measured in rods of different materials. The PZT is clamped onto them by means of a simple plastic cylinder, as shown in Fig. 1, or a standard clamp with an enlarged opening. Care is taken to avoid undesired electrical contacts. The liquids are contained in thin-walled plastic tubes that are sealed by standard rubber stoppers with inserted metal plugs, as shown in Fig.2. The PZT plate is clamped to the plugs as before.

The sound wave is generated by a slight hit with a hammer on one end of the rod (or tube). The wave travels back and forth several times, activating the PZT. The electric signal from the PZT is recorded by an oscilloscope with a digital memory and a plotter.

The velocity of the sound wave in the material is equal to the quotient of twice the length of the rod (or tube) divided by the average time between two adjacent peaks on the plots.

Results for several metals and dielectrics are shown in Figs. 3 and 4. Oscilloscope traces for two iron rods of different length are given in Fig. 5. In Fig. 6 three oscilloscope traces for liquids are shown. In these traces the attenuation of the wave is clearly shown.

Numerical values of the velocity of sound, as calculated

Table I. The velocity of sound for different materials (m/s).

	Measured Values	Handbook[4] Values
Metals		
Iron	4737(4450[2])	5189
Copper	3509	3813
Brass	2727	3451
Aluminum	4122	5102
Dielectrics		
Glass	2683	4717
Plexiglas	1213	—
Liquids		
Alcohol	1176	1162
Water (tap)	1727	~1500
Carbon tetrachloride	1070	940

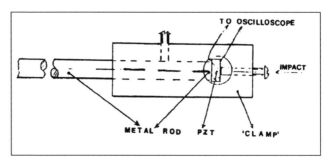

Fig. 1. PZT plateholder for solid rods.

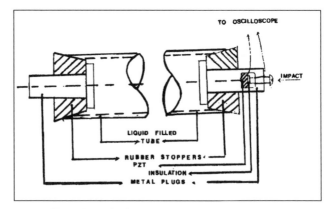

Fig. 2. PZT plateholder for liquids.

from the various traces, are presented in Table I. The results, compared with handbook values,[4] are in good agreement for metals and liquids (between 1 and 20 percent). The glass and plastic samples show a discrepancy of about 40 percent. For the sake of comparison, the velocity of sound in iron, measured in our laboratory using Nuffield's method, is shown in the table.

References

1. Judith Bransky, *Phys. Teach* **27**, 637 (1989).
2. "Waves and Oscillations," Teachers Guide, Unit 4, *Physics, Nuffield Advanced Science* (Penguin Books, New York, 1971), pp. 52–54.
3. Ceramic PZT-5A can be obtained in the United States, subject to availability, from Vernitron in Ohio, (216)232-8600. (This company is also located in Thornhill, Southampton, England). Vernitron is willing to work with schools and colleges seeking this ceramic material.
4. *Tables of Physical and Chemical Constants* (Longmans, London, 1978).

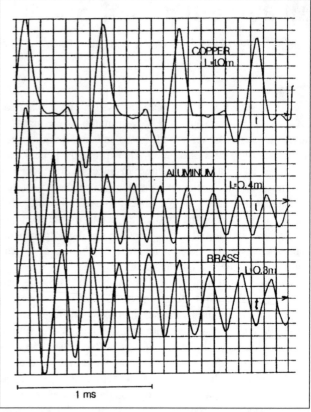

Fig. 3. Oscilloscope traces of the PZT transducer output for three iron rods. L = length of rod.

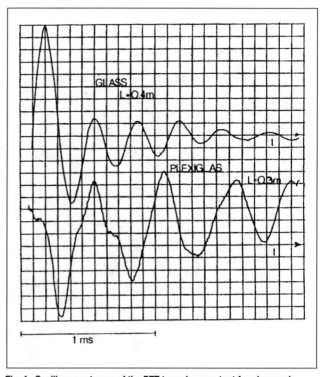

Fig. 4. Oscilloscope traces of the PZT transducer output for glass and Plexiglas rods.

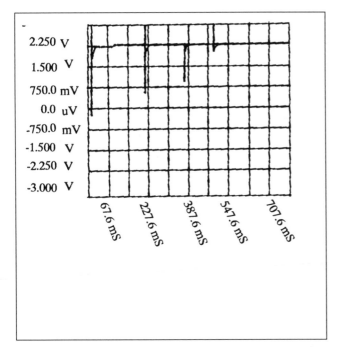

Fig. 5. Oscilloscope traces of the PZT transducer output for two iron rods of different lengths.

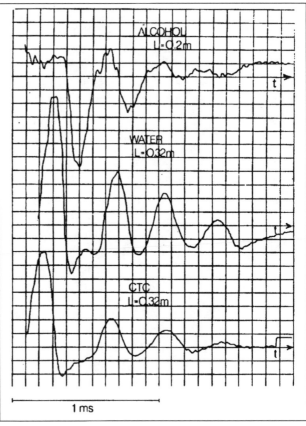

Fig. 6. Oscilloscope traces of the PZT transducer output for three liquids. CTC = carbon tetrachloride.

A Sound-Wave Demonstrator — For about $10?

Charlotte Farrell (Retired), Vestal Central High School, Vestal, NY 13850

For $10? Yep. And here's how we did it. And why. It's not much of a secret that physics often deals with abstract phenomena. Most of us run into those moments when all we want is a concrete model. If it's an inexpensive model that requires no time to set up and is also sturdy enough for students to "play with," so much the better. So if longitudinal waves and compressions and rarefactions have ever been the bane of your existence (and your students'), here's an idea for you.

The occasion was a two-week workshop for local physics teachers.[1] We were playing the part of students as each of our number gave a teaching demonstration.

Nancy Harvey (West Middle School, Binghamton) placed a wooden framework holding 25 suspended index cards on the demonstration desk in front of us (Fig. 1). When she touched the card at one end, a longitudinal wave moved down the length of the apparatus, reflected at the end, rippled back, and reflected once or twice more before damping out.

"How does it work?" the "students" wanted to know. "The cards don't appear to touch."

Nancy allowed a few thoughts to be expressed. Then we discovered that each card had a magnet glued to its face so that like poles were adjacent. This allowed each card to

Table I. Parts list.

Key	#	Dimensions (cm)	Description	Approx. cost 24 demos
A	48	2.0 x 1.2 x 63.5	Pine parting stop (25 each)	$39.20
B	96	2.0 x 3.6 x 30.5	1 x 2 #2 pine (12 in each)	22.08
C	24	2.0 x 3.6 x 59.7	1 x 2 #2 pine (23½ in each)	11.04
D	48	2.0 x 8.8 x 17.8	1 x 4 #2 pine (7 in each)	7.00
	48	57.2 (length)	Suspension rods ¼ in smooth, cold-rolled steel rods (22½ in each)	40.00
	600		Magnets (Radio Shack #64-1885)	90.00
	336		#6 slotted flat-head screws (1¼ in)	18.00
	1248	2.1 (length)	Spacers (drinking straws with a diameter larger than the holes in the index cards) approx. 173 straws	– –
	600	20.3 x 12.7	Index cards (5 x 8 in)	21.36
	small amount		Any suitable glue (e.g. Goop by Eclectic Products)	5.91
			Approx. total cost	$254.59
			Approx. cost for one demonstrator	$ 10.61

"push" the next without actually touching it. The analogy to air molecules propagating a sound wave is close.

Nancy then went on to explain condensation, rarefaction, and wavelength with a wonderful economy of words. She sketched the traditional representation of longitudinal waves on the board, and it even looked like the wave on the appa-ratus.

Later, Carl Stannard (SUNY, Bing-hamton), one of the workshop's directors, placed the wave apparatus in front of us again. He vibrated the first card sending waves chasing down the line of cards. They soon settled into a standing wave. The middle card hung almost at rest while the cards on either side flapped back and forth. Don't do this in front of your classes unless you're prepared to answer their questions!

Carl then explained that we would be setting up a manufacturing assembly line so that each of us would have a longitudinal wave demonstrator to take back to our classes.

A picture of the apparatus (Fig. 1), a diagram (Fig. 2), a template showing the placement of the magnets on the index cards (Fig. 3), and the list of materials (Table I) gives most of the information you need to build one for yourself or set up an assembly line at your next physics teachers' meeting.

The lumber came from a lumber yard and the steel rods from a steel dealer. (Quarter-inch piano wire from a hobby shop will also work.) The magnets came from Radio Shack. Carl bought out the entire stock of several Shacks in the area.

We found it necessary to be reasonably neat about gluing the magnets to the index cards and punching the suspension holes. If the magnets don't line up, the wave action suffers.

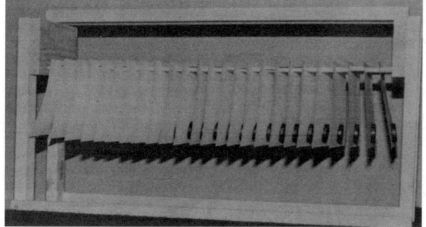

Fig. 1. Wave demonstrator showing the index cards separated by pieces of drinking straw.

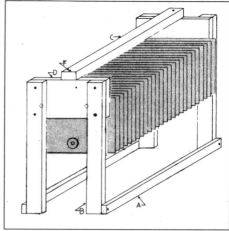

Fig. 2. Details of assembly of the wave demonstrator.

Figure 3 can be enlarged to scale and used as a template to assure that all the cards are identical.

Half of the magnets must be glued with the north face toward the cards and half with the south face. Naturally we had to keep track of which was which and alternate them in the final assembly.

The spacing of the suspended cards is important. Andy Telesca (Johnson City High School), another workshop director, obtained the drinking straws (spacers) through high-level negotiations with a public-spirited fast-food franchise. The drinking straws must be larger in diameter than the suspension holes. Any arrangement that keeps the cards about 2.1 cm apart would probably work.

The straws were cut to 2.1 cm length, and the frames assembled except for the final screw (labeled F in Fig. 2). Then the suspension rods (precut) were inserted into blind holes drilled in the end pieces (shown as broken circles in piece D in Fig. 2), and the spacers and cards (with magnets alternating faces) were threaded onto them. The other ends of the rods were inserted into the blind holes at the other end of the apparatus, and screw F was inserted to complete the assembly.

Voila! Twenty-four longitudinal wave demonstration models in less than two hours for about $10 each.[2]

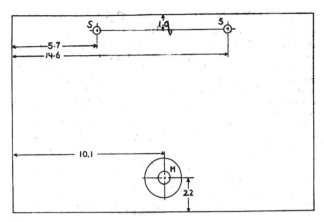

Fig. 3. Template showing the placement of magnets (M) and suspension holes (S) on 5 x 8-in index cards. Dimensions on the template are in cm.

References

1. This two-week summer workshop is part of STEP UP (Southern Tier Educators Program for Understanding Physics) and is supported by the New York State Education Department.
2. The apparatus was designed by the author, aided by Mark Stephens, Equipment and Laboratory Specialist, SUNY, Binghamton.

Wave Interference Patterns Displayed on the Overhead Projector

Richard A. Secco, University of Western Ontario, London, ONT N6A 5B7, Canada

A wave interference pattern generated in a water-filled ripple tank is a common laboratory demonstration for high-school and first-year university physics courses. In order to integrate this demonstration in a classroom lecture, we have designed and built a transparent apparatus for use on an overhead projector. The apparatus, shown in Fig. 1, produces a double-source interference pattern, shown in Fig. 2, by a dc, motor-driven, double-cam assembly. One cam translates the continuous rotational motion of the motor shaft, via a slotted disk, to an oscillating translational motion of the spring-loaded, double-point-source assembly. The second cam, with its lobe oriented 180° from the lobe of the first cam, acts as a counterbalance. The tank and support arm for the motor and source assembly are made of Plexiglas, which is the key to overhead projection. Although we used a variable dc power supply, a simple battery and rheostat combination would serve equally well. Since the tank walls produce reflections, the double-source frequency must be adjusted, via the rheostat-controlled motor current, to give a stationary wave interference pattern. The material costs including battery and rheostat are less than $25, and the apparatus takes about eight hours to build.

Thanks to Ron Tucker for building our apparatus.

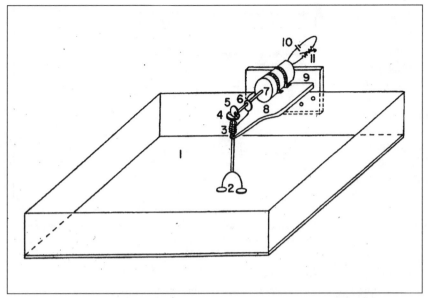

Fig. 1. Double-source Plexiglas ripple tank. 1) Plexiglas tank; 2) double-point-source assembly; 3) spring; 4) slotted disk; 5) active cam; 6) counterbalance cam; 7) dc motor (6 V); 8) Plexiglas support arm; 9) mounting back plate; 10) battery; 11) rheostat.

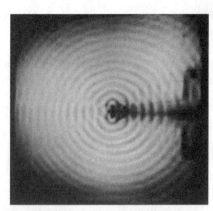

Fig. 2. Double-source interference pattern photographed from the projector screen.

Note: Don't forget to raise the projector focus to the water surface for a sharp interference pattern projection!

A Standing Wave Simulator

Robert H. March, Dalhousie University, Halifax, Nova Scotia, Canada B3H 3J5

This simple device can show, when used on an overhead projector, many combinations of boundary conditions and normal modes for vibrating strings or air columns in pipes. It is based on the idea that a twisted narrow band has a projection that is mathematically equivalent to the envelope of a vibrating string.

A common elastic band is held (under slight tension) at each end by a flat clip. Each clip is rendered free to turn by a piece of beaded chain. The outside end of each chain is supported by a wire frame (coat-hanger wire works well). Adequate rotational friction is important so a minimum length of chain, four beads, is used. Additional friction, if required, can be obtained by wrapping some string between the middle two beads. The tension of the band is not critical. When mounted with about 20 percent elongation, this model worked well. The moss section is 1 mm x 6 mm, which worked somewhat better than 0.5 mm x 6 mm. The entire apparatus can be assembled from scratch in about 20 minutes at a cost of less than $1.

Figure 1 shows the effect as an overhead projector would and also illustrates the construction. A cardboard mask on the projector will eliminate the distraction of the mechanics. Shown are two-and-a-half loops with the boundary conditions appropriate for one end fixed and one end free. As many as six or seven half wavelengths can be shown.

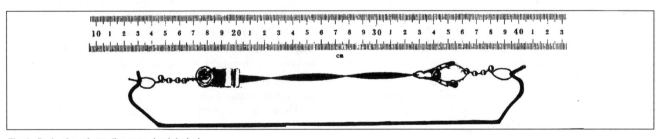

Fig. 1. Projection of standing wave (and device).

The Helium-Filled Organ Pipe

Brian Holmes, Department of Physics, San Jose State University, San Jose, CA 95192

Filling an organ pipe with helium raises its fundamental frequency since sound travels faster in helium than in air. Neglecting end corrections, an organ pipe of length L open at both ends has a fundamental frequency f = v/2L; other allowed frequencies will be integer multiples of this. Since the speed of sound in air and in helium is 331 m/sec and 970 m/sec respectively,[1] one expects that the result of replacing air with helium will be to multiply the frequency by 2.93, the ratio of the two velocities. Many introductory physics books include problems based on this increase.

Unfortunately, experiments seem to contradict the theory described above. For instance, when we sound an organ pipe with helium the frequency rises between 25% and 40%, far less than the predicted 193%. In fact, the change we observe depends on the orientation of the pipe.

Why is there such an apparent discrepancy between theory and experiment? Faulty experiment! To understand this we need to discuss how an organ pipe makes sound.

In an organ pipe a gas exits from a windway, crosses a gap, and strikes the upper lip of the opening. The gas stream oscillates back and forth across the upper lip. As the gas stream oscillates, it alternates between going inside the pipe and outside the pipe.

Evidently, when the gas enters the pipe it drags with it some gas from outside the tube. Therefore, the gas inside the pipe includes air from outside the pipe. So blowing helium through an organ pipe will not result in a pipe entirely filled with helium.

The speed of sound in a gas is proportional to the square root of its density, which is in turn proportional to the molecular mass M. So we get

$$v_1/v_2 = (M_1/M_2)^{1/2},$$

where v_1, is the speed corresponding to molecular mass M_1. If the gas inside the pipe is an equal mixture of helium and air, the average molecular mass is about 16 gm/mole, and the speed of sound should be a factor of $(28/16)^{1/2} = 1.32$, or 32% higher. This is within the range mentioned above. Orientation could change the pipe's frequency, because buoyancy effects change the relative proportions of helium and air inside the pipe.

To observe the expected 193% rise in pitch, the pipe should be sounded while surrounded by helium. We fill a large garbage bag with helium, taking care to secure it so that is does not escape to the ceiling. Then we use helium to sound the pipe inside this bag, taking care that the open end of the pipe is not too close to the side of the bag. We observe a frequency rise of 174%; the remaining discrepancy is probably due to small amounts of air in the bag. As a lecture demonstration, this experiment works best if the garbage bag is transparent so that students can observe what is going on inside the bag.

Reference

1. T. Rossing, *The Science of Sound,* (Addison-Wesley. 1982). We have quoted values for 0°C; temperature changes affect each gas in the same proportion.

Chladni Plates: How Big Can They Be?

John M. Pitre,[*] Department of Physics, University of Toronto, Toronto, ONT MSS IA7 Canada;
pitre@faraday.physics.utoronto.ca

The use of Chladni plates for demonstrating the nodal lines on resonating surfaces has been with us since 1787 when E.F.F. Chladni first created patterns using sand on vibrating plates.[1]

Chladni plates of various shapes have been a standard classroom demonstration; photographs of several figures are presented in a book by Mary Waller.[2]

My interest in this subject was rekindled in June of 1995 at the annual meeting of the Ontario section of the AAPT when George Vanderkur demonstrated some patterns by using a violin bow to excite vibrations on a reasonably sized plate. This demonstration, I thought, would be a good introduction to standing waves on two-dimensional structures since in our first-year course, Physics for the Life Sciences, we cover standing waves on strings and in air columns (basically one dimensional) and then proceed to discuss resonances on the basilar membrane inside the cochlea of the human ear. However, what is a reasonable size for a demonstration in many classrooms is woefully inadequate for classes of 200 or more such as we have at the University of Toronto.

Our standard response when a demonstration is too small for our large classes is to make a small apparatus and then use a video camera to project to one or more monitors. Another solution for this demonstration would be to use transparent Chladni plates and an overhead projector.[3] Although these procedures would work, I find that intermediate technology often removes immediacy and creates a barrier for some students. The straightforward solution is to just make bigger plates. The question was, "How big can they be?"

Our first attempt was a sheet of aluminum (1 m square; 1/8-in thick) from the workshop. We drilled a hole through the center and supported the plate on a heavy laboratory stand with a diameter of 2.5 cm. Although very clear patterns could be set up using a violin bow, it did take some practice; the usual tendency was for the plate to make large-amplitude, low-frequency unstable oscillations, possibly due to the swaying of the stand itself. This certainly was not suitable since several professors would be using the apparatus and they had no desire to become accomplished "platists" before using the apparatus. What we needed was a demonstration that worked every time with little skill required on the part of the lecturer.

In our next attempt we simply cut 10 cm off each side of the plate. This pleased the demonstration staff since now the stand and plate with a width of 80 cm could be carried through a standard doorway. To our surprise the change in operation was dramatic. As long as the demonstrator bowed with enough vigor, Chladni patterns appeared each time with little or no practice. However, the vigor of the bowing was wreaking havoc on our violin bow; the number of tattered horsehairs indicated that the number of demonstrations per bow would not be large. Having visited the Hands-On Science Museum in Ann Arbor, Michigan in the summer of 1995, I recalled a Chladni plate demonstration with a more robust bow of tubular steel and catgut. The "bow" in Fig. 1 shows an alternative that works extremely well when used with a little rosin. It is a simple hacksaw with the blade replaced by about a half a dozen strands of nylon fishing line. In fact, when bowing gently with this crude instrument it is much easier to generate standing-wave patterns than when using the violin bow.

Fig. 1. Resonance pattern for a square plate supported at the center and bowed at the midpoint of one side.

Fig. 2. Resonance pattern for a square plate supported at the center and clamped at the midpoint of one side.

Figure 1 shows the pattern that is easiest to generate when the plate is bowed at the midpoint of one of the sides. The pattern formed by the white sand was made more visible by spray painting the aluminum plate a flat black. This photograph was taken during the 1996 summer semester; students are sitting up to 40 feet away from the apparatus.

Figure 2 is a photograph taken during the 1995–96 winter semester and shows the pattern generated when a nodal line is forced to pass through a certain point. The student at the right is holding the plate at the midpoint of one side; the plate is being bowed about 25 cm from the corner. The patterns in both figures are very easy to generate. More complicated patterns at higher frequencies can be generated but they take more practice. For example, with the student holding the midpoint of the plate as shown and with the bowing a few centimeters closer to the corner, patterns containing circles can be generated. One resonant pattern is a single large circle with eight spokes and another is a rectangular grid with edges parallel to the plate diagonal with the grid enclosing four well-defined circles. With care and practice, more sharply defined patterns can be produced than those shown.

So how big can the plates be? Practically, the limitation on size is a function of the sturdiness of the stand. About 80 to 100 cm square seems to be the limit for l/8-in aluminum and the stand we describe if you place one foot on the base of the stand as you bow. I'm sure that with a thicker plate

and/or a sturdier stand, an even larger apparatus could be constructed; however, for lecture rooms similar in size to ours the apparatus shown here is more than adequate.

The author was the 1995 recipient of the Canadian Association of Physicists' Medal for Excellence in Teaching Physics.

References
1. E.F.F. Chladni, *Entdeckungen über die Theorie des Klangen*, translated excerpts in R.B. Lindsay, *Acoustics: Historical and Philosophical Development* (Dowden, Hutchinson, and Ross, Stroudsburg, PA, 1973), p. 155.
2. M. Waller, *Chladni Figures: A Study in Symmetry* (Bell, London, 1961).
3. P.J. Ouseph, "Chladni plates for overhead projectors," *Am. J. Phys.* **59**, 665 (1991).

The Doppler Demonstrator

William P. Brown, Irondequoit High School, Rochester, NY 14617-3093

To illustrate the Doppler effect, two simple but effective overhead projection demonstrations can be used. Instead of drawing several diagrams illustrating the different wave formations as the speed of a source increases and reaches the speed of sound or greater, make a set of concentric circles ($r_1 = 3$ cm, $r_2 = 6$ cm, $r_3 = 9$ cm) out of heavy-duty plastic sheets or Plexiglas. These permanent wavefronts (plastic circles) can be easily and quickly rearranged to demonstrate the Doppler effect and other related phenomenon (Figs. 1, 2, & 3). The fact that the radii are always the same helps the student understand that once a wave is in the air its speed is constant and will always travel the same distance per unit time. If the source moves, then the origin of each successive wave moves, and the resulting pattern shows an apparent wavelength that is shorter preceding the moving source and longer trailing the source.

In the second demonstration, a spring is stretched over the overhead projector. The support illustrated (Fig. 4) was made out of a 60-cm section of support channel for a suspension ceiling. A 90° "V" was cut 10 cm from each end and folded up to make a "C-shaped" support, and a 15-cm section of wave demonstrator spring was stretched across the 40-cm gap between the two ends. A piece of tape or clay is attached to the center to represent the wave source. When the source on the spring is held and moved parallel to the

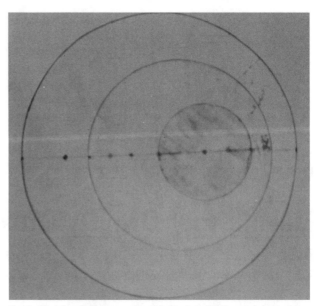

Fig. 1. Plexiglas circles are arranged to illustrate the Doppler effect when a source travels less than the speed of sound.

spring, the spring will compress on one side and stretch on the other (Fig. 5). On the screen the spring will look like a wave and be shorter in front of (hence, the higher frequency) and longer in back of the moving source.

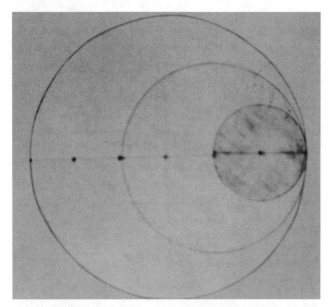

Fig. 2. The Plexiglas circles are quickly moved to illustrate a source moving at the speed of sound.

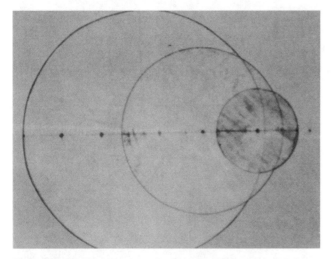

Fig. 3. Now the circles are arranged to demonstrate the sonic boom when the source is moving greater than the speed of sound.

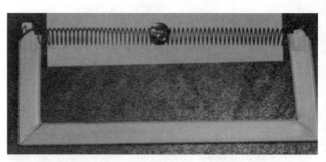

Fig. 4. The evenly stretched spring represents a wave source at rest.

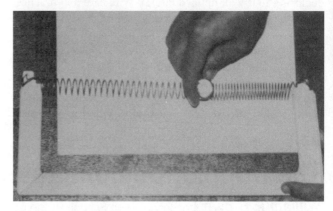

Fig. 5. The Doppler demonstrator is compressed in the direction of motion, showing an apparent decrease of the wavelength in front of the moving source.

Making Your Own Dynamic Loudspeaker

Allen Keeney and Brant Hershey, Department of Physics, Lebanon Valley College, Annville, PA 17003; A_Keeney@lvc.edu, B_Hershe@lvc.edu

A loudspeaker is a familiar everyday device that depends on electromagnetic force for its operation. Speakers are excellent examples of simple devices that use many different physical concepts. A dynamic loudspeaker uses a magnetic field and moving electrons to produce a Lorentz force, which in turn causes a set of longitudinal

pressure waves to propagate through air. Thus a speaker can be used to teach about electricity, magnetism, properties of waves (including the principle of superposition), and sound.

Figure 1 is a cutaway diagram of a speaker built using the technique described here. The basic components are: supporting ring, paper surround, cone, voice coil, metal core, and ferromagnet.

The supporting ring simply holds the speaker over the magnet. The surround is a folded paper region acting as a spring, which allows the cone to vibrate when small forces are applied to it. The cone itself is made of construction paper; it moves when a periodic alternating force is applied, thus pushing the air and producing the sound. The voice coil provides a path for the alternating electric current, which produces a magnetic field that reacts with the permanent magnetic field to produce Lorentzian forces on the speaker causing it to vibrate. The magnet is simply the source of the magnetic field; the metal core acts as a magnetic field extender to direct the magnetic field.

Materials needed.
- Construction paper (student's choice of color)
- Permanent magnet (of box or cylindrical shape)
- Iron bolt or short iron bar (approximately 1 cm diameter by 2 cm long)
- Enameled 30-gauge magnet wire (15 to 20 m long)
- Ring stand and metal ring
- Glue (preferably from a hot glue gun but other glues work)

The cone. Using a compass and scissors cut a circle out of the construction paper of the same radius as the outside of the supporting ring. Cut a smaller circle (diameter 2 cm) out of the exact center of the circle. Cut a straight line from the outside of the circle toward the center (Fig. 2). Form the speaker cone by overlapping the two edges and gluing them together.

Now cut a strip of construction paper 2.5 cm wide by 8

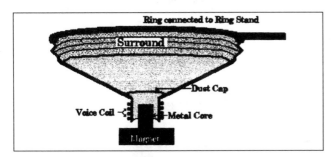

Fig. 1. Cutaway view of homemade cone speaker.

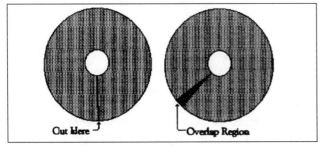

Fig. 2. Cut on line and glue paper over itself to make cone with hole.

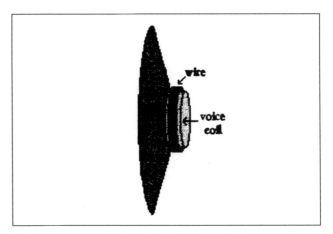

Fig. 3. Side view of cone with voice coil attached to back.

cm long. Wrap this paper into a donut with a 1-cm overlap and glue ends to create a paper loop with a diameter of 2.2 cm. The loop is the base for the voice coil. Now wrap the enameled 30-gauge wire around this cylinder. For a radius of 2.2 cm, this is about 110 to 150 wraps. A shorter length of 32- or 34-gauge wire can also be used. For ease of wrapping, place your finger or a dowel inside the paper loop to provide support. Be sure to allow 5 cm on each end to be lead wires. Glue the loop to the back of the cone as shown in Fig. 3. At this point, a small circle of paper can be glued to the cone to act as a dust cap by covering the hole in the center of the speaker.

Optional. An LCR meter can be used to determine the impedance at the standard frequency of 1 kHz. The impedance should be between 4 and 8 Ω. We used 16 m of 30-gauge wire, which yielded an impedance of 6.6 Ω. If the impedance is found to be less then 4 Ω. the voice coil should be rewrapped using a longer wire before attaching it to an amplifier.[1]

The surround. Cut a piece of construction paper 4 cm wide with a length slightly longer than π times the diameter of the cone. Fold the paper down the center lengthwise. Then fold the paper the opposite direction 1 cm in from each edge (see Fig. 4). The two center sections should form a V-shaped section. Make a series of cuts in this V-shaped section, about one cut per cm. The cuts allow you to fold the paper into a ring. Touch the two long edges of the paper together so that the paper makes a ring as shown in Fig. 5.

Attach the bottom of the surround to the cone with hot glue or rubber cement; attach the top of the surround to the ring with tape.

Fasten the whole speaker assembly to a ringstand. Set a permanent magnet[2] on the table and place the iron bolt on top of it. Lower the speaker assembly so that the iron bolt is inside the voice coil.

Connections. Remove enamel from the ends of the wire

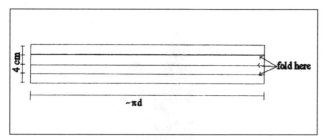

Fig. 4. Folding pattern for the surround.

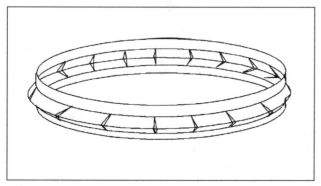

Fig. 5. Finished surround.

by heating with a soldering iron or by scraping with a razor blade and connect the two leads of the voice coil to a function generator. Always start with low voltages. High voltages may cause the voice coil to become hot, especially if 32- or 34-gauge wire is used. Feel the voice coil with your finger every once in a while, if the wire begins to get warm, decrease the amplitude. Frequencies from about 100 to 15,000 Hz should be audible from the speaker. Extremely low frequencies of 1 or 2 Hz can be used to see more effectively the electromagnetic forces on the speaker. You can also experiment with the effect of the magnetic field by

moving the speaker up or down, effectively lowering and raising the magnetic field passing through the coil. In our speaker, we noticed a resonant frequency for the speaker at about 20 Hz, which can also be an interesting demonstration. Finding the resonant frequency is easy: simply vary the frequency until the speaker's amplitude increases dramatically. Resonant frequencies for commercial woofers are typically between 20 and 50 Hz.

The speaker can be attached to an old radio or other amplifier. By adding an oscilloscope on the output wire, you can see the many components of music. This provides an excellent demonstration of the superposition principle, since students can see the many frequencies. Beat frequencies can also be demonstrated by attaching two function generators to the speaker and varying their frequencies. This allows the student to hear the beats as well as see them on the oscilloscope.

The classroom experiment of producing an ordinary loudspeaker has led us into discussions of electromagnetic fields and sound waves with our students, turning what could have been a dry theoretical topic into an exciting application.

References

1. A method of measuring impedance without using an LCR meter can be found in David Weems, *Designing, Building, and Testing Your Own Speaker System With Projects*, 2nd ed. (Tab Books, Blue Ridge Summit, PA, 1984), pp. 169–170.
2. We used a rectangular ferromagnet bought at Radio Shack for less than a dollar. The larger ceramic refrigerator magnets are also acceptable.

Experiments with Sharp Acoustical Pulses

Hubert Biezeveld, Rijksscholengemeenschap West-Friesland, Hoorn, The Netherlands, *and Louis Mathot,* Waterlant-College Amsterdam, The Netherlands

One can make a generator for sharp electrical pulses simply by putting together a stroboscope and a small photovoltaic cell. If these are not available, then one can use an LDR (light-dependent resistor), a resistor, and a bakery (see Fig. 1). An audio-amplifier with a loudspeaker, when fed with this signal, will give sharp clicks. Two experiments which use this "click-generator" will be described.

A. Measuring the Speed of Sound

The sharp clicks are produced near the opening of a pvc draintube (diam 80 mm; length about 1.30 m, not critical). A microphone is installed sideways into the tube and receives the direct as well as the reflected pulses (see Fig. 2). Both signals are shown in the oscilloscope display of Fig. 3. With this setup, we found for the speed of sound: $v = 2 \times 1.4/2 \times 3.6 \times 10^{-3} = 3.4 \times 10^{-2}$ m/s $\pm 2\%$.

B. Fourier's Theorem is Sound

According to Fourier, each periodic signal is composed of a series of pure sine waves, each with its own amplitude, frequency, and phase. The sharp clicks form such a signal. One can easily prove the existence of the Fourier components with the setup of Fig. 4.

With the stroboscope on e.g. 90 Hz, switch the sine generator to 91 Hz, 181 Hz, 271 Hz, etc. Each time this is done beats will be heard, formed by the Fourier components of the signal and the auxiliary sine wave. With some care, seven or more of the components can be heard.

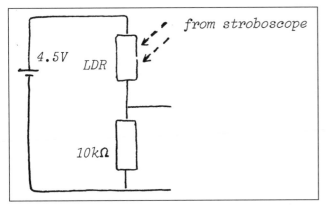

Fig. 1. A "click-generator."

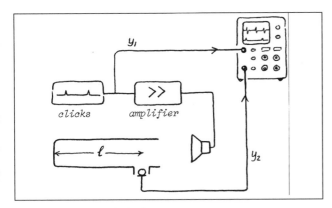

Fig. 2. Reflecting acoustical pulses.

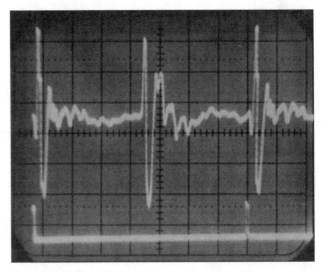

Fig. 3. Timebase 2 ms/div; l = 1.24 m; pulses from solar cell.

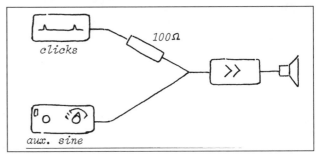

Fig. 4. Producing beats with sine and Fourier components.

THERMAL PHYSICS

Mechanical Equivalent of Heat

F. Paul Inscho, Maryville High School, 825 Lawrence Avenue, Maryville, TN 37801

Here is a suggestion for an improvement in apparatus that is commonly used to measure the mechanical equivalent of heat.

The standard apparatus consists of a heavy cardboard tube about 1 m long and 4 cm in diameter with two cork stoppers to fit the ends of the tube. I've found it difficult to locate tubes of these dimensions, and when I did use these tubes they had a very short useful lifetime. Also, if a student fails to hold the stopper in place, or if the tape holding the stopper comes loose, you will find buckshot or BB's all over the floor, and the experiment has to be repeated. So I constructed my own permanent tubes that work very well; four such tubes cost me less than $25.

Materials

Buy 4.5 m of 1½-in (3.81-cm) PVC pipe (STM D2665 330 PSI @ 73°C) and cut it with a regular saw into four equal lengths. For each tube, attach a PVC endcap to one end with PVC cement. For the other end, purchase (perhaps as a unit) an expandable cap of rubber, a steel plate (5.08 cm in diameter), a stove bolt, washer, and thumb screw (see Fig. 1). When the thumb screw is tightened, the rubber expands inside the tube, and the steel plate pulls tight against the end of the tube.

Method

The experiment calls for the use of lead shot, but this may be difficult to find in some areas. If so, steel BB's may be used with some modification. Because of the differences in the specific heat of lead (0.038 cal/g-°C) and steel (0.106 cal/g-°C), cool the steel 1 to

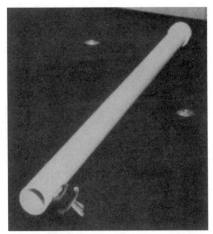
Fig. 1. Tube and end cap.

Sample Data

Mass of shot (steel)   814 g (0.814 kg)

Initial average temperature of shot   21.2°C

Final average temperature of shot after

rotating   23.7°C

KE gained = PE lost = (0.814 kg) (100 m) (9.8 N/kg)

KE = 8.0×10^2 J

Heat gained by shot:

        Q = (m) (c) (Δt)

        Q = (814 g) (0.106 cal/g-°C) (2.5°C)

        Q = 220 cal

Comparing KE and Q, it is determined that

        1 cal = 3.7 J from this experiment.

Discrepancy = (4.2 J/cal) = (3.7 J/cal) = 0.5 J/cal

Relative discrepancy = (0.5 J/cal) / (4.2 J/cal) = 0.12 or 12%

Mass of shot (lead)   786 g (0.786 kg)

Initial average temperature of shot   17.3°C

Final average temperature of shot after rotating   24.1°C

KE gained = PE lost = (0.786 kg) (100 m) (9.8 J/kg)

KE = 7.7×10^2J

Heat gained by shot:

        Q = (m) (c) (Δt)

        Q = (786 g) (0.038 cal/g-°C) (6.8°C)

        Q = 200 cal

Comparing KE and Q, it is determined that 1 cal = 3.8 J

Discrepancy = (4.2 J/cal) – (3.8 J/cal) = 0.4 J/cal

Relative discrepancy = (0.4 J/cal) / (4.2 J/cal) = 0.098 or 10%

2° below room temperature; the lead should be cooled 3 to 4° below room temperature. This will give better symmetry for temperatures above and below room temperature. It will therefore partially correct for heat flow from and to the room, which in our case was at 22°C.

Prior to class, cool approximately 750 g of shot to below room temperature by placing them in a calorimeter cup, which is then placed in a 2000-ml beaker of ice and water.

Ask your students to determine the mass of a 9-oz (approximately 250-ml) Styrofoam cup. Quickly transfer the cooled shot to the foam cup and weigh it again to determine the mass of the shot. Place a plastic cover with a small hole or slit in the center over the top of the cup (perhaps the cover from your morning coffee). Insert a thermometer through the slit, getting the bulb well down into the shot. Allow the thermometer to come to equilibrium and record the temperature. It should be below room temperature.

Immediately transfer the shot into the prepared PVC tube, close the end with the expandable closer, and rotate the tube vertically approximately 100 times. Be sure all the shot hits the bottom of the tube before each rotation. This rotating procedure simulates the shot falling through a distance of 100 vertical meters. We are making an assumption that in "falling" through this 100 m the potential energy (PE) of the shot at the top is totally converted to kinetic energy (KE) at the bottom, and the KE in turn is converted into heat.

After rotating the tube 100 times, quickly open it and pour the shot back into the foam cup. Put the cover back on the cup, and insert the thermometer as before. Allow the temperature to come to equilibrium, and record the temperature. The difference in the two recorded temperatures measures the heat gained by the shot while falling.

Calculations

Ideally, heat converted from the KE gained in falling should equal heat gained (calories) by the shot. The KE at the bottom should equal the PE at the top of the 100 m. This is measured in joules, and the number of joules and calories are compared.

Comments

These results were obtained by using thermometers with a range of –2 to 52°C (larger degree size produced a more accurate reading). The students wore ordinary cotton work gloves to minimize heat transfer from their hands.

This experiment, if carefully done, will not only illustrate the theory and concepts of the relationship of mechanical energy to thermal energy, but also produces reasonable numerical values.

Results obtained with this apparatus are as good or better than with the cardboard tube. There is much less risk of having to pick the shot off the floor, and I also have a piece of permanent equipment that can be used from year to year. Since I have three physics classes and 75 to 80 students per year, the PVC tubes are a decided advantage.

A New Apparatus for Measuring the Mechanical Equivalent of Heat

Akio Saitoh, 2085-22 Mise-cho, Kashihara-shi, Naraken, 634 Japan

James Prescott Joule, an English scientist, performed a famous experiment in 1843 with an apparatus that determined the equivalence between heat and work with considerable precision.

We present a new apparatus for measuring the mechanical equivalent of heat that can be constructed at low cost (Fig. 1).

A hollow cylinder, with a diameter of 14 cm and length 7 cm, is mounted on a shaft, 0.4 cm in diameter. The shaft rotates on ball bearings to reduce friction to a minimum; however, when small lead grains (lead shot about 0.15 cm diam) are put inside the cylinder, work has to be supplied to turn the cylinder.

As the cylinder is turned n times by a constant torque, L, an amount of work

$$W = 2\pi Ln$$

is done. Since the torque, L, depends on the speed of rotation, the cylinder must be turned at a constant speed. It takes about 70 sec to turn the cylinder 30 times. The torque, L, is measured by a torque wrench which reads directly in Newton meters.

As the cylinder rotates, the lead grains are lifted by the 12 vanes and then fall back to the bottom of the cylinder. Kinetic energy is converted to heat energy, and therefore the temperature of the mass (m) of the lead grains is raised by ΔT.

There is a small hole at the side of the cylinder for insertion of a thermometer (Fig. 2) capable of measuring to 1/20 deg. The heat Q is

$$Q = mc\Delta T$$

where c is the specific heat of lead (0.031 cal/g K). Consequently, the mechanical equivalent of heat J is

$$J = W/Q = \frac{2\pi Ln}{mc\Delta T}.$$

The apparatus is made of plastic which has a very low thermal conductivity. The vanes (7 x 3 x 0.3 cm) and ends are attached to the cylinder with cement.

To minimize heat loss, the initial temperature of the small lead grains should be that of the room.

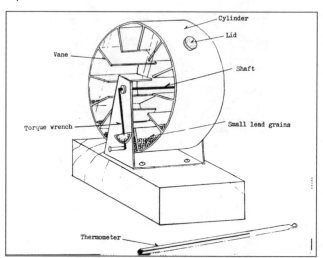

Fig. 1. An apparatus for measuring the mechanical equivalent of heat.

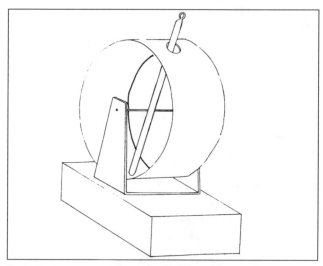

Fig. 2. The temperature of the small lead grains Is measured by the thermometer that Is Inserted from the side of the cylinder.

In our experiment, the small lead grains are initially at room temperature (20.00°C), and the final temperature is found to be 20.35°C. Therefore,

$$\Delta T = 20.35°C - 20.00°C = 0.35°C.$$

Also,
$$L = 0.13 \text{ Nm}$$
$$n = 30 \text{ times}$$
$$m = 500 \text{ g}$$
$$c = 0.031 \text{ cal/g K}.$$

From the above values, we obtain J = 4.5 J/cal.

This experiment was carried out many times with good results.

Viewer for Brownian Motion

Bill Reid, Jacksonville State University, Jacksonville, AL 36265

Robert Brown discovered in 1827 that small particles suspended in a fluid undergo random, irregular movement. This "Brownian motion" is produced by statistical fluctuations in the bombardment of the particle by molecules of the fluid. Although we do not directly view molecular motion, but only a consequence of it, the phenomenon provides students with a visual model, albeit imperfect, of the thermal motion of molecules.

Several science supply houses[1,2] sell small chambers for confining smoke particles under a microscope and observing them strongly illuminated against a black background. We have built several chambers from the transparent plastic "blister packs" in which tiny model automobiles, faucet washers, or other merchandise are sold. Materials used in construction are shown in Fig. 1.

We carefully open a blister pack for faucet washers, about 4.2 x 2.8 x 1.5 cm, by cutting a rectangular aperture about 1 x 1.5 cm in the cardboard backing with a utility knife, and remove the contents. (This opening will later serve as an orifice for the introduction of smoke.) We cut a square opening slightly smaller than a microscope slide cover glass in the top surface. (This will later serve as the viewing window.) Its location should be such that the most intense part of the beam will be directly beneath it in the completed apparatus.

A small, flattened, clear glass "marble" (about 1.8 x 0.9 cm) such as florists use in decorative arrangements serves as a code light-concentrating lens. A hole slightly smaller than this "lens" is cut in the side of the blister.

Through these three apertures, we spray flat black paint until the whole interior is covered. After the paint dries, we mount the lens on the side and the cover glass on the top, using clear silicone rubber cement, and making sure all crevices are sealed completely. When the cement has cured, the chamber is ready for use. The hole cut in the bottom cardboard should be closed with black electrical tape after smoke is admitted.

We also prepare a "spotlight." We open a discarded 35-mm slide holder, remove the color slide, and replace it with aluminum foil. With the point of a wooden pencil we make a circular hole about 4 mm in diameter in the foil. When placed in a projector with the lens racked out, this will produce a spot a few centimeters in diameter. (Ray Carpenter and Dick Minnix at VMI first showed me this trick.)

To use the Brownian Motion Viewer, strike a match, blow it out, and insert it in the bottom opening while it is still

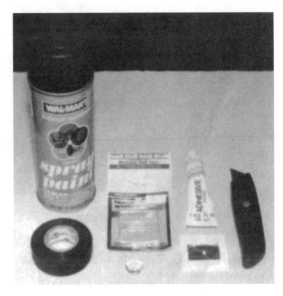

Fig. 1. Materials used in construction of viewer and "spotlight" slide.

smoking. Remove the match and close the opening with black electrical tape. Place the apparatus on the stage of a microscope with the turret set for overall magnification of about 35. The marble lens should be turned to face the slide projector, which should be about a meter or so away on your left or right. The slide projector should be placed on books or blocks so that the beam shines into the marble lens horizontally. Adjust the projection lens so the light is concentrated on the marble lens. Move the apparatus about on the stage until the smoky cone of light inside the apparatus is underneath the microscope's objective lens. Look through the eyepiece and focus. You will find tiny, randomly dancing points of light visible, executing Brownian movement. If a great deal of convective "streaming" is occurring, it may be necessary to wait a few minutes until some kind of temperature equilibrium is reached. The streaming won't stop, but will become much slower. The microscope cover glass over the viewing port is fragile. Always focus the microscope moving the barrel upward; otherwise, you may smash the glass. The viewer in use is shown in Fig. 2. Immediately below the camera, but not visible, is the slide projector illuminating the smoke.

Several other methods of construction are possible. The entire blister pack may be pried from the cardboard, appro-

Fig. 2. Student Assistant Michelle Tew viewing Brownian motion in "blister-pack" chamber.

priate apertures cut, all sprayed with flat black, and then reassembled with silicone cement. The cover glass is not absolutely essential. If a portion of the clear plastic is temporarily covered with tape while spray painting, a clear viewing port will be left when the tape is removed, but the plastic is imperfect optically, and the points will appear as "commas." Another alternative for a makeshift lens may be procured from a ceramic crafts store for a few cents. This is a spherical, small-necked flask about 3 cm in diameter, which is used as a breakaway mold for ceramic grapes. When filled with water, it serves as a short-focal-length lens, but the larger size requires a larger blister pack, which in turn seems to aggravate convective streaming of the smoke particles.

References

1. Sargent-Welch 1986 Catalog—Biology, Chemistry and Physics, p. 590, Catalog #4860B.
2. Central Scientific Co. 1987–88 Physics and Chemistry Catalog, p. 3, Catalog #71270.

A Simple Apparatus for Demonstration of Gaseous Diffusion

Roger A. Key *and* **B. D. DePaola,** Department of Physics, Cardwell Hall, Kansas State University, Manhattan, KS 66506

Gaseous diffusion has been a difficult concept to demonstrate in a large classroom. Past demonstrations have used complex apparatus[1] or have relied on dangerous gases such as bromine in order to be visible to the class.[2] The demonstration described here requires a minimum amount of safe, inexpensive equipment and shows the effect in a highly visible qualitative, as well as a quantitative, way.

The apparatus is constructed from the following parts:
- ringstand
- clamp
- small unglazed clay flowerpot (a glazed container will not allow the gas to diffuse)
- plastic or metal disk large enough to cover the top of the pot

- water or mercury manometer
- length of rubber hose to connect the flowerpot with the manometer
- beaker or vessel large enough to invert over the flower pot
- short length of stiff tube, which is affixed to the center of the plate
- a small amount of helium and/or argon

Seal the drainage hole of the flowerpot with stopper or clay; cover the top of the pot with the disk, and connect the pot with the hose to one side of the manometer (refer to Fig. 1). Clamp this apparatus onto a sturdy ringstand. Fill the beaker with helium and quickly place it over the pot. Because of their smaller mass and size, the helium atoms

Fig. 1. Apparatus in use about 30 s after the addition of helium to the beaker. Helium fills the beaker and is diffusing through the clay of the flowerpot. The manometer shows the increase of total pressure in the flowerpot.

ed away from the ringstand, the effect of diffusion is seen in reverse; the helium diffuses out of the pot while the air diffuses in (Fig. 2). In Fig. 2, the measured pressure is seen to equilibriate at about −14 cm of water. This negative value of equilibrium pressure is due to the helium diffusing out of the open-ended beaker, thereby allowing the helium in the pot to begin flowing out again. The "anomaly" is removed by continuously purging the beaker with a gentle stream of helium.

The diffusion effect can be seen to different degrees by using different gases. Argon is a gas that can be used without precautions and is heavier than air. By standing the large beaker on the lecture table, filling it with argon, and then lowering the flowerpot into the beaker, the manometer will show a decrease in pressure as the air diffuses out faster than the argon diffuses in. Even oxygen produces a measurable effect, since it diffuses more slowly than air.

Our data were taken with a stopwatch, a cassette tape recorder, and the apparatus shown. For the helium data, we first started recording with the cassette player. The large beaker was placed above the clamped flowerpot and filled with helium. The pot was then immersed in the helium by rapidly lowering the beaker. The experimenter lowering the beaker gave a verbal mark and the other experimenter then spoke the relative manometer readings into the tape recorder. The data were later transcribed using a stopwatch and the recorded tape, and then were converted from relative to gauge pressure by subtracting the equilibrium reading of the manometer. This method produced data whose error bars in both pressure and time are within the size of the circles on the graph shown here.

The argon data were taken in the same manner with the exception that the flowerpot-beaker system was inverted, since argon is heavier than air. In the graph, the magnitude of the argon data has been doubled to show the effect more clearly.

The experiment was repeated with oxygen. A maximum water displacement of 1 cm was observed in the manometer. The maximum pressure differential for oxygen occurred about a minute after the gas was added to the beaker and lasted for several minutes.

Thus we have a highly visible demonstration of the diffusion of different gases through a porous material. The demonstration does not require complex or dangerous apparatus, and the results can be qualitatively explained to students in the most introductory physics courses. The demonstration can also be used in more advanced classes to stimulate discussion that might include topics such as partial pressures, porosity of ceramic, and how the size and mass of atoms of the gases used quantitatively effect diffusion rate.

diffuse through the porous material of the pot faster than the air molecules inside the pot can diffuse out. The result is a rapid increase in the partial pressure of helium and a slow decrease in the partial pressure of the constituent gases of air inside the pot. This is seen in the dramatic change of liquid level in the manometer, indicating the increase of total pressure. Caution should be exercised since the effect is very large and can turn short water manometers into fountains.[3] Students can easily see the change in pressure as registered with the manometer. We have achieved manometer displacements of nearly 70 cm of water, corresponding to a pressure difference of over 6.5 kPa, as depicted in Fig. 2.

After some time the levels in the manometer will again equalize. Equilibrium in the manometer while the beaker is still inverted over the flowerpot indicates that the mixture of gases inside the flower pot is the same as the mixture of gases immediately outside the pot. When the beaker is lift-

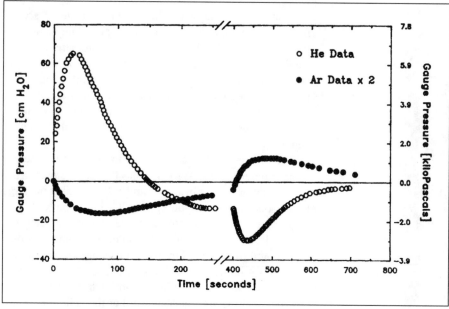

Fig. 2. Pressure with respect to time for helium and argon. The manometer reading has been translated to gauge pressure for the plot. Argon pressure has been doubled for clarity.

References

1. H.F. Meiners, *Physics Demonstration Experiments* (Ronald Press, New York, 1970), p. 784.
2. *Ibid*, p. 821.
3. We used a 1-m, colored-water manometer. Mercury manometers will also dramatically demonstrate the effect.

Measuring the Heat Produced by a Single Candle

William S. Wagner, Northern Kentucky University, Highland Heights, KY 41076

A forced-air calorimeter box was constructed using a 48-qt Styrofoam cooler and two small dc motor fans—one used as an intake fan and the other as an exhaust fan (Fig. 1). A layer of polystyrene insulation was added to the interior walls of the cooler to help reduce the heat transfer by conduction. A source of heat such as a candle or light bulb is placed in the box, and the temperature difference between the intake air and the heated exhaust air is measured. The temperature difference between the interior and exterior surfaces of the box must also be measured, because even with the extra insulation there is a non-negligible amount of heat conducted through the walls. By using these measured temperature differences and the specified flow rate of the fans in cubic feet per minute (CFM), the heating rate of a heat source can be determined by

$$P = 0.59 \text{ (CFM)} \Delta T_{air} + 0.54 \, \Delta T_{walls} \qquad (1)$$

where P is the heat output rate in joules per second (watts) and the temperature differences are in °C. [See theory section for derivation of Eq. (1).] The first term in Eq. (1)—call it the forced-air or convection term—would be the same for any forced-air calorimeter box so constructed. But the sec-

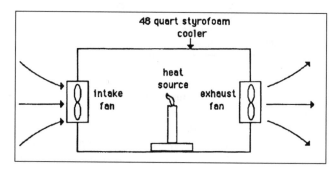

Fig. 1. Sideview of forced-air calorimeter box. Both fans are 12 V DC, 27 CFM fans and are available from Radio Shack, #273-243.

ond term—the conduction term —depends on the thermal conductivity of the box plus the physical dimensions of its surface area and thickness. (See theory section for determination of thermal conductivity.)

The precision of the calorimeter is determined by using sources of known heat output and performing the experiment. (See results.) Two mercury thermometers were positioned outside the box with ring stands and clamps to monitor the intake and exhaust air. Digital thermometers with small temperature-sensing probes were used to measure the

Table I. The results for the fan-flow rates. Percent discrepancies are calculated by comparing the measured heat output with the electrical input power as measured by the voltmeter-ammeter method. The measured, electrical power input was 96 W (116 V × 0.828 A) for the 100-W bulb, and 86 W (116 V × 0.74 A) for the power resistor.

Heat Source	27 CFM (12 V)				20 CFM (9 V)			
	ΔT_{air}	ΔT_{walls}	P	Discrepancy	ΔT_{air}	ΔT_{walls}	P	Discrepancy
100-W bulb	4.8°C	23°C	89 W	−7%	6.2°C	32°C	90 W	−6%
3 100-W bulbs	16°C	35°C	274 W	−5%	21.5°C	43°C	277 W	−4%
150-Ω power resistor	5°C	4°C	82 W	−5%	6.5°C	5°C	80 W	−7%
1 candle	4.5°C	5°C	75 W	N/A	6°C	6°C	74 W	N/A
2 candles	9°C	9°C	148 W	N/A	12°C	14°C	149 W	N/A

box surface temperatures by taping the probes to the interior and exterior walls of the box.

Theory

The heat output rate P is given by

$$P = \frac{mc\Delta T_{air}}{t} + \frac{kA\Delta T_{walls}}{d} \qquad (2)$$

where the first term (the convection term) accounts for the heat used to raise the temperature of the air as it is forced through the box by the intake and exhaust fans. Composing the first term are: ΔT_{air}, the temperature rise of the forced air; m, the mass of the air; c, the specific heat of air; and t, the time in seconds. The second term (the conduction term) accounts for any heat that is not forced out of the box by the air flow and hence conducts through the walls. The factors in the second term are: k, the thermal conductivity of the walls; A, the surface area of the box; ΔT_{walls}, the temperature difference between the inside and outside surface; and d, the thickness of the walls.

In order to reduce the equation to its final form [Eq.(1)], replace m by $\rho \times V$ (density × volume) and then associate volume/time with the fan flow rate. Thus the first term becomes

$$\rho \times (\text{flow rate}) \times c \times \Delta T_{air} \qquad (3)$$

Using handbook values for the density of air (1.29 kg/m^3), the specific heat of air (963 J/kgC°), and designating flow rate in CFM (CFM = 4.72 × 10^{-4} m^3/s), since these are the units specified for the fan, one arrives at the convection term in Eq. (1).

The conduction term is evaluated by measuring A and d for the box and calculating k as follows:

Disconnect the fans, seal off their openings, and place a small known source of heat output in the box. A 15-W incandescent bulb was used for this purpose, giving a ΔT_{walls} of 27°C. The thermal conductivity equation is then used to solve for k, yielding $k = 0.025$ J/(s • m • °C).

Conclusions

The results (Table I) seem to be accurate and consistent as evidenced, respectively, by the small and uniformly negative discrepancies for both the power resistor and the light bulbs. Fan flow rates don't affect the final results, i.e., 27 CFM and 20 CFM yield very similar heat-output rates.

When candles are used for the heat source, the conduction term is a smaller proportion of the total heat output than when light bulbs are used. This is probably due to the fact that a candle is a smaller source of heat than a light bulb, and hence almost all of the thermal energy is forced out of the box when a candle is used as the heat source. The conduction term is also quite small when the power resistor is used as the heat source. This is because the power resistor is in the shape of a cylinder 2.54 cm in diam by 20.3-cm long and was placed in the box with its length parallel to, and in line with, the air flow. Since the fans are 7.6 cm in diam and the resistor is only 2.54 cm in diam, almost all of the thermal energy is forced out of the box. Also, note that when two candles are placed in the box, the measured heat output is double the single candle output, which helps to verify the validity of the method. Finally, the heat-producing rate of a single candle is found to be about the same as a human being at rest, viz., 75 W = 65 kcal/hr = 256 BTU/hr.

Demonstrating Adiabatic Temperature Changes

R.D. Russell, Auburn University at Montgomery, Montgomery, AL 36193

When an ideal gas expands and works against its environment, without the loss or gain of heat, the internal energy of the gas decreases. The first law of thermodynamics and the ideal gas equation dictate that the temperature T and pressure P of an ideal gas follow the relation

$$TP^{(1-\gamma)/\gamma} = \text{constant}$$
$$\gamma = C_P/C_v$$

during an adiabatic expansion.[1]

The adiabatic expansion of an ideal gas is a useful process for illustrating the difference between the concepts of heat and internal energy. In addition, many important thermodynamic processes (e.g., the Carnot cycle and the formation of clouds in the Earth's atmosphere) involve adiabatic expansion. A simple, yet effective, way of illustrating adiabatic temperature changes is to produce a cloud in the laboratory in a manner analogous to cloud formation in the atmosphere.

Two simple and inexpensive variations of the apparatus

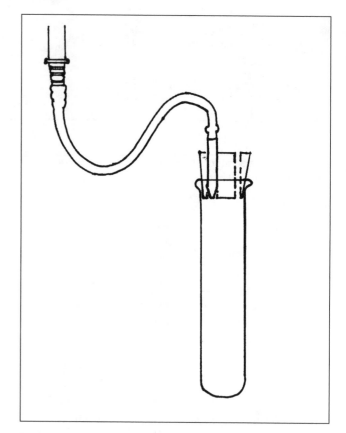

Fig. 2. A cloud chamber constructed from a test tube and water tap.

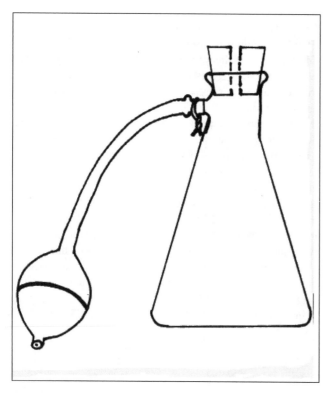

Fig. 1. A cloud chamber constructed from a filtering flask and a hand pump.

needed to conduct the demonstration are pictured in Figs. 1 and 2. The apparatus in Fig. 1 consists of a one-liter filtering flask with a hand pump attached to the side neck. A one-hole rubber stopper plugs the opening in the top of the flask. The apparatus in Fig. 2 is constructed from a 25 x 200 mm test tube. A two-hole stopper plugs the opening. An eyedropper is inserted in one hole, and a length of rubber tubing connected to a water faucet is fitted over the protruding end of the eyedropper.

To produce a cloud to illustrate adiabatic expansion, air near saturation is compressed in either the flask or test tube apparatus and then allowed to expand rapidly. As the temperature of the expanding air decreases, the relative humidity will exceed 100% and condensation will occur. To decrease the saturation ratio needed to produce condensation, however, condensation nuclei should first be introduced into the flask or test tube. The apparatus of choice

Apparatus for Teaching Physics

should be inverted, and then a match should be burned an inch or so beneath its opening.[2] It is important that the visible smoke particles produced near the beginning and end of the burning are not allowed to enter the flask or test tube since the smoke particles tend to mask the desired effect. The adiabatic expansion demonstration is then conducted as follows.

In the bottom of the side-neck flask a small amount of water is placed to provide a source of moisture. Air is pumped into the flask while the opening in the stopper is plugged by a finger. Upon removing the finger, the compressed air rapidly expands with an audible hiss, and a dense cloud forms in the flask.

In the test tube air is compressed by carefully turning on the water tap and adding a couple of inches of water while the opening in the rubber stopper is blocked by a finger. Removing the finger allows the air to expand, and a cloud

forms in the top of the test tube. A faint plume of water droplets may be observed to emanate from the opening in the stopper.

Adiabatic temperature changes may be demonstrated effectively and at low cost using either the flask or test tube apparatuses

References

1. F.W. Sears and G.L. Salinger, *Thermodynamics, Kinetic Theory, and Statistical Thermodynamics*, 3rd ed. (Addison-Wesley, New York, 1975), pp. 102–108.
2. R.G. Fleagle and J.A. Businger, *An Introduction to Atmospheric Physics*, 2nd ed. (Academic Press, New York, 1980), pp. 92–98.

Measurement of a Thermodynamic Constant

Aaron McAlexander, Central Piedmont Community College, Charlotte, NC 28235

The more successful experiments used in the open laboratory for introductory physics at Central Piedmont Community College all tend to meet certain criteria in the areas of instructional value, difficulty in execution, scientific validity, potential for student interest, and safety. The application of such criteria substantially restricts the number of experiments considered suitable for use in the open laboratory, especially in areas such as thermodynamics. For this reason, I was particularly interested when I discovered "Apparatus for measuring c_p/c_v by Rüchhardt's method" described in scientific supply catalogs. The catalog descriptions of the experiments led me to believe this experiment might meet most, if not all of the above criteria.[1,2]

The experiment is described in Zemansky's *Heat and Thermodynamics* in general terms similar to those used in the catalogs.[3] The apparatus consists primarily of a large, gas-filled jar (or aspirator) of volume V, fitted with a glass tube with a precision bore of cross-sectional area A in which a metal ball fits snugly like a piston (Fig. 1).

When the apparatus has been assembled with the ball in equilibrium within the tube, any displacement of the ball from its equilibrium position produces a change in the pressure of the gas in the jar proportional to the ball's displacement. Therefore, if the ball is displaced and released, it

should oscillate with simple harmonic motion. The period of the ball's oscillations should be short enough so that the compressions and rarefactions of the gas in the jar may be considered adiabatic.

The basic equation for the period of a simple harmonic oscillator,

$$T = 2\pi(-y/a)^{1/2}, \qquad (1)$$

can be combined with the expression for the bulk modulus of a gas at low pressure,

$$B = -\Delta P/(\Delta v/v) = \gamma P, \qquad (2)$$

to yield

$$T = 2\pi(mV/\gamma PA^2)^{1/2}. \qquad (3)$$

The adiabatic constant of a gas γ is equal to the ratio of the molar heat capacity of the gas at constant pressure to its molar heat capacity at constant volume, that is

$$\gamma = c_p/c_v. \qquad (4)$$

The essence of the experiment is, therefore, to measure

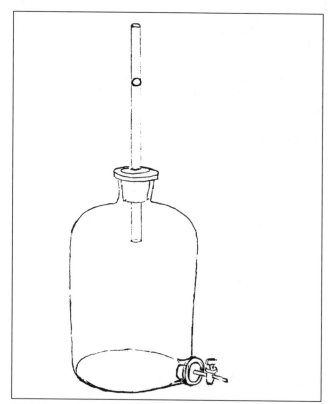

Fig. 1. Apparatus for determining c_p/c_v of a gas by Rüchhardt's method.

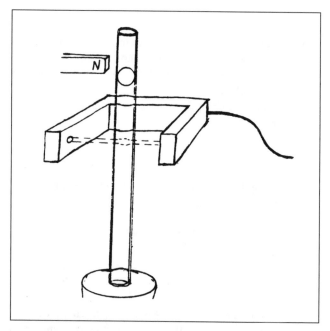

Fig. 2. A photogate timer can be used to obtain a precise measurement of the oscillation period of the ball. The ball easily can be manipulated within the tube by using a strong permanent magnet.

the period of oscillation of the ball in the tube, and to use this information, along with atmospheric pressure and the

dimensions of the tube, the ball, and the jar, to calculate c_p/c_v of the gas in the jar:

$$c_p/c_v = 4\pi^2 Vm/PA^2T^2. \tag{5}$$

The experiment is not as simple as it first appears. Our first attempt with the experiment was to measure c_p/c_v for air (normally available in the open laboratory). We soon discovered that surgical cleanliness (not normally available in the open laboratory) is required to prevent dust particles or debris from causing the ball to lodge in the tube immediately upon its introduction. Even with the required cleanliness (multiple cleanings with acetone-moistened lens paper on a stiff wire), friction between the ball and the tube was a problem.

Frictional damping was so severe that the ball would not execute a sufficient number of continuous oscillations to allow a measurement of the oscillation period with the needed accuracy. Attempts to use larger initial amplitudes to produce series of oscillations of greater duration led to the discovery that, above a nominal amplitude of about 50 mm, the period of oscillation increases with amplitude.

Further research uncovered some suggested modifications to the apparatus for Rüchhardt's method. The 1970 edition of *Physics Demonstration Experiments* suggested using a tapered tube (slightly larger at the top) and maintaining a continuous flow of gas in through the stopcock at the bottom of the aspirator and out through the tube and around the ball.[4] (I wondered why a $100 + aspirator was preferable to a gallon jug.) The slow flow of gas around the ball is stated to provide enough energy to the ball that it will oscillate indefinitely. This publication also describes the construction of an aneroid/photoelectric pressure detector which feeds the output to an oscilloscope. The oscillation period of the ball is determined from the oscilloscope trace. Using an electromagnetic release for the ball also is suggested.

The modifications suggested above would all doubtlessly improve the performance of the apparatus, but we judged that they violate the simplicity criterion. We therefore opted for less complex modifications (Fig. 2).

Our first recommendation is that a strong permanent magnet be used to manipulate the ball within the tube. The magnet can be used to move the ball up and down repeatedly, until a sufficient section of tube is clear of dust and debris. The magnet also can be used to move the ball to the desired amplitude, and the ball can be released at will simply by moving the magnet away horizontally.

The second recommendation is to use a photogate timer with a pendulum mode (such as PASCO ME9215) to measure the oscillation period of the ball. A photogate of the type used with air tracks easily can be arranged so that the beam passes horizontally through the tube and is interrupted by the movement of the ball. (In the "pendulum" mode, the PASCO photogate timer displays the time between the first and third interruption of the beam, which is the period of the ball in this case.)

One catalog description states that the determination of c_p/c_v within $\pm 1\%$ of the accepted value is possible. Using the magnet and the photogate timer, and with either air or helium as the gas in the jar, we have found such results to be the norm.

References

1. *Klinger Educational Physics Cat.* 984, p.15, aspirator KH 2001; precision glass tube with ball, KH 2002.
2. *Central Scientific Company Physics/Chemistry Cat.* 1985, p. 185, c_p/c_v Measurement Apparatus, 37105; 10-1 glass aspirator, 37104.
3. Mark W. Zemansky, *Heat and Thermodynamics*. 4th. ed. McGraw-Hill, 1957), pp. 127–128.
4. H.E. Meiners, *Physics Demonstration Experiments*, (Ronald Press, 1970), pp. 716–717 and 801–804.

Isothermal and Adiabatic Measurements

William W. McNairy, Department of Physics and Astronomy, Virginia Military Institute, Lexington, VA 24450

The Adiabatic Gas Law Apparatus manufactured by PASCO scientific[1] is a useful tool for measuring the pressure, temperature, and volume of a variety of gases undergoing compressions and expansions. Gases studied in this column represent the three general classifications: monatomic (argon), diatomic (nitrogen), and polyatomic (carbon dioxide). The apparatus is intended to qualitatively study adiabatic processes. An adiabatic process may be simulated by rapidly changing the volume of an enclosed gas, allowing little time for heat transfer between the system and its environment. Measurement of the pressure and volume of this gas can yield a value for the adiabatic gas constant, γ. If the volume is changed in small steps and if the gas is given sufficient time to come to thermal equilibrium after each change, measurements of pressure and volume will then correspond to an isothermal process. An ideal gas (one in which the pressure is not too large), regardless of classification, will have the pressure inversely proportional to the volume for an isothermal process.

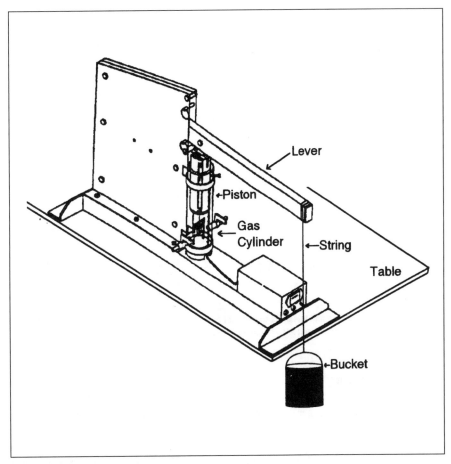

Fig. 1. Schematic of Adiabatic Gas Law apparatus showing the addition of the bucket suspended from the lever arm for isothermal studies. (Adapted, with permission, from the instruction manual for this apparatus, PASCO scientific, Publication #012-05110C, 1/94.)

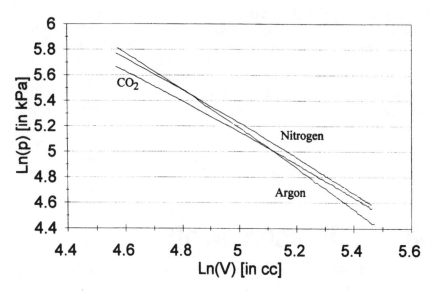

Fig. 2. Plot of raw data only for the adiabatic compressions of three categories of gases. Slopes of each line should equal the corresponding value of the ratio of specific heats.

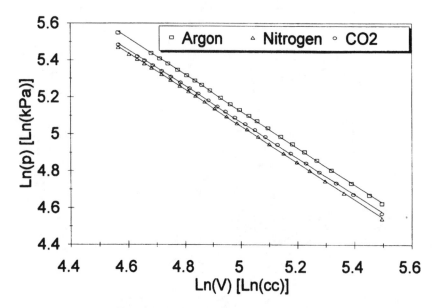

Fig. 3. Plot of both raw data and linear fits to each set of data for the isothermal compression of the three categories of gases. Slopes of each line should equal −1.

Adiabatic Processes

Thermodynamic theory gives a relation between the pressure and volume for a gas undergoing an adiabatic process as,

$$P_i V_i^\gamma = p_f V_f^\gamma = constant \qquad (1)$$

where γ = ratio of molar specific heat at constant pres-

sure to the molar specific heat at constant volume = C_p/C_V. This ratio is equal to 5/3 for monatomic gases, 7/5 for diatomic gases, and 4/3 for "poly-atomic" gases. In reality, γ varies for polyatomic gases depending on the complexity of the gas: for carbon dioxide the value is actually 1.30. In order to perform a linear regression on the data, we take the natural logarithm of both sides of Eq. (1). Rearranging terms, we obtain

$$1n(p) = -\gamma 1n(V) + constant \qquad (2)$$

Thus a plot of $1n(p)$ vs $1n(V)$ for a given gas undergoing an adiabatic compression should have a slope equal to the negative of the ratio of specific heats. Since the thermal sensor lags behind the pressure and volume sensors, data on $p(T)$ and $V(T)$ were not used for measuring the adiabatic gas constant.

The adiabatic process is simulated by rapidly compressing gas in a cylinder by forcefully pushing down on a lever that is attached to a piston in the cylinder, whereas for an isothermal process the volume must be changed slowly. Figure 1 illustrates the adaptation of this apparatus to perform isothermal measurements. Gases are introduced into the cylinder by use of valves mounted at the bottom of the cylinder. It is important to keep the flow rate of gas very low; the temperature sensor uses very fine nickel wire wound on a frame near the bottom of the cylinder. If a gas is introduced into the cylinder too quickly, these wires could be damaged. To prevent this from occurring, we use modified Mylar balloons as gas storage devices. Many helium Mylar balloons found in stores have a "self-sealing" mechanism: a thin plastic sleeve inside the balloon that collapses after the balloon is inflated, keeping the gas inside. In order to access the stored gas, this inner sleeve must be removed. We found that inserting and subsequently removing a piece of rubber or Tygon tubing (approximately 3/16-in O.D.) will result in the inner sleeve being pulled outside the balloon. We cut the sleeve off near its end and removed it with fine tweezers.

Then we reinserted the rubber tubing into the balloon, leaving about a foot of tubing outside the balloon. The mouth of the balloon is sealed to the tubing with electrical tape; the open end of the tubing is clamped with a bulldog clip. This device allows for long-term storage and easy removal of gas.

The adiabatic compression of the gas is achieved by forcefully pushing down on the lever. Pressure and volume data can be recorded during the approximately 100-ms period of the stroke by operating the *Data Monitor* software in "Oscilloscope Mode." The data are saved on disk and imported into a spreadsheet program. Raw data corresponding to the times after the stroke has been completed is deleted so as not to skew the linear regression. The spreadsheet then converts the raw data from the pressure and volume sensors into kPa and cc, respectively, using calibration data given by the manufacturer. Figure 2 shows sets of typical data for ln(p) vs ln(V) for adiabatic compressions of the three classifications of gas studied. Results of the linear regressions corresponding to these data are presented in Table I. General agreement can be seen between theory and experiment, with discrepancies on the order of 3 to 6%.

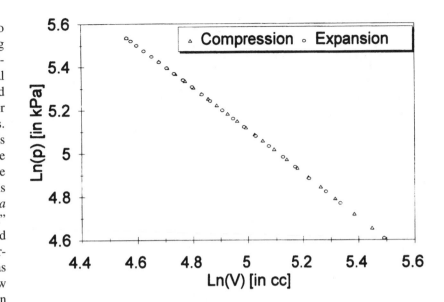

Fig. 4. Plot of raw data only for isothermal compression and expansion of argon gas. Slope should equal −1 for both processes.

Isothermal Processes

The ideal gas law states

$$p\,V = n\,R\,T \qquad (3)$$

Taking the natural logarithm of both sides and rearranging terms, we obtain

$$\ln(p) = -\ln(V) + constant \qquad (4)$$

This equation shows that the slope of a plot of ln(p) vs ln(V) for any classification of ideal gas is equal to −1. To create an isothermal process, we clamped the Adiabatic Gas Law apparatus to the edge of a table with the free end of the lever projecting over the edge of the table. We hung a one-gallon bucket from the end of the lever, as shown in Fig. 1. The length of the string was such that the bucket is below

the top of the table when the lever is at its highest point (the gas in the cylinder is at its maximum volume), and is short enough so that the bucket does not reach the floor when the lever is at its lowest point (minimum gas volume). With the software operating in "Monitor Input" mode, an option can be chosen to display the volume, temperature, and pressure data each second while only storing the data taken every 15 s. (Note: a series of increasing numbers in the leftmost column of the data are displayed *only* on rows of data that will be stored in the computer file.)

Lift the lever to its maximum height, and hold it for about 15 s, to allow the gas to come to thermal equilibrium with the room. Initiate data-taking by the computer; after the first point is recorded, allow the lever to fall to a new equilibrium position with only the empty bucket attached. As may be seen from the raw temperature data displayed every second on the computer screen, the temperature of the gas rapidly decreases to near room temperature in about 10 s or less. After the second point is recorded, gently and quickly place a 0.500-kg mass in the bucket: the gas is compressed somewhat and shortly comes to thermal equilibrium at its newer and smaller volume and higher pressure. Repeat this procedure of adding a 0.500-kg mass each time, until a total of 22 data points are collected. (The process can be reversed: remove masses one at a time and then lift the lever for the final data point.) Since this process occurs slowly (in effect), any thermal energy produced by friction between the cylinder walls and the piston will have sufficient time to flow

Table I. Data for Adiabatic Compressions.

Gas Type	γ (Theoretical)	γ (Experimental)	%Discrepancy
Monatomic (Ar)	1.667	1.555 ± 0.004	6.9
Diatomic (N_2)	1.400	1.345 ± 0.003	4.0
Polyatomic(CO_2)	1.30	1.251 ± 0.002	3.8

Table II. Data for Isothermal Processes.

Gas Type	Theoretical Slope	Experimental Slope	% Discrepancy
Monatomic (Ar): Compression	−1.000	−0.998 ± 0.003	0.2
Monatomic (Ar): Expansion	−1.000	−0.992 ± 0.002	0.8
Diatomic (N_2): Compression	−1.000	−0.996 ± 0.003	0.4
Polyatomic (CO_2): Compression	−1.000	−0.983 ± 0.003	1.7

from the gas before the next data point is taken.

Plots of $\ln(p)$ vs $\ln(V)$ for isothermal compressions using all three categories of gases are shown in Fig. 3; a similar plot for the isothermal compression and expansion of argon is shown in Fig. 4. Table II shows the results of linear regressions for these plots. Typical discrepancies between theory and experiment for the isothermal processes are on the order of 1%, providing an excellent confirmation of the theory.

Acknowledgments

The author would like to acknowledge stimulating and informative discussions held with Mary Ellen Niedzielski of PASCO scientific and with Philip B. Peters, D. Rae Carpenter, Jr., and Richard B. Minnix of Virginia Military Institute.

Reference

1. The apparatus (Part Number TD-8565) was used with the Series 6500 Laboratory Interface (CI-6500) and the software program *Data Monitor* running on a 386-based PC computer. Parts come from PASCO scientific, P.O. Box 619011, Roseville, CA 95661-9011; 1-800-772-8700.

The Thermometric Property of a Diode

Fred W. Inman and Dan Woodruff, Department of Physics, Mankato State University, Mankato, MN 56002-8400

We often introduce the concept of temperature by telling our students that "temperature is what a thermometer measures" and by this we mean that a temperature scale can be introduced based upon some thermometric property, e.g., thermal expansion of a liquid or solid, the behavior of an ideal gas at constant pressure or volume, or electrical resistance. The oldest thermometric property, of course, is the physiological sensation of "hot" and "cold" and this naturally led to the introduction of thermometers and temperature scales for more quantitative measurements. Even today, where we have a much more satisfactory understanding of temperature in terms of the laws of thermodynamics, the practical measurement of temperature still relies heavily on various thermometric properties. What we present here is a simple way to implement the thermometric property of a semiconductor diode to produce a "thermometer" with a very nearly linear dependence upon temperature over a wide range of temperatures. This thermometer utilizes components that are readily available in most physics laboratories, or can be purchased at reasonable cost.

The current I in an ideal pn junction is related to the diode potential V by the relation[1]

$$I = I_0 \exp\left(-\frac{eV_0}{kT}\right)\left[\exp\left(\frac{eV}{kT}\right) - 1\right] \qquad (1)$$

where I_0 and V_0 can be considered constants. If the temperature is not too high, then the exponential term in the square bracket is large compared with one and the equation simplifies to

$$I = I_0 \exp\left[\frac{e(V - V_0)}{kT}\right] \qquad (2)$$

If we arrange for a constant current to flow in the diode, then the exponent becomes a negative constant (I is less than I_0), and we see that V is a linear function of T. that is,

$$V = V_0 - bT \qquad (3)$$

where b is a constant whose value depends upon the current in the diode.

144

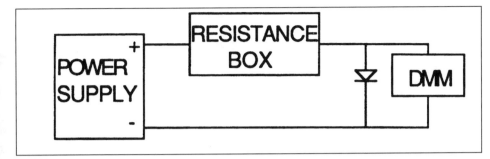

Fig. 1. Experimental arrangement.

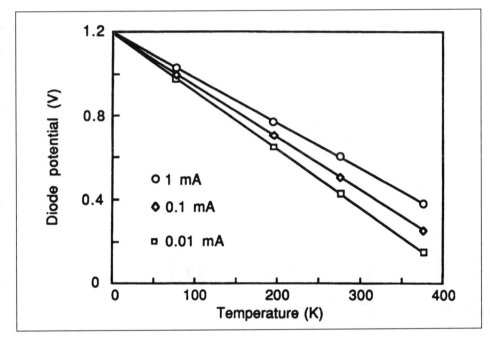

Fig. 2. Typical results of diode potential vs temperature.

squares fits for a typical diode at three different currents. The intercepts were equal within the standard deviations of the fits. The uncertainties in the slopes and intercepts of the fits were each approximately 1% or less.

Several experiments are possible with this diode thermometer. Students could choose the melting and boiling points of water to establish the calibration of the thermometer, then use it to measure other temperatures. It might not be convenient to use liquid nitrogen, but dry ice is usually readily available and its sublimation temperature could be determined. Also, other temperatures could be measured: body temperature, the lowering of the melting point of ice with the addition of NaCl, the melting point of mercury (which can first be solidified with dry ice), and so on. Also, the apparatus can be simplified. The resistance box can be replaced with a fixed resistor and the power supply with a 9-V battery (or better, two 9-V batteries in series). The diodes can be lN914 or equivalent (Radio Shack #276-1122) and if digital multimeters (DMMs) capable of reading at the millivolt level are not already on hand, they can be purchased at low cost (e.g., Radio Shack #22-171 for about $25) and will be useful in the laboratory for other electrical measurements.

Discussion of the theory leading to Eq. (3) could be omitted, but the students should express the calibration temperatures in degrees Celsius and assume the linear relation between voltage and temperature for two or more different currents. They could then be asked to speculate about the significance of the fact that these linear calibrations at different currents intersect at a common temperature of about −273°C.

Figure 1 shows a circuit that can be used to implement Eq. (3). If the power supply voltage is large compared with the diode voltage (about 1 V or less), then the current in the diode is approximately constant for small changes in the diode voltage. We used a power supply that produced 40 V and with the resistance box set the current to 1 mA, 0.1 mA, and 0.01 mA. We used four calibration temperatures: boiling point of liquid nitrogen, dry ice and acetone, and the melting and boiling points of water. Insulated wires were connected to each lead of the glass-encapsulated diode, and the diode was covered with a heatshrinkable sleeve for insulation. This sleeve was found not to be necessary for most temperature measurements, but if the diode is to be immersed in a conducting medium of low resistance, it would be required. We tested four diodes and found that they performed equally well, i.e., the linear least-squares fits of V vs T were equally good, and the intercepts, V_0, were equal within experimental error. Figure 2 shows the least-

Reference

1. S.M. Sze, *Physics of Semiconductor Devices* (Wiley & Sons, New York, 1969), pp. 96–102.

4

Electric Charge, Electrostatics

Experiment to Measure *e/m* for an Electron

Lawrence A. Ferrari, Queens College of the City University of New York, Flushing, NY 11367-1597, **and Kenneth E. Jesse,** Professor Emeritus, Illinois State University, Normal, IL 61790-4560; laf$phys@qc1.qc.edu; kejesse@rs6000.cmp.ilstu.edu

Measurement of the charge to mass ratio, *e/m*, for an electron is a classic physics experiment and one that can now be done in an undergraduate or high-school physics laboratory. Many physics laboratories purchase the apparatus as a unit from a commercial manufacturer. Unfortunately, in our experience, this apparatus has a high initial cost and one of the key elements, a discharge tube, has a limited lifetime; replacement cost is between $450 and $600.

In their classic text on experimental atomic physics, Harnwell and Livingood[1] discuss approximately ten different methods of measuring *e/m* for electrons, including several for ions. The most accurate measurement of *e/m* for an electron by one of these techniques, magnetic deflection or focusing, has been done by Wolf[2] using the method due originally to Busch.[3,4]

The basic concept of magnetic focusing is shown in Fig. 1. Electrons injected at the origin with velocity components parallel and perpendicular to the uniform magnetic field, $\mathbf{B} = B_0\mathbf{k}$, spiral in a helical path about $\mathbf{B}$. After each complete revolution the electrons are focused, that is, they pass through the *z* axis. Points labeled $N = 1$, $N = 2$, etc. are the focus

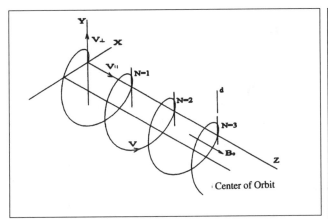

Fig. 1. Schematic showing concept of magnetic focusing. Electrons leave the electron gun at the origin with velocity components parallel ($v_{\parallel}$) and perpendicular ($v_{\perp}$) to the magnetic field direction. After one complete revolution they return to the z axis, i.e., are brought to a focus, at the point labeled $N = 1$; after two revolutions electrons are focused at $N = 2$, etc.

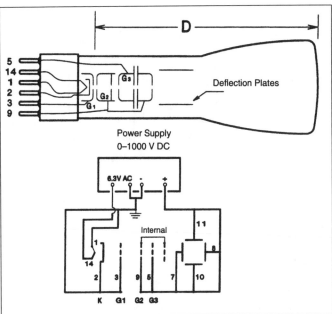

Fig. 2. Schematic of 3BP1 A cathode ray tube electrode structure and wiring diagram used in this experiment. Tube pin numbers are given; certain features such as the conducting coating that provides the return path for the electron current are not shown.

points. At the distance $z = d$ the electrons have completed three complete revolutions. In an experiment an observation screen is located at a fixed distance from the injection point and the electrons are focused at the screen when the time to reach the screen is an integral number of periods of revolution.

In this column we describe experimental apparatus to measure e/m of an electron using the magnetic deflection or focusing technique. The apparatus consists of a relatively inexpensive off-the-shelf cathode ray tube (CRT) and a simple inexpensive solenoid magnet that can be easily fabricated from common materials by an unskilled person. The apparatus is so easy to build that it is an excellent special project for a high-school student. The value of e/m is determined by measuring the focuses of the electron beam as a function of magnetic field strength, which is similar to the basic Busch experiment. The CRT is placed in the magnetic field generated by the solenoid. Data are obtained using exciting currents of less than 10 A (which can be supplied by an automobile battery if a conventional power supply is not available). With this apparatus we find that untrained students can obtain a value of e/m with a probable error of less than ± 5%. This is certainly not as good as the accuracy that can be obtained with the apparatus of Neher,[5] but more than satisfactory for the undergraduate general physics laboratory and certainly remarkable given the low cost of the apparatus. The experiment is simple enough so that students can obtain all of the necessary data in a two-hour laboratory period and get a simple lesson in electron optics at the same time. The general features of this experiment were presented by author Jesse the January 1994 meeting of AAPT in San Diego.

Theory

First, we note that a small misalignment of the CRT within the solenoid, which is very difficult to eliminate, guarantees that an electron will have a small transverse velocity component with respect to the magnetic field direction. However, a misalignment that is too large can cause the electron beam to miss the exit hole in the electron gun and thereby either not produce a spot on the CRT screen or produce an erratic spot that cannot be used for analysis.

The basic formula for this experiment is obtained as follows. Let V be the potential difference between the anode and the cathode of the CRT electron gun. The component of the electron's velocity parallel to $\mathbf{B}_0$ is determined from $\frac{1}{2}mv_{\parallel}^2 = eV$, and the time T for the electron to reach the CRT screen at distance $z = D$ from the gun is $T = D/v_{\parallel}$.

The electrons will be focused when

$$\left(\frac{eB_0}{m}\right)T = 2N\pi, \qquad N = 1, 2, 3, \ldots$$

Combining these equations we obtain

$$e/m = \frac{8N^2\pi^2}{(DB_0)^2}\,V \qquad (1)$$

Quantity eB_0/m is the cyclotron frequency. This is the fundamental formula used in this experiment.

The external magnetic field is produced by a solenoid that approximates an infinite solenoid in the central region where the CRT is located. Therefore, we write $B_0 = \mu_0 nIF$ where $B_{inf} = \mu_0 nI$ is the field within an infinite solenoid with n turns/meter, and F is a correction factor due to the finite length of the solenoid. Thus, we obtain

$$e/m = \frac{8N^2\pi^2}{(\mu_0 nFD)^2}\frac{V}{I^2} \qquad (2)$$

or rearranging:

$$(I/N)^2 = \left(\frac{m}{e}\right)\frac{8\pi^2}{(\mu_0 nFD)^2}\ V \qquad (3)$$

Thus, by plotting the ratio of the focus current to the focus number squared, $(I/N)^2$, versus the accelerating potential V, we get a straight line the slope of which is proportional to m/e and, thus, e/m is readily obtained.

Experimental Apparatus

We use a 3BPlA cathode ray tube in this experiment because of its low cost, convenient size, modest accelerating potentials, and availability.[6] Other tubes using electrostatic focusing should also be satisfactory.

A schematic diagram of the CRT electrode structure and the wiring diagram used for this experiment is shown in Fig. 2. The tube pin numbers are given in the figure; K is the cathode (pin #2).

In the usual mode of operation, grid G1 is biased a few volts negative with respect to the cathode in order to limit the beam current and prevent the beam from burning a spot into the CRT screen. Grid G3 (anode #1) is the focusing electrode. For this experiment grid G3 is connected to grid G2 (anode #2) so that there is no electrostatic focusing in the electron gun. The deflection plates (pins #7, 8, 10, 11) are also connected to G2. Grid G1 is placed at the same potential as the cathode. With this simplified wiring arrangement we have not observed an overly bright spot on the CRT screen. With G3 or anode #1 (pin #5) connected to G2 or anode #2 (pin #9), the maximum accelerating potential difference that can be applied is 2300 V.

We have found that certain tubes produce erratic beams at the lower accelerating potentials, which are well below the usual operating voltage of this tube. For these tubes the voltage must be increased until there is a stable spot. This effect might be reduced by biasing G1 negative but this point has not been explored. We use a 0 to 1000-V power

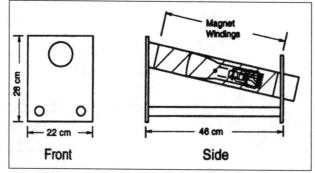

Fig. 3. Diagram of the stand used to hold CRT and magnet. Dimensions are approximate; all materials must be nonmagnetic.

supply for the accelerating voltage V. Data can be obtained with V as low as 200 V, but the focuses are ambiguous due to the presence of stray magnetic fields; this leads to relatively large error in determining the current value at focus. Reliable data can be obtained with $250 \leq V \leq 800$ V if the first focus, $N = 1$, is ignored at the lowest voltage value. For voltages greater than about 800 V there is little transverse displacement of the electron beam, which also makes detection of the focus ambiguous. For this tube, the distance D from between grid G1 and grid G2 to the CRT screen is $D = 19 \pm 0.1$ cm and can be measured directly off the CRT (see Fig. 2).

The magnetic field is produced by a solenoid magnet consisting of 305 turns of #16 copper magnet wire (about 1 kg of copper: wire diameter, including insulation is 1.36 mm) wound on the center section of a 60-cm (approx) length of Schedule 40, 3½-in (nominal) PVC (polyvinyl chloride) tubing. Total length of the windings is $\ell = 41.3 \pm 0.1$ cm. This length is not critical as long as the central 19-cm section has the required uniformity. The Biot-Savart law can be used to calculate the magnetic field variation along the axis of the solenoid.

The ratio of the field B_z in the magnet to that in an infinite solenoid $F = B_z/B_{inf}$ averaged over the center 20 cm of the magnet is $F = 0.967$ on the axis and $F = 0.996$ at radius $\rho = 0.2$ cm. We have found that without special centering jigs the CRT can be moved 1 to 2 mm laterally in the magnet. Therefore, in our data analysis we use a value $F = 0.985$, which is the average of the values of F obtained at $\rho = 0, 0.1$, and 0.2 cm. The axial field off axis is calculated by applying the single-turn coil formula given in Smythe[7] to the 305 coils in the magnet. The correction factor can be neglected; i.e., let $F = 1$ if its calculation is too involved to explain to students since this will introduce an error of only about 3%. Epoxy varnish is applied to the windings to prevent students from unwinding the coils.

Figure 3 is a diagram of the stand used to hold the CRT and the magnet in our general physics laboratory. This is only a suggested way of mounting the CRT. The key requirement is that all materials, including screws, be nonmagnetic. The screen end of the CRT rests directly on the PVC tubing and the rear of the CRT is centered along the magnet axis by a homemade tube socket. Electrical connections to the CRT pins are made with bare "butt" electrical connectors for size #12 or #14 wire. The connectors are drilled out about halfway with a #43 or #42 drill to allow for a snug fit on the pins. The butt connectors rest in holes drilled in a cylindrical piece of Bakelite, or other insulating material, about 3 cm in axial length and with diameter sized to just slide into the PVC tubing. The easiest method of assembly is to first place the connectors, with wires soldered to them, on the CRT pins and then slide the socket over the wires and onto the connectors. An aluminum strap screwed to both the tube socket and the PVC tube at the rear keeps the CRT in position.

The front and rear faces of this stand are made from 0.9-cm thick PVC, but plywood or any other nonmagnetic material will do just as well. The magnet tube is glued to the front and rear faces. At the bottom, PVC tubing with an outside diameter of 3 cm is glued to the front and rear faces to give additional rigidity. Readers who would like additional construction details should contact the authors.

Experimental Results

Figure 4 is a plot of $(I/N)^2$ versus accelerating potential difference V. These data were obtained in four different sets of experiments with magnet currents measured at the first three focuses, and include the effects of using different multimeters to measure the magnet current and of repositioning the CRT within the magnet. The error bars represent the standard deviation of the mean of at least ten different current readings at each voltage and are typically less than $\pm 3\%$ of the average value. The straight line drawn through

the data points is plotted using Eq. (3) with the experimental values of n, F, and D, and the generally accepted value of e/m for an electron. The data points at 250 V and 300 V lie off the straight line; this result is probably due to stray magnetic fields, but we did not investigate this point thoroughly. The magnetic field strength along the center 20-cm section of the solenoid on axis is 8.97 G/A. The smallest currents are those at the first resonance at which $I \approx 2$ A. We estimate the value of the earth's magnetic field in our laboratory to be about 1 G; this value includes the distortion, etc., due to the structural steel and reinforcing rods in the concrete in the building. This value of stray field is approximately 5% of the axial field strength in the magnet at the first focus and can therefore affect the data at this focus. Magnetic materials in the electron gun might also contribute to magnetic field distortion.

In Fig. 5 we show a similar plot of a set of data obtained by two undergraduate students in a two-hour laboratory period. The error bars show the standard deviation of the mean of six current values at each V; i.e., currents at the first three focuses were measured. When first plotted these data fell just below the straight line drawn in the figure. On seeing this result, the students realized that the particular multimeter used to measure the current read low by 2%. When this correction was included, the plot shown in Fig. 5 was obtained.

From a least-squares analysis of the data points in Fig. 4

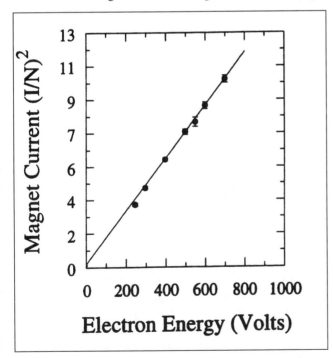

Fig. 4. Graph at magnet current $(I/N)^2$ versus accelerating potential difference or electron energy V. Data were obtained in four different sets of experiments.

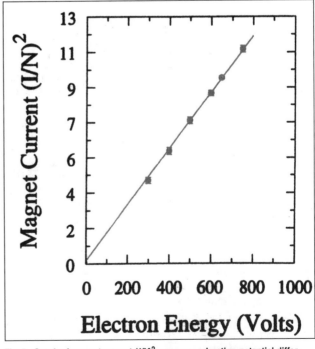

Fig. 5. Graph of magnet current $(I/N)^2$ versus accelerating potential difference or electron energy V. The data was obtained by undergraduate general physics students M. Leibovici and K. McClean in a two-hour laboratory period.

we obtain

$$e/m = 1.71 \pm 0.06 \times 10^{11} C/kg \qquad (4)$$

Similarly, a least-squares analysis of the data points in Fig. 5 gives

$$e/m = 1.70 \pm 0.07 \times 10^{12} \; C/kg \qquad (5)$$

These results differ by 2.8% and 3.3% respectively, from the handbook value of

$$e/m = 1.7588 \times 10^{12} \; C/kg$$

The experimental error given in Eqs. (4) and (5) was obtained using the following values of the relative errors: $\delta \ell \ell = 0.1/41.3$, $\delta \#/\# = 2/305$ (number of turns), $\delta \; F/F = 0.01$, $\delta \; D/D = 0.1/19$, and $\delta \; b/b = 0.0245$ for the data of Fig. 4, and $\delta \; b/b = 0.0277$ for the data of Fig. 5 (b is the slope of the least-squares analysis of the data points in Figs. 4 and 5. The relative error for b is obtained using the average standard deviation of all the data points shown in the respective figure.).

Comment

The total cost of the basic components, the CRT, and the solenoid magnet to do this classic physics experiment is less than $75. The required power supplies, meters, etc., are typical of equipment that is usually available in physics laboratories. We have used a variable high-voltage supply, but, this is not a strict requirement. A fixed-voltage supply can be used as well, but the accuracy might suffer a small amount.

Acknowledgments

Author Ferrari would like to thank Prof. J. Neuberger for bringing Prof. Jesse's work to my attention and for his continued interest in this experiment. The work at Queens College could not have been completed without the generous support of Dean Norman L. Goldman and the many contributions of E. Kuhner.

References

1. G.P. Harnwell and J.J. Livingood, *Experimental Atomic Physics* (McGraw-Hill, New York, 1933), Chap. IV, pp. 112–152.
2. F. Wolf, "Eine Präzisionsmessung von e/m_0 nach der Methode von H. Busch," *Ann. Physik* **83**, 849–883 (1927).
3. H. Busch, "Eine neue Methode zur e/m Bestimmung," *Physik. Zeitschr.* **23**, 438–440 (1922).
4. H. Busch, "Berechnung der Bahn von Kathodenstrahlen im axialsymmetrischen elektromagnetischen Felde," *Ann. Physik.* **81**, 974–993 (1926).
5. H.V. Neher, "Busch tube for determining e/m for the electron," *Am. J. Phys.* **29**, 471–475 (1961).
6. These tubes can be obtained for about $60 from: Daily Electronics Corporation, 10914 N.E. 39th Street, Suite B-6, Vancouver, WA 98682, 800-346-6667; or Thor Electronics Corporation, 321 Pennsylvania Avenue, P.O. Box 707T, Linden, NJ 07036, 800-666-8467.
7. W.R. Smythe, *Static and Dynamic Electricity*, 3rd ed. (McGraw-Hill, New York, 1968), p. 291.

A Simpler Soft-Drink-Can Electroscope

Haym Kruglak, Western Michigan University, Kalamazoo, MI 49008-5151

Construction of an electroscope from a soft-drink can has been described by R.D. Edge,[1] but the method requires careful cutting and assembly of several components. Here is a simpler model in which the opening tab of the can is used as a support for the electroscope leaves.

Tape the soft-drink can horizontally to an inverted Styrofoam cup. Cut two leaves (~0.04 x 0.006 m) from thin household aluminum foil and bend one end of each into a hook. Suspend the leaves one above the other from the hor-izontal can tab, following the arrangement shown in Fig. 1.

The electroscope is readily charged inductively by bringing up to the rear of the can a Styrofoam picnic plate that has been rubbed with wool or one of the "miracle" fabrics, touching the can, and then removing the plate.

Rubbing the can with the charge plate does not give it a residual charge. However, if you cut a strip (~0.15 x 0.03 m) from the middle of the plate, charge it, and place it on top of the can, the electroscope is charged by contact. You can show that the small piece of cloth used to charge it has an opposite charge by bringing the cloth near the leaves. In like fashion, the electroscope can be charged with opposite polarity by placing the small charging cloth on top of the can.

The electroscope is simple enough to be assembled in front of a class in a couple of minutes. A desk lamp with a high-intensity bulb may be used to shadow-project the electroscope onto a wall or screen.

Reference

1. R.D. Edge, *Phys. Teach.* **22**, 396 (1984).

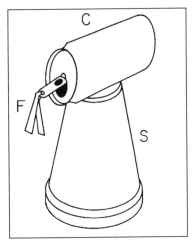

Fig. 1. A soft-drink can electroscope. C = soft drink can; S = Styrofoam cup; F = aluminum foil leaves.

A New Device for Studying Electric Fields

Gary Benoit, Sackler Sciences Center, *and Mauri Gould,* Department of Education, Clark University, Worcester, MA 01610

The gold-leaf electroscope has been a standard tool in the study of static electricity for many years. Although it is a simple device, its use is limited by the fragile nature of its gold leaves. In addition, some students have difficulty interpreting the significance of the behavior of the leaves. In the context of developing a laboratory for a discovery-based course involving static electricity, we wished to use an electrometer that would be sufficiently sturdy to allow constant handling by the students. The device we developed satisfies this requirement and makes possible some additional measurements that cannot be done with a metallic-leaf electroscope.

We describe here an inexpensive and sensitive electrometer that uses a newer type of field-effect transistor. The practical operation of this device is simple, students learn to use it quickly, and the device is easily assembled for a cost of less than $5. Although it has a low cost and a robust nature, the main advantage of the electrometer is its sensitivity. Several applications of the electrometer that exploit this sensitivity and the differences in its response to positively and negatively charged objects are included.

Transistors in General

Most transistors use semiconducting materials such as crystalline silicon with small amounts of impurities introduced into the silicon to give positively and negatively

doped regions. The microscopic structures are fabricated on silicon wafers and are produced by introducing atoms that have either three (aluminum) or five (phosphorus) electrons in the valence shell.

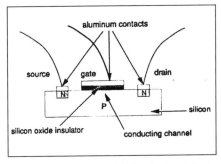

Fig. 1. Pictorial diagram of the insulated gate field-effect transistor (IGFET). Wires from the source, drain, and gate of the IGFET are shown.

The presence of aluminum ions produces regions in the silicon crystal with electron holes, giving the region net positive conductors. In contrast, phosphorus produces regions with extra electrons and net negative conductors. A p-n junction forms where the positive and negative regions meet. Current can easily go in only one direction across the p-n junction.

IGFET and VMOS Power FET

The IGFET (Insulated Gate Field-Effect Transistor),[1] often referred to as a MOSFET (Metal Oxide Semiconductor Field-Effect Transistor), has its limitations.

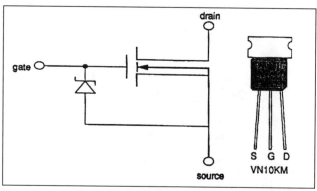

Fig. 2. Schematic of a VMOS Power FET showing the internal Zener diode.

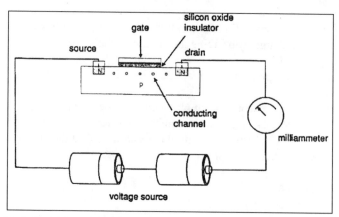

Fig. 3. Pictorial circuit indicating how the gate controls the current through the conducting channel of the IGFET. The contacts to the drain, gate, and source are aluminum.

A pictorial diagram of the IGFET[2] is shown in Fig. 1. Note that there are p-n junctions at the ends of the die. The body of the transistor is made with silicon doped with impurities giving the crystal an excess of holes and therefore making it a p-type crystal. A piece of aluminum insulated from the die by a thin layer of silicon dioxide is called the gate. One lead wire is connected to each n island at opposite ends of the die, and a third wire is attached to the gate. These wires are denoted as the source, drain, and gate, respectively. The presence of the insulator between the gate and the crystal forms a capacitor. Since the gate is part of a capacitor, the input resistance is extremely high and there is almost no dc current in the gate circuit. The gate oxide layer is very thin and therefore a large voltage difference, such as might be created by a static charge, would destroy the insulation. For this reason it is necessary to take special precautions to protect the IGFET from static electricity.

The VMOS Power FET (Vertical Metal Oxide Semiconductor Power Field-Effect Transistor) was first introduced in 1976.[3] Whereas the IGFET has only *horizontal* active structures fabricated near the surface of the silicon chip, a VMOSFET uses many parallel connected structures that allow vertical conduction. Most important, for our purposes, is the fact that it can pass high current and withstand higher voltage, making it a relatively rugged device. The VMOS structure also makes the gate capacitance much higher than an IGFET and allows the gate to withstand a higher static charge.[4]

The transistor used in the electrometer, a VN10KM produced by Siliconix Inc.,[3] has a Zener diode as an integral part of the silicon die. In contrast, a Zener diode is not part of most IGFET's. A Zener diode is a p-n junction that is doped to allow current in the reverse bias direction after a specific voltage is reached. The diode is connected between the gate and source leads as shown in Fig. 2. When the Zener voltage breakdown is reached (at about 15 V), charge can flow from the gate circuit to the source, thus limiting the voltage across the gate capacitor and protecting the oxide insulation.

IGFET Operation. The function of an IGFET can be understood by studying the circuit shown in Fig. 3. With zero voltage across the gate, no charge flows between the source and the drain. A positive voltage on the gate attracts electrons in the region below the gate. These electrons induce a thin n-type channel in the p-type silicon between the source and drain, permitting current through the channel. The gate voltage and the physical and geometrical properties of the semiconductor determine the current. The higher the positive gate voltage, the greater the channel current.

Electrometer Circuit. The VMOS circuit is shown in Fig. 4. The 10-MΩ resistor on the gate helps to limit the charging and discharging currents. A resistor in the drain circuit limits the current through the light-emitting diode (LED). The brightness of the LED indicates the current that is drawn from the battery through the drain-channel-source circuit. It is also possible to measure the current by connecting a milliameter to the posts marked A and B.

A parts list for the VMOS electrometer is given in Table I. The parts are assembled on a small piece of perfboard with a 0.1-in spacing. The board is attached by bolt D to a piece of 1/8-in plastic as shown in Fig. 5. For convenience we used a socket for the VMOSFET, 330-Ω resistor, and LED, but it is possible to solder directly to all the components. When soldering wires to the VMOSFET and LED, a small soldering iron and a heat sink should be used. (A clip used to make wire connectors makes an excellent heat sink.) Be sure to use thin resin core solder.

Electrometer Operation. When the unit is first turned on, the LED usually glows and remains on. This effect is due to the presence of static charge that has built up on the gate sensing lead. In this case it is necessary to remove the charge by touching the sensing wire with one finger while touching another finger to post C (the ground). This straightforward procedure must be done whenever the LED

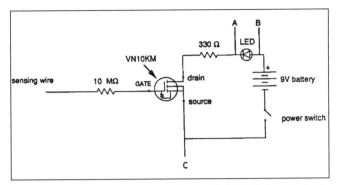

Fig. 4. Schematic of the electrometer utilizing a VN10KM FET. The cathode of the Zener diode is shown connected to the gate, and the anode is connected to the source of the VMOS Power FET.

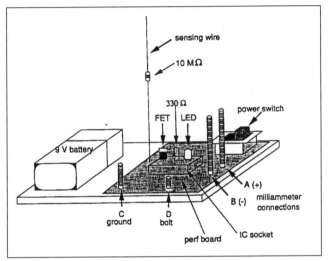

Fig. 5. Relative placement of the components of the VMOS electrometer. The polarity of the posts is shown for measuring the direction of the current.

glows and does not respond to a nearby charged object. The intensity of the light from the LED is proportional to the amount of charge. Positively charged objects brought within a meter or less of the sensing wire will cause the LED to glow. The closer the charged object, the brighter the glow until the LED glows independently of the position of the object. In this case, it is necessary to reset the VMOS electrometer as already described.

When a positively charged object is brought near the sensing terminal, a voltage is produced across the gate-to-source capacitor of the VMOS Power FET, conduction between the source and the drain occurs, and the LED glows. If the induced voltage does not exceed the threshold voltage of the Zener, there is no gate-to-source current. In this case, when the object is removed, the VMOS will stop conducting drain current and the LED will cease to glow.

If a sufficiently large positive charge is placed near the sensor wire, the charge will induce a voltage larger than threshold voltage of the Zener diode, and the diode will con-

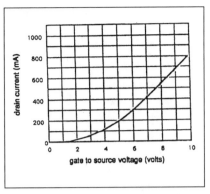

Fig. 6. Transfer curve for VN10KM Power MOSFET.

duct, allowing charges to go to the source (see Fig. 4). When the object is removed in this case, the LED continues to glow because charge has flowed from the gate circuit through the Zener into the source-drain output circuit. Since the balance of charge has been changed on the gate, a voltage difference remains to turn on the VMOSFET when the object is removed.

When a negatively charged object is brought near the sensor wire, the charge repels electrons onto the gate. When the gate is negative, the LED does not glow since a positive charge on the gate is required to cause the VMOSFET to conduct. The negative charge on the gate causes the Zener to conduct in a forward direction. If the negative charge is removed from the vicinity of the sensor wire, the gate becomes positive and remains so since electrons have been removed from the gate. The LED now glows. If the negative charge is again brought near the sensor wire, the LED ceases to glow.

Applications

On dry days, a positively charged rod will cause the LED to glow from as far away as one meter. Since the sensitivity of the device is good, it will work even on a damp day, although the rod must be brought closer to the sensing wire. The closer the rod is to the gate wire, the brighter the LED glows until the LED remains on whether the rod is present or not.

As already discussed, the LED also glows when a *negatively* charged object is moved *away* from the gate wire. This difference gives us a straightforward way of determining that there are two types of charges. For example, assume that an object is rubbed on a piece of wool. The device will easily detect the charge on the rod, but this device is so sensitive that it will also detect the opposite charge on the wool.

A number of other observations can be performed with the VMOS electrometer that are difficult to do with a conventional gold-leaf electroscope. Some of the observations that we have made include the following:

■ The device can be used to determine if the charge on an object has the same effect as the charge that comes from other sources such as a battery. A connection of the positive side of a 3-V source (e.g., two 1.5-V cells in series)

Table I. List of parts for the VMOS electrometer*

Part	Approximate cost
VN10KM FET	$0.59
330-Ω ¼-W resistor	0.08
10-MΩ ¼-W resistor	0.08
LED	0.40
Single- or double-pole slide switch	0.40
9-V transistor battery	1.00
9-V battery connector	0.20
14-hole IC socket (optional)	0.40
Perfboard	
Scrap 1/8-in plastic	
½-in 4/40 bolts and nuts	

* Various nuts and bolts are also needed as shown in Fig. 5. Most of the parts can be found at Radio Shack or at a local electronic parts store. Although many small parts come in packages that contain more than is needed for the device, the approximate prices given in the table are for a single unit. The VN10KM FET can be purchased from Active Electronics, which has retail stores in Santa Clara, CA; Chicago, IL; Westborough, MA; Woburn, MA; Detroit, MI; Mount Laurel, NJ; Long Island, NY; and Seattle, WA. However the minimum mail order is $25. If you have difficulty obtaining the FET, you may send $2 to the authors who will send you a tested FET.

to the sensor wire and the negative side to the ground (post C) turns on the LED. If the battery connections are reversed, the LED does not go on. This simple demonstration yields convincing evidence that static charges are the same as current charges, and therefore is an inexpensive alternative to some elaborate apparatus that use hundreds of volts to show this equality.

■ Another interesting demonstration is to determine whether it is possible to place opposite charges on different parts of the same insulating rod. Rub one end of a PVC pipe with plastic wrap and the other end with wool. Hold the pipe in the center and test both ends of the pipe with the VMOS electrometer. It would be interesting to determine how many charged spots can be produced on an insulating pipe or rod.

■ Make a capacitor using aluminum foil and waxed paper. Cut two pieces of aluminum foil, each approximately 25 x 5 cm. Cut two pieces of waxed paper somewhat larger than the foil. Make a sandwich of paper, foil, paper, foil, and roll into a cylinder. Put a piece of bare copper wire on each piece of foil so that the two wires become part of the capacitor and stick out enough to make connections to the foil. Charge the capacitor by connecting it momentarily to a battery. Does the capacitor have a measurable charge? Connect one side of the capacitor to the ground and the other side to the gate wire. Be sure the positively charged side of the capacitor goes to the gate of the device.

■ The device makes an excellent detector of the electric fields that surround TV and computer monitors. Students will be surprised to note the approximate intensity of the electric field near a color TV.

■ It is interesting to measure the field strength as a function of the distance from a charged object. Figure 6 shows that there is an approximately linear relationship between the gate voltage and the drain current for currents greater than 120 mA. Below this the current is nonlinear. Replace the transistor battery with a 9-V power supply and reduce the value of the 330-Ω resistor to 30 Ω. Then install a meter rated at 300 mA full scale across A and B. Also remove the LED from the circuit. In order to approximate a point source of charge, it is suggested that a small aluminum or steel ball be placed on the end of 25 cm of insulating material such as a PVC pipe. The pipe can be mounted on a small piece of wood.

Conclusions

We believe that the VMOS electrometer is a useful low-cost, rugged device for the study of static electricity. Further, it can be used as a "black box," and students will not find it essential to understand all the electronic principles involved. More information about its construction and use is available from the authors.

We thank S. Leslie Blatt and Harvey Gould for helpful discussions and careful reading of the manuscript. We also thank Joseph Priest for his encouragement.

References

1. See for example, F.M. Mims III, *Getting Started in Electronics* (1983). This book can be purchased through Radio Shack, catalog no. 276-5003.
2. *Small-Signal FET Data Book*, Siliconix Inc. (January 1986).
3. *VMOS Power FET Design Catalog*, Siliconix Inc. (1979).
4. *Power MOSFET Transistor Data*, Motorola Inc. (1984).

Electric Field and Gaussian Models

Richard S. Murphy *and **Charles Montefusco**,* Western New England College, Springfield, MA 01119-2684

Most people who have taught science courses have noted that three-dimensional models are more effective representations than the best of blackboard sketches. As an example, no matter how clearly we present our blackboard sketches of certain electric charge configurations and their associated Gaussian surfaces, there are always a few students who have difficulty visualizing the arrangement; i.e., their eyes get "glassy."

So to help the students' visualization we built three-dimensional models. Figures 1 A and 1 B are photographs of the models for spherical and cylindrical charge configurations, respectively. Figure 1C is a photograph of the model representing a charged capacitor. These models are made of plastic with the charged surfaces red and blue. The Gaussian surfaces are clear plastic to represent their imaginary nature. The area vector is represented by a suction dart.

Everyone in the class can now see the Gaussian surfaces and their physical relationship to the electric field lines and the charges.

Fig. 1B. A cylindrically charged surface.

Fig. 1A. A spherically charged surface.

Fig. 1C. A charged parallel plate capacitor.

The Automatic Electrophorous

R.A. Morse, St. Albans School, Washington, DC 20016

This inexpensive electrostatic generator demonstrates the principle of electrostatic induction and can be substituted for more expensive generators in many electrostatics experiments. It can be assembled rapidly using only simple tools and is a good project for students or for a teacher workshop.

Materials
- inexpensive phonograph turntable
- an LP record
- six aluminum soft drink cans
- a 20 x 30-cm (8 x 12-in) piece of fine-grain Styrofoam, 1.3- to 2.5-cm, (0.5- to 1-in) thick
- four plastic soda straws with flexible ends

- aluminum foil
- a glue stick
- tape
- fur or wool
- a 20-cm (8-in) length of 2 x 6-in lumber
- some screws or nails

Construction

Refer to Fig. 1 and proceed as follows. Tape four soda cans onto the LP record, standing them upright at opposite ends of diameters, tangent to the edge of the record. Put the record on the turntable. The edge of the record should overhang the edge of the base, or at least come within a centimeter or so of the edge. Fasten the Styrofoam to the side of the lumber using nails or screws to form the upright leg of an "L" with the wood as the base of the L. (You could just tape it securely to the wood block using masking or duct tape.)

Set the L next to the turntable with the edge of the record close to the foam, and mark the height of the top of the soda cans against the foam. With a pencil poke two holes in the foam 3 or 4 cm above the level of the tops of the cans, separated by about 10 cm. Take two of the flexible soda straws, crimp the long end of one slightly and slide it into the long end of the other, making a long "straw" about 30-cm long with two flexible ends. Make another such long straw; then use a glue stick and aluminum foil to cover the straws smoothly with a single layer of foil, leaving a flag of foil about 5 x 5 cm on one of the flexible ends of each long straw. Slide the straws through the holes in the foam as in Fig. 1. Adjust the straws so that the flag on one straw brushes the top of a can as it passes close to the surface of the foam, and the flag on the other straw brushes the top of a can about a quarter turn away from its closest approach to the foam. Take two more soda cans and bend their tabs upright. Hang these cans by their tabs on the ends of the straw projecting through the other face of the foam, as shown in the figure.

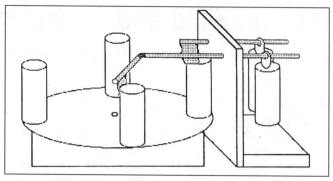

Fig. 1. The automatic electrophorous. This apparatus won second place in the low-cost division of the 1990 AAPT Apparatus Competition.

Operation

Slide the foam away from the turntable and charge it by rubbing it with a piece of wool or fur. Slide the foam back into position so that the moving cans pass close to the charged surface of the foam. The negatively charged foam induces negative charges to flow from the can through the foil-covered straw to the collector can, giving it an excess of negative charge. As the connection is broken by the rotation of the record, the now positively charged can moves on to the second brush. Since it is now some distance from the charged foam, negative charges from the second brush run back onto the can, thereby partially neutralizing the excess positive charge and leaving the other collector can with an excess positive charge. The moving cans take the place of the electrophorous plate in the process of charging by induction. The machine will work with only one can, but the rate of charging is improved with more. The collector cans can be connected to each other through a series of neon bulbs to see the charging cycle in action, or the charge can be collected with a Leyden jar. This generator can also be hooked up to an electrostatic motor. The flexible ends of the combined straws allow the flags and the other ends to be bent to adjust the positions of flags and collectors. Other devices can be connected to the collector cans and the generator can be used to supply charge for a variety of electrostatic demonstrations.

Toy Moved by Frictional Electricity

Akio Saitoh, 2085-22 Mise-Cho, Kashihara-Shi, Nara-Ken, 634 Japan

The "Owl With Unsteady Eyes" (Fig. 1) is a toy moved by frictional electricity. The mechanism of the toy is shown in Fig. 2. Two aluminum plates 18 cm x 11 cm) are fixed to a Styrofoam plate so that they are 1.5 cm apart and parallel to each other with their planes vertical. One of the plates A is connected to the large aluminum plate C (20 cm x 25 cm) placed on another Styrofoam plate; the other B is grounded.

A small metal screw and a U-shaped wire are attached to each end of a drinking straw. The straw is capable of rotating freely on a horizontal needle passing through its center of gravity. This needle is placed between the two plates as shown. A bakelite sheet shaped like an owl is attached to the two plates, A and B.

When a negatively charged polystyrene sheet rubbed with fur is brought close to plate C, a positive charge will be induced in plate C and will leave plate A negatively charged. Therefore, a positive charge will be induced in plate B, and there will be an electric field between the two plates.

The screw is charged when it contacts one of the plates, and it will then move rapidly backwards and forwards between the two plates as it transfers charges between the plates. The owl's eyes are connected to the U-shaped wire,

Fig. 1. Photograph of the toy called "Owl With Unsteady Eyes."

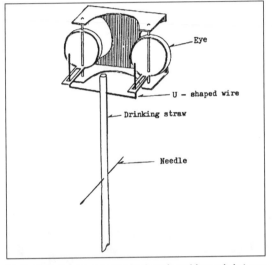

Fig. 3. When the screw moves backwards and forwards between the two plates, the owl's eyes also move.

as illustrated in Fig. 3, so they move back and forth as the screw moves.

This toy demonstrates the forces on a charged object in an electric field and electrostatic induction.

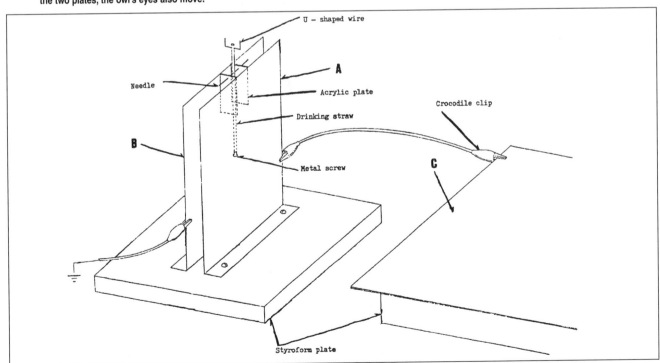

Fig. 2. The mechanism of the toy.

Lightning Rod

Wang Da-yuan, Lumiao High School, Hubei Province, China

A transistor radio that is turned to maximum volume, but not tuned to a station, will enable one to hear electrostatic discharges. This is accomplished by winding several turns of wire around the radio and then bringing an electrified rod (plastic rod rubbed with fur) near one end of the wire. If you quickly bring the rod up to the wire, a loud crack (static) will be heard. If you bring it up slowly, a series of moderate static noises will be heard. If the wire has a sharp point and you hold the rod some distance away, a continuous thin whistle will be heard.

The Kelvin Water-Drop Electrostatic Generator — An Improved Design

Se-yuen Mak, Department of Curriculum and Instruction, The Chinese University of Hong Kong, Shatin, N.T., Hong Kong

One of the most interesting and impressive demonstrations of static electricity is the experiment using the Kelvin water-drop electrostatic generator. When the electric field is building up, a downward water jet will change into a water spray around the bottom cans. A fascinating scene with threads of water falling along the electric field lines like an inverted fountain (Fig. 1) will be observed. The equipment can be connected to a number of gadgets, such as an electroscope, a neon bulb, the bell-and-chime kit,[1] or an electric windmill, to exhibit a number of electrostatic phenomena. These demonstrations will attract the attention, provoke the interest, and arouse the curiosity of every person over four years old. They also provide teachers a lot of questioning opportunities serving different purposes. Some will lead pupils to make careful observations; others will encourage them to construct hypotheses, develop explanations, and discuss their findings.

No one would deny that such a generator is an asset to have in every elementary physics laboratory. Unfortunately, the traditional design of the apparatus (Fig. 2) is not as easy to construct as described in the literature.[1,2] In particular, the mounting and alignment of tin cans of different sizes is tedious and time-consuming. The apparatus is also not as popular as claimed. Since its performance relies heavily on weather conditions, it is seldom used in places where air conditioning is uncommon (probably most high schools the world over) or where relative humidity is high almost all year round (as in Southeast Asia or England). The multi-can arrangement is also very bulky to store and not durable if iron cans are used. With all these hurdles, little wonder that a

Fig. 1. Water spray from one side of Kelvin water-drop generator (photo taken at temperature 24 °C, relative humidity 65%).

reliable commercial product is not on the market.

An Improved Design

We have built and tested a modification of the traditional water-drop generator setup, employing the same principle but with several advantages in design. The apparatus has been tested many times and has never failed to work for us when the humidity is below 80%. To build a similar apparatus (refer to Fig. 3), you will need:

2 *stainless-steel kitchen vessels*
 (In principle, any metal containers will serve. We chose the lunch carrier because it is inexpensive and readily

available to us in several sizes. Stainless-steel saucepans and their lids are another alternative. Aluminum vessels could be used.)

2 *insulating bases*
(Use saucers from plastic flower pots or lids from plastic containers.)

2 *mildly stiff PVC-coated copper wires* (of just sufficient length to criss-cross between covers and cans without touching each other or the bench)

2 *hypodermic syringes*
(Needles will be removed.)

1 *plastic strip*
(approximately 30 by 5 cm with clips at either end to hold the syringes)

1 *aquarium T-piece*
(Ours was originally used for connecting air hoses.)

1 *meter of rubber tubing*

1 *retort stand and clamp*

Note that in contrast to the traditional setup of Fig. 2, you need only two "cans" instead of four or six because the insulated bottom cans store both water and charge, and the middle hollow cans are replaced by the covers from the kitchen vessels. Moreover, the setup can be mounted or dismounted within two minutes, and once dismounted occupies very little storage space.

Construction Details

For the pair of bottom cans we substituted two seamless lunch carriers (see Fig. 4; one measures 18 cm in both diameter and height; the second 16 cm in both diameter and height, which means that for storage the smaller can can be placed inside the larger). Placing the plastic lids under each can bottom keeps contact between can and bench surface to a minimum. Also, if the diameter of the base is smaller than that of the can, stray droplets from the water spray that miss the cans will not wet the base; in that way the bottom cans remain well insulated during the experiment.

In our setup, the covers of the lunch carriers become the "middle cans." First we remove the plastic knob from the cover and enlarge the hole at the center (by pounding in a metal cone or using a round-headed hammer directly). The enlarged hole looks like the crater of a volcano. Such a geometry enhances the charge concentration near the hole and facilitates the charging-by-induction process.

We found that 1-ml hypodermic syringes make excellent water jets. First, remove the needle and cut off the opposite end (see Fig. 5a), which will leave a corrugated tunnel about 0.6 mm in diameter and 6 mm long. Install an insulating collar, made from a short length of rubber tubing, around the syringe and fit it into the enlarged hole of the cover (Fig. 5b).

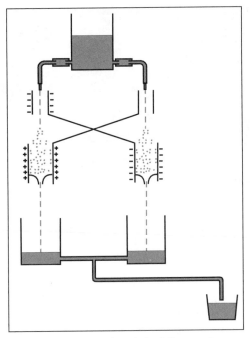

Fig. 2. Traditional water-drop electrostatic generator design with six tin cans. Mountings not shown.

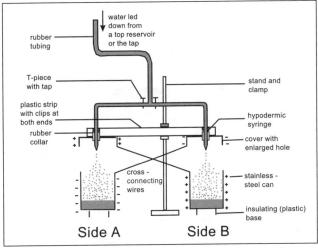

Fig. 3. Schematic of improved water-drop electrostatic generator setup.

Assembly

We hang a water container with an outlet about a meter above the can covers. (Water may be used directly from the tap if a steady flow at a low speed can be maintained for a long time, and if there is no dirt or rust in the water). As shown in Fig. 3, the water is led downward by the rubber tubing, branches at the T-piece (where rate of flow is controlled by built-in taps), and each branch of the tubing is connected to the top of a syringe. The outside of the syringe and rubber tubing must be kept clean and dry and connected in such a way that no water drips from the outside of the tubing.

Fig. 4. Apparatus components: stainless-steel lunch carriers, their covers, and syringes mounted on plastic strip.

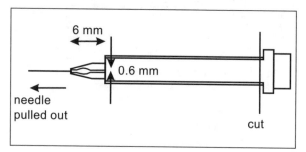

Fig. 5a. Modifying the hypodermic syringe.

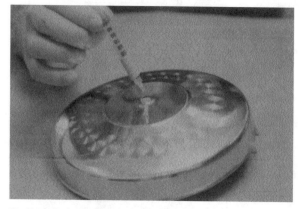

Fig. 5b. Inserting collared syringe into cover.

By clipping the syringes at each end of the plastic strip and clamping the plastic on a laboratory stand, the covers are mounted in the air. Position the two cans directly below their respective covers with the inserted syringes. Separations between the two cans and between each cover and bottom should be at least 15 cm. This ensures that the electrostatic induction between cans or between can and cover is negligible compared with the induction near the crater. In this way, the charge near the crater will not be pulled away by the charged cans.

The pair of copper wires, separated by as much space as possible, connect the right cover to the left can and the left cover to the right can. To obtain a steady flow, press the rubber tubing momentarily many times at the beginning of the experiment to get rid of air bubbles trapped in the water path.

As the flow starts, water running through the rubber tube and plastic syringe loses electrons by contact with the rubber and the plastic. To speed up the charging process, grip the A side of the branched tubing with two fingers and for about 20 seconds let the water run down only through syringe B. This water that has lost electrons gathers in pail B, providing a positive charge. Because of the wired cross connections, a positive electric field is produced in the region surrounding syringe A. That attracts electrons in the water column, causing the water flowing through A to be negatively charged, and driving positive charge over to syringe B. The water in can A thus becomes negative, which through the cross connections produces a negative field in the region of syringe B. The charges and electric fields thus build up exponentially.

In our design, the charged crater is separated from the running water by two thin insulating layers—the walls of the rubber tubing and the syringe. Although the electric field is weakened by the presence of the dielectrics, the distance between the water path and the crater has been reduced from about 5 cm in a traditional model to less than 2 mm. As a result, the electric field in the region acting on the water is much stronger in our improved model. As with the Van de Graaff generator, the water-drop generator should be cleaned with alcohol if it is to be used on a wet day. You may also want to blow hot air on the syringes to keep them dry.

Remarks

We encourage both high-school and university teachers to try this simplified version of a "classic" apparatus. Replace components with equivalents in the local market. If the new design is used as the baseline for improvement, the performance of the apparatus will rely much less on prayer.

References
1   *Demonstration Experiments in Physics*, edited by R.M. Sutton (McGraw-Hill, New York, 1938), pp. 261–262.
2. *A Potpourri of Physics Teaching Ideas*, edited by D.A. Berry (American Association of Physics Teachers, 1978), pp. 133–135.

Capacitance, Resistance, Circuits

Measuring Capacitance and the Dielectric Constant

Ellis D. Noll, Jacksonville Episcopal High School, Jacksonville, FL 32211

Although most teachers and students of physics have experimentally determined capacitance, an experimental determination of dielectric constant is less frequently accomplished in physics courses. This note describes an inexpensive transistor switch circuit (Fig. 1) by which capacitance and dielectric constant can conveniently be measured.[1]

Describing the Circuit

The transistors act as switches in this circuit. When one transistor conducts, the other is nonconducting. To understand how the circuit works, one must understand how a transistor becomes conducting or nonconducting. A transistor must have its emitter base forward biased for it to conduct. For the PNP transistor, both its base and collector terminals are negative with respect to its emitter when it conducts. Since the emitter base PN junction is then forward biased, an emitter base current exists. Consequently, an emitter to collector current exists also, since the emitter is more positive than the negative collector. (The presence of the 1.5-V dry cell produces a negative potential on the PNP collector and a positive potential on the NPN collector.) The NPN transistor behaves in like manner. When the emitter base is forward biased (base and collector are positive with respect to the emitter), base to emitter current flows, causing collector to emitter current. There are no special requirements for the transistors: however, they must be protected from overheating by the 200Ω current-limiting resistors.

Measuring Capacitance

To see how the circuit can be used to measure capacitance, start with the square wave voltage such that the emitter of the two transistors is positive and the base is negative. As explained before, the dry cell produces a positive potential on the NPN collector and a negative potential on the PNP collector. Thus, we start with the PNP transistor conducting. Since the battery and capacitor are in the closed loop containing the conducting PNP transistor, the capacitor is charged with its lower plate at the higher potential. Upon reversal of the square wave potential, both transistor bases

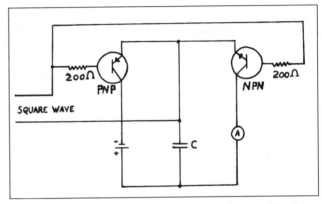

Fig. 1. Transistor switch circuit used to measure capacitance and the dielectric constant.

are positive while both emitters are negative. Thus, the PNP transistor is turned off. Only the NPN transistor conducts, causing the capacitor to discharge through the ammeter (0-100 μA). This charging-discharging cycle occurs at a frequency F of the square wave signal while a current I exists in the ammeter. The charge q transferred to the capacitor and delivered to the ammeter circuit in a time F^{-1} is

$$q = I/F. \qquad (1)$$

From the definition of capacitance, $C = q/V$ and Eq. (1), the capacitance for our circuit becomes

$$C = I/FV, \qquad (2)$$

where V is the potential difference across the capacitor (the charging battery voltage).

For a constant frequency F and charging voltage V, the capacitance C is directly proportional to the current I. Hence, once the current is determined for a standard capacitor C_1, an unknown capacitance C_2 is given by the expression

$$C_2 = (I_2/I_1) C_1. \qquad (3)$$

Also, a graph of current I vs. frequency F is a straight line of slope CV. Hence, the capacitance can be determined from the slope of this graph. Capacitors also can be connected in series and parallel to study the laws of equivalent capacitance.

Measuring Dielectric Constant

Replace the capacitor in Fig. 1 with two parallel metallic plates separated by a thin dielectric such as can be obtained from the wrapping on a cigarette pack. The thickness d of the dielectric can be determined by light interference, employing the traditional PSSC interference experiment.[2] The thickness of the dielectric is given by the equation

$$d = (N\lambda L)/2, \tag{4}$$

where L is the length of the glass plates and N represents the number of light (or dark) interference fringes counted per centimeter of length.

To determine the dielectric constant, an arbitrary but high square wave frequency will be required. Since the capacitance will most probably be in the picofarad range, a high frequency will be required to obtain an appreciable current, as predicted by Eq. (2).

To obtain the equation needed for determining the dielectric constant, start with the equation for the capacitance of a parallel plate capacitor:

$$C = (K\epsilon_o A)/d, \tag{5}$$

where A is the area of either of the parallel plates, ϵ_o is the permittivity of free space, and K is the dielectric constant. Combining Eq. (2) with Eq. (5) and substituting the dielectric thickness d from Eq. (4) gives:

$$K = (N \lambda I L)/(2 \epsilon_o F V A). \tag{6}$$

Conclusion

I have obtained good results with polyvinyl chloride, a plastic packaging material (K = 3.18). Mylar (K = 3.1) should also be a good substance for this experiment if you can obtain some in sheets as large as the capacitor plates.

Even if the dielectric constant of the thin film is unknown, the experiment is still valuable since students measure a quantity which has frequently received only mathematical treatment in our physics courses.

References

1. This circuit was originally described by R.G. Martin. See R.G. Martin, "An electronic 'reed switch'," *The School Science Review,* **62,** 117 (1980).
2. Physical Science Study Committee, *Physics Laboratory Guide*, 2nd ed. (D.C. Heath & Co., Boston, 1965). p. 33.

Printed Circuit Board Capacitors

Chris Emery, Amherst Regional High School, 21 Mattoon Street, Amherst, MA 01002

Capacitors may be easily fabricated using a commercially available double-sided printed circuit (PC) board. Using a capacitance meter to measure the value of *C*, students may verify the relationship between capacitance, plate area and dielectric constant, and thickness. Once the value of each capacitor is known, predictions for series- and parallel-connected capacitors may be made and compared with measured totals. Various lab activities provide meaningful methods of making the transition between the theoretical model of a parallel plate capacitor and actual circuit components.

Construction

Obtain double-sided PC board material from an electronic supply and surplus dealer or the local Radio Shack.[1] This material is easily cut with a hacksaw or jig saw, using a fine-tooth blade. Smooth rough edges with a file or sandpaper, then check to make sure that no copper foil pieces produce a short circuit between the two sides when finished. Various sizes and geometric shapes (square, rectangular, circular, etc.) are useful for challenging student computational skills. To obtain an accurate value of dielectric thickness, *d*, etch (using ferric chloride, also available from Radio Shack) a supply of small pieces of board and have students measure *d* with a micrometer. To facilitate electrical connection to each of the boards, solder a Fahnestock clip to each surface of the copper foil. These clips will accept banana plugs as well as various diameters of solid or stranded wire.

Operation

Cut a piece of 2 x 12 x 2-cm pine with several slots (approximately 0.6 cm deep) at regular intervals as an aid in mounting the capacitors for lab work (refer to figures). This method of supporting the boards is not necessary when making individual measurements, but it does minimize the effects of hand/body capacitance that can result from physically holding the board. In addition, when connecting the capacitors in series or parallel, this regular ordering of the boards (along with the connecting wires) provides a valuable visual reinforcement of series and parallel wiring schemes. Since the values of capacitance exhibited by these boards is in the picofarad (pF) range, avoid working on a metal desk or table; such a surface may introduce additional capacitance into the circuit. Figure 1 shows a single capacitor having a value of 934 pF connected to the meter; in Fig. 2, three similar capacitors are connected in parallel resulting in a value of 2800 pF.

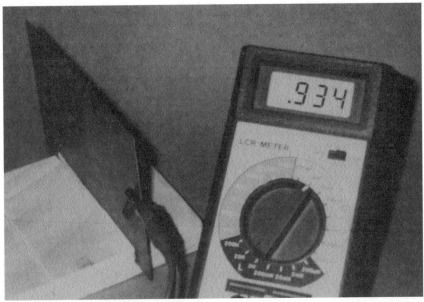

Fig. 1. Single capacitor having a value of 934 pF.

Classroom/Lab Use

1. Determining dielectric constant

Measure appropriate dimensions to determine the surface area A, and with a micrometer measure the dielectric thickness d of a piece of material from which the copper has been etched.

Measure the value of capacitance C, and solve for dielectric constant k.

Sample measurements and calculation:
d (thickness) = 1.57×10^{-3} m
l (length) = 14.8×10^{-2} m
w (width) = 11.5×10^{-2} m
C (measured) = 450×10^{-12} F

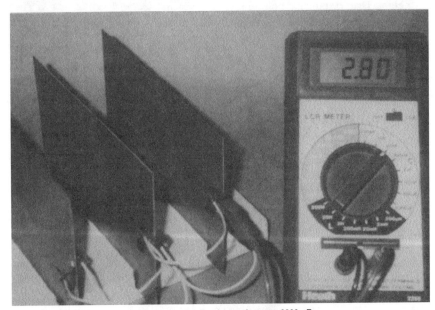

Fig. 2. Three capacitors connected in parallel. Total capacitance = 2800 pF.

$$k = \frac{Cd}{\epsilon_o A} = \tag{1}$$

$$\frac{(450 \times 10^{-12}\text{F}) \times (1.57 \times 10^{-3}\text{m})}{(8.85 \times 10^{-12}\text{F/m}) \times (170 \times 10^{-4}\text{ m}^2)} = 4.70$$

2. Determining values of irregularly shaped capacitors

Using the value of k and d just obtained, measure the appropriate dimensions of the capacitor to determine plate area. Solve for C and verify with a measurement using the capacitance meter.

3. Series- and parallel-connected capacitors

Having measured/calculated the values of capacitance for several pieces of PC board, connect them in series or parallel. Calculate a predicted value of capacitance, and measure.

Reference

1. Other sources of double-sided PC board include: Kelvin Electronics, 10 Hub Drive, Melville, NY 11747 and Omnitron Electronics, 280 N Midland Avenue, Building Z-2A, Saddle Brook, NJ 07662.

A Homemade Leyden Jar

Haym Kruglak, Department of Physics, Western Michigan University, Kalamazoo, MI 49008

The Leyden jar was the first artificial capacitor used by the early experimenters with static electricity. It was invented by P. van Musschenbroek in 1746 at Leyden, The Netherlands. He received a severe shock when he removed a bare connecting wire, and said he "would not take another shock for the kingdom of France."[1]

An effective Leyden jar for classroom use can be assembled with readily available and inexpensive materials.[2] You will need: a wide-mouth glass jar with plastic cover; an eye bolt; two nuts and two washers for the bolt; aluminum self-adhesive tape,[3] or household aluminum foil and rubber cement; a piece of flexible copper wire. Line the inside and outside of the jar with aluminum foil to about two-thirds of jar height. Drill or punch a hole in the jar cover and secure the eye bolt in it. Fasten the flexible conductor to the bottom

of the bolt so as to make contact with the inner conducting lining of the jar.

The Leyden jar can be charged with a basic Van de Graaff electrostatic generator[4] or Wimshurst machine. Capacitance of our jar is 0.6 nF.

References

1. F. Cajori, *A History of Physics* (Dover, New York, 1962), p. 125.
2. CENCO and Sargent-Welch catalogs no longer list Leyden jars of fixed capacitance. They still offer a dissectable Leyden jar.
3. Available in hardware stores as aluminum foil tape.
4. CENCO #31028G or its Sargent-Welch equivalent.

The Flexible Capacitor: An Electrostatic Demonstration Using Batteries

Robert A. Morse, St. Albans School, Washington, DC 20016 *and* **Diego Enciso,** Cass Technical High School, Detroit, MI 48201

An important problem of nineteenth-century physics concerned the identity of the several different kinds of electricity.[1] One part of this problem is to show that electrostatic forces exist between the plates of a capacitor as charge flows onto them, thus demonstrating the identity of static and current electricity. This note describes a relatively inexpensive and dramatic demonstration of this effect using a capacitor with one plate made of flexible aluminized Mylar™ film. The process was devised by the authors during work on the CASTLE project.[2]

For this demonstration you make a capacitor from a sheet (approximately 9 x 14 inches) of aluminum foil, a sheet of typing paper (approximately 8½ x 11 inches), and a sheet of 0.25-mil Mylar film.[3] Tape the aluminum foil to a blackboard or other flat surface; tape the paper over the foil, and then tape the Mylar over the paper, as shown in Fig. 1. Attach clip leads to the foil and the Mylar and connect them to a battery of about 200 V or more. When the connection is made, the wrinkled Mylar will be pulled tightly against the paper for about 10 seconds or so. With proper lighting, the

phenomenon is visible from a good distance, especially if large pieces of Mylar are used. The effect can be seen when as few as 150 V are used, but at 500 V the effect is quite dramatic.

A battery of several hundred volts can be

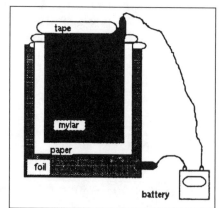

Fig. 1. The flexible capacitor.

assembled for about six cents a volt by snapping together a series of the least expensive 9-V transistor batteries you can find, or photoflash batteries of 300 to 500 volts can be purchased for about ten cents a volt from a good camera shop.[4] Although these batteries have a fairly high internal resistance, care should be taken to avoid electrical shock; you may wish to put a current-limiting resistor in the circuit.

A neon bulb in series with the capacitor will flash several times as the charging progresses, and there is sufficient capacity to flash the neon bulb on discharge as well. The charge and discharge process should be repeated several times so that students can be sure of their observations.

We have tried this demonstration with Mylar cut from aluminized balloons without success, and 1-mil Mylar is too thick to show the effect. Since the proper material does not seem to be readily available at retail, a 25- x 50-cm piece may be obtained from R.A. Morse at St. Albans School, Washington, DC 20016 at cost. Send $1 and a stamped, self-addressed envelope with your request.

References

1. M.H. Shamos, *Great Experiments in Physics* (Dover Publications, New York, 1959), p. 130.
2. M.S. Steinberg et al., *Electricity Visualized: The CAS-TLE Project* (PASCO scientific, Roseville, CA, 1990). Supported by NSF grant MDR-9050189.
3. Dan Sullivan of Dunmore Corp., Newtown, PA was especially helpful in obtaining for us large quantities of the 0.25-mil aluminized Mylar film known as 25 Dun-Met.
4. Mallory PF497, 510 V, about $50 retail; Eveready No. 493, 300 V, about $30 retail.

Solar Approach to Ohm's Law

M. H. Ansarizadeh and E. F. Walker, Texas Southern University, Department of Computer Science and Physics, Houston, TX 77004

As a result of a recent overhaul of our introductory physics laboratory curriculum, a solar panel with a flood lamp has now replaced the traditional power supply (or dry cell) in our Ohm's Law experiment. The setup incorporates the use of a flood lamp for activating the solar panel as part of a simple circuit illustrated in Fig. 1. Together, the lamp and solar panel function as a variable power supply having an output controlled by the lamp height (i.e., the distance between the lamp and the solar panel). The solar panel, milliammeter, and coil are connected in series, and the millivoltmeter is connected in parallel with the coil to allow for measurement of the voltage across the coil. In order to obtain optimum results, the lamp is aligned vertically above the panel and neighboring setups are spaced a minimum of 1 m apart. Routinely, a variety of solar panels, operating between 0.45 V and 9 V, purchased from the Edmund Scientific Company (101 E. Glouster Pike; Barrington, NJ 08007) are used. Using various lamp heights, voltage and current readings are recorded for further analysis in order to verify the proportionality between voltage and current in the circuit.

Experimental analyses completed with data collected using the solar approach compare very favorably with experimental analyses completed with data collected using a traditional, non-solar approach.

One outcome of the solar approach to the verification of Ohm's Law is that the solar panel and flood lamp together provide an excellent avenue through which inverse square law behavior may be demonstrated (assuming the flood lamp to be a point source). The output power generated by the solar panel varies inversely as the square of its distance from the light source, and students are able to see this relationship both analytically and graphically.

Both the Wilson textbook[1] and the Serway and Faughn textbook[2] are used within the physics curriculum at Texas Southern University. The Wilson textbook devotes an entire chapter to solar energy technology; the Serway and Faughn textbook devotes a section to solar houses in its chapter on

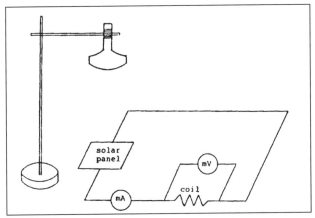

Fig. 1. A hood lamp and solar panel function as a variable power source for a simple circuit.

heat. There is little time in lecture to devote to these topics, but as a result of the laboratory approach described here and because they are of current interest students have been motivated to read these sections of these books on their own.

Thus, what started out as a routine overhaul of laboratory exercises resulted in a new approach for studying Ohm's Law and yielded a new experiment for demonstrating inverse square law behavior.

References

1. J.D. Wilson. *Technical College Physics*. 2nd ed. (Saunders, Pennsylvania, 1987), pp. 614–620.
2. R.A. Serway and J.S. Faughn, *College Physics* (Saunders, Pennsylvania, 1985). pp. 275–278.

Transient Lamp Lighting with High-Tech Capacitors*

Melvin S. Steinberg, Smith College, Northampton, MA 01063

Contemporary capacitor technology can provide enormous capacitance in compact nonpolar units (Fig. 1) that make transient lamp lighting feasible for instructional use. High volumetric efficiency is achieved by employing (a) etched aluminum plates with aluminum oxide dielectric and glycol-based electrolyte or (b) activated carbon granules with ion-permeable separator and sulphuric acid electrolyte. l have found that both types are useful in demonstrations and hands-on experiments designed to promote development of circuit concepts.

Aluminum capacitors are preferable for introductory student experiences because they have very low equivalent series resistance (ESR) and may be cut open to reveal simple capacitor architecture. In charge/discharge experiments, where optimum lamp lighting time is about half a second, I use 25,000 μF and 5,000 μF capacitors that have been manufactured to my specifications. Nonpolar aluminum units with this much capacitance are not normal production items, but they may be obtained from Mallory by special order (see below).

Transients lasting tens of seconds are desirable for investigating the transition from transient to steady-state flow. Because aluminum capacitors of the required capacitance are unacceptably large and costly, I use carbon granule capacitors which provide up to one farad in the volume of a pocket watch. These "Supercaps" are marketed by NEC as backup voltage sources for computers—designed to maintain working memory for up to 30 days in the event of power failure.[1] They have some ESR, which behaves like the internal resistance of batteries. Disassembly is not recommended, because the electrolyte is a skin irritant, and the stacked cell architecture may be confusing to beginners.

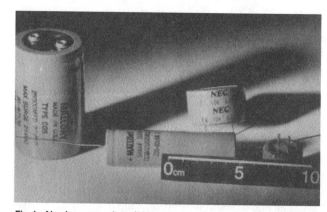

Fig. 1. Aluminum capacitors (20 V nonpolar): 25,000 μF (far left) and 5,000 μF left center. Supercaps (10 V nonpolar): 0.47 F right center and 0.10 F far right.

Applications

Charging and Discharging Processes. Hands-on experiments with the circuit shown in Fig. 2 provide evidence of electrostatic forces in electric circuits and of competition with electromotive forces. Some useful experiments are: (a) observation of half-second transient lamp lighting while the capacitor is charging and also when the capacitor is discharging after the battery is removed; (b) doubling the voltage by adding a second 4.5-V battery after the capacitor has been charged, which makes the lamps brighter during subsequent discharging; and (c) reversing the polarity of the

*Editor's Note: *Professor Steinberg's apparatus received a second place award in the 1986 AAPT Apparatus Competition in Columbus, OH.*

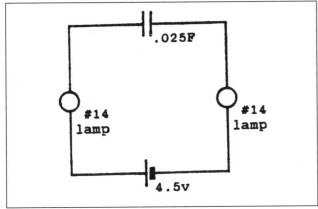

Fig. 2. Circuit for charging/discharging experiments.

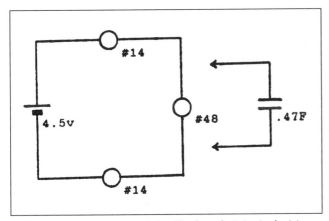

Fig. 3. Circuit for studying the relationship of transients to steady states.

battery after charging, which causes discharging (followed by recharging with reversed polarity) in which the lamps are again extra bright.

A less expensive 0.005 F capacitor can be used with # 48 (high resistance) lamps instead of # 14s to obtain approximately the same lighting time, though with some sacrifice of light output. Both lamp types have short warmup time.

Equipotential Property of Wires. Group activity: Parallel the 0.025 F capacitors for an entire class—all 10 or 20 or 30 of them—and charge to 4.5 V. Then remove the battery and short-circuit the capacitors while they are discharging very slowly through the # 48 lamp. The sudden lamp turn-off demonstrates that the shorting wire cannot sustain a potential difference for a significant length of time. Thus, a wire will, in effect, always have uniform potential.

Demonstration: This experiment may be performed with a 0.47 F Supercap. Note, however, that the ESR of this type of capacitor can prolong discharge sufficiently for the lamp to light up again if the shorting wire is removed too soon. Therefore, an instructor will want to hold the wire in place for several seconds.

Transient Processes and Steady States. Hands-on experiments with the circuit of Fig. 3 provide evidence that steady-state voltage division is established by excess charges built up during transients on wires and their metallic extensions: (a) The # 48 lamp is normally on and the # 14s are off. The on/off conditions suddenly reverse when the capacitor is connected across the # 48 and then slowly revert back to normal; (b) Disconnecting the battery, after the steady state is reached, reveals delayed turnoff of the # 48 lamp, due to discharge from the wires and capacitor plates attached to them: and (c) Repeating (a) and (b) with less capacitance then reveals why lamps in ordinary circuits turn off so rapidly. Try a 0.10 F Supercap first, and the 0.025 F and 0.005 F.

Purchasing Information

Mallory has agreed to supply the following etched aluminum capacitors by special order:

Part Number	Capacitance Max.	Voltage	ESR	Cost
CG253U020V3C3NL	25,000μF	20 volts	0.04 ohms	$8.61
TCG502U020N3L1N	5,000μF	20 volts	0.15 ohms	$3.44

I am indebted to Paul H. Forssander, applications engineer at Mallory's Indianapolis facility, for designing these capacitors and arranging for their manufacture. For minimum purchase of $200, and allowing 8-20 weeks for delivery, orders should be addressed to:

Mallory Capacitor Company
P.O. Box 372
Indianapolis, IN 46206

I will personally undertake to provide smaller quantities at cost.

Carbon granule capacitors may be obtained in any quantity from suppliers of Nippon Electric Company components. NEC calls these devices "Supercaps." The Supercaps of interest are:

Catalog Number	Capacitance Max.	Voltage	ESR	Cost
FA1A474Z	0.47 F	10 volts	4 ohms	$12.70
FA1A104Z	0.10 F	10 volts	8 ohms	$9.50
FAOH105Z	1.0 F	5 volts	2.5 ohms	$8.50

The 0.47 F Supercap is more expensive than the 1.0 F but is probably a better buy because of its greater maximum voltage and energy storage capability.

Maintenance

Supercaps have a 3- to 7-year life expectancy, limited by electrolyte dryout. The life expectancy of the aluminum capacitors is considerably greater (precise information not available).

The electrolyte of the aluminum capacitors may penetrate the dielectric over years of disuse, resulting in low-leakage resistance. However, the dielectric can be reformed by applying the maximum permitted voltage for a few minutes (until the leakage current drops). For preventive maintenance, it is recommended that this "forming voltage" be applied once a year for 15 min in each direction. Twelve D-cells in series, applied to one's entire collection of capacitors connected in parallel, should work very well for the 20-V units described above.

Can Markings

The nonpolar capacitors described here are placed in cans that were manufactured for use with polar units. Consequently, the cans will typically come with signs suggesting polarity. These signs should be ignored, however, for the capacitors really are nonpolar. To be reassured about this, look for "20VNP" stamped on the can or can sleeve. It stands for "20 Volts Not Polar."

Reference

1. A.J. Juodikis, "Supercapacitors Serve As Standby Power Sources," *Electronic Design*, Sept. 30, 1982, p. 159.

Making an Old Measurement Experiment Modern and Exciting!

Paul D. Schulze, Department of Physics, Box 7963, Abilene Christian University, Abilene, TX 79699-7963; schulzep@nicanor.acu.edu

Determination of the temperature coefficient of resistance of a resistor and a thermistor has been part of the introductory physics laboratory for years. I've been using a new approach that incorporates several advantages over the traditional method. These advantages include: teaching students how to linearize data in order to utilize least-squares techniques; continuously taking data over desired temperature range; using up-to-date data-acquisition techniques with standard laboratory equipment;[1,2] teaching the use of spreadsheets to analyze and graph data, thus eliminating many manual manipulation mistakes; enjoying a much more interesting approach than traditional methods;

and, getting reliable results within acceptable experimental ranges.

The apparatus list for this experiment is given in Table I, and a schematic of the experimental arrangement is shown in Fig. 1. The procedure is basically to (1) set up the apparatus, (2) heat water continuously over the desired temperature range, (3) transfer data directly from Vernier's Data Monitor acquisition program[3] to a spreadsheet, and (4) analyze and graph using linear regression techniques. If the teaching of spreadsheet use is not desired, an alternative approach would be to use Vernier's new Graphical Analysis for Windows® program.

The resistance of a resistor changes with temperature according to $R = R'(1 + \alpha \Delta T)$ or $\Delta R / R' = \alpha \Delta T$. For a thermistor this change can be expressed as

$$R = R' \exp \{\beta[(1/T - (1/T')]\}$$

or

$$1n(R/R') = \beta[(1/T) - (1/T')]$$

Here α and β are the temperature coefficients of resistance. For the thermistor, T is in kelvins. R' is the resistance at some arbitrarily chosen T'. Using PASCO's 6500 interface, the water temperature and voltage across the resistor can be read simultaneously on two analog inputs. If you use a current-limited power supply with the voltage turned to

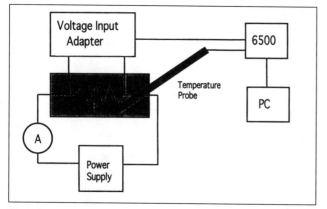

Fig. 1. Schematic of experimental arrangement.

Table I. Suggested apparatus.

1. PC – 286 or higher
2. PASCO CI-6500 computer interface (which includes Vernier's Data Monitor program)
3. PASCO CI-6508 input adapter box
4. PASCO CI-6505 temperature probe
5. PASCO PI-9596 student dc power supply
6. Sargent-Welch 2836X thermistor apparatus
7. Sargent-Welch 2836Y resistance coil
8. Spreadsheet or graphical analysis program capable of linear regression and graphing
9. Connecting wires
10. Optional digital multimeter (for setting and/or monitoring current)

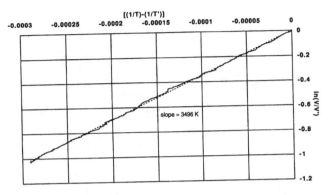

Fig. 2. Spreadsheet plot of ln $(\Delta V / V')$ as a function of $[(1/T) - (1/T')]$ for thermistor. Solid line is data; dashed line is regression line. Slope = β = 3496 ± 8 K. Accepted value is 3530 ± 80 K.

maximum and the current limit set to some reasonably low current, regulation at a constant current can be maintained as the water temperature is continuously changed. Since $V = IR$ with I constant, R can be replaced by V in the preceding equations. Then, $\alpha = (\Delta V/V')/\Delta T$ and $\beta = \ln (\Delta V/V')/ [(1/T) - (1/T')]$ for the resistor and thermistor respectively. Thus instead of measuring the resistance, the PASCO 6500 reads the corresponding voltage across the resistor or thermistor as a function of temperature.

Using a suitable spreadsheet or the new Vernier program, linear regression techniques can be applied so that α and β can be found from the appropriate slopes. For example, you can find β from the slope of $\ln(\Delta V/V')$ vs $[(1/T) - (1/T')]$.

Figure 2 shows a typical student plot of data for the thermistor. The experimental value for β was 3496 ± 8 K, which is well within the accepted value 3540 + 80 K.[4]

Similar results can be obtained for the resistor.

Teachers with different interface/data acquisition systems should be able to adapt this approach to their own systems so that their introductory students can also enjoy doing a standard measurement laboratory in this nontraditional and interesting way.

References

1. PASCO scientific, P.O. Box 619011, Roseville, CA 95678-9011.
2. Sargent-Welch Scientific Company, P.O. Box 1026, Skokie, IL 60076-8026.
3. Vernier Software, 8565 SW Beaverton-Hillsdale Highway, Portland, OR 9722-52429.
4. Sargent-Welch 2836X thermistor apparatus data sheet.

An Apparatus for Teaching Series and Parallel Circuits

Richard Forrest, Rochester High School, Rochester, MI 48307

Most introductory physics programs include a unit on series and parallel circuits. For the first-year student, it is a challenge to build circuits, measure values, and still clearly see the circuit layout. Breadboards offer a convenient way to build circuits, but the layout is usually difficult for beginners to see, and circuits built using loose wires with alligator clips are a virtual "sea" of wires and clips. Faced with this dilemma, I developed a series and par-

allel circuit board (Fig. 1) that easily accommodates various components and test equipment and allows students to readily follow the circuit.

The design employs a 25- x 33-cm piece of 6-mm (¼-in) plywood through which 24 holes are drilled with a 5.5-mm (7/32-in) bit. Drill the holes according to the pattern in Fig. 2. Insert the base of an alligator clip snugly through each hole. Following the pattern of heavy black lines in Fig. 2,

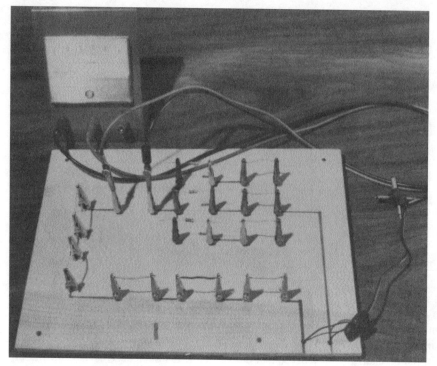

Fig. 1. Series and parallel circuit board.

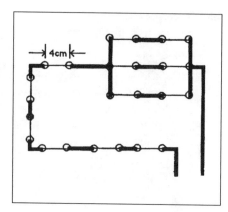

Fig. 2. Circles represent hole locations for 7/32-in drill.

use 22-gauge insulated wire to connect adjacent alligator clips underneath the board. Cut wires of sufficient length to attach to the screw terminals on the clips. Draw the heavy black lines in Fig. 2 on the board itself so students can see where the "hidden wires" are in the circuit. Next, the wire leading into the parallel section is twisted together, soldered, and taped with wires from the closest end alligator clips in the parallel section. Use the same procedure for con-

necting the three alligator clips on the opposite end to the wire leading out of the parallel section. The thin black lines in Fig. 2 represent "jumper wires" between clips on the top side of the board. Jumper wires can thus be replaced by ammeters, resistors, light bulbs, or other components. Alligator clips should be spaced about 4 cm apart along the circuit to accommodate jumper wires. A 3- to 12-V variable DC voltage source is adequate for most experiments. I use a 300-mA battery eliminator, which can be connected to the circuit board with a 9-V snap connector. Small wooden blocks can be attached on each lower side corner to serve as legs. Also, the portion of each alligator clip protruding through the bottom of the board can be crimped into an oval shape to prevent removal.

Using the Sound Board As an Analog-to-Digital Card

Kirk Hansen, Mark Harnetiaux, and Peter B. Siegel, Physics Department, California State Polytechnic University, Pomona, CA 91768; PBSIEGEL@csupomona.edu

Over the past few years, sound boards (or sound blaster cards) have become very inexpensive, and are standard items on most personal computers. Their primary use is for audio applications in multimedia and computer games. However, they can also serve as an analog-to-digital (A-to-D) card for data acquisition, and thus offer a very inexpensive way to interface computers with equipment in the laboratory, classroom, or at home. In fact, the line input to our sound board, Sound Blaster 16, is essentially a single-channel 8-bit A-to-D converter capable of sampling 22,000 times per second in direct mode. This data

logger is hiding in many computers, and we describe here one way we have used ours.

Reading the sound card can be done with just a few lines of computer code. For example, we read our Sound Blaster 16 card with the following Pascal lines of code run in DOS:

```
port[$226] : = 1;    {reset the sound blaster}
delay(3);            {wait at least 3 microsec}
port[$226]: = 0;     {reset the port}
delay (100);         {wait at least 100 microsec}
```

```
for i: = 1 to 30000 do
  begin
    port [$22c]: = 32;   {initiate the A/D conversion}
    while port[$22e]<128 do;  {check to see if the
                              A/D is done}
    x[i]: = port[$22a];   {store the signal in an array}
  end;
```

This program reads the sound card in direct mode 30,000 times in succession, with a sampling rate of 22,000 times per second for our card. Writing 32 (or 20h, which is a one in the fifth bit and zeros everywhere else) to port[$22c] initiates an 8-bit direct mode A-to-D conversion. When the conversion is completed, the seventh bit in port[$22e] changes from zero to one. So when port[$22e] is greater than 127, the data can be read from port[$22a]. The actual voltage of the signal is equal to (port[$22a] – 127)*5/127. Input can be done via the line or microphone input on the card. The microphone input has a built-in amplifier, whereas the line does not. In the direct mode it is best to run the program in DOS, since in a Windows environment the sampling rate might not be uniform.

In one application, we use our personal computer as an electrocardiograph. This is done by putting the (amplified) electrical signal produced by the heart muscles into the line input of the sound card. We amplify the signal using a high-accuracy 8-pin instrumentation amplifier from Analog Devices, chip number AMP-02FP.[1] A schematic of how the amplifier chip is connected is shown in Fig. 1. The gain, G, of the amplifier is given by the formula $G = 50{,}000/R_G + 1$. We used a switch for three different values of R_G: 50Ω, 15Ω, and 5Ω, producing amplifications of 1000, 3333, and 10,000 respectively. A sample signal from a volunteer is shown in Fig. 2. The noise level is less than one percent.

This setup provides an inexpensive (under $50) electrocardiograph to be used for biology or biophysics laboratory experiments. For example, sampling the sound board in a loop enables one to measure the time between heartbeats very accurately, to one part in 20,000. In Fig. 3 we graph the time between heartbeats as a function of beat number. The oscillations are due to breathing. These variations can be used as an exercise in statistical analysis, and we find a large range in the percent variance of the times for a subject at rest. For certain individuals, the standard deviation of the time between heartbeats can be as low as 2% of the average time. For others it can be as large as 15%.

Thus, the sound board can be a useful A-to-D card in the laboratory. Not only can it be used to record the students' voices, but also lets them put their heart into their physics experiments.

Reference

1. We purchased the Analog Devices AMP-O2FP from Allied Electronics, 11030 Arrow Route, Suite 214, Rancho Cucamonga, CA 91730. Call 800-433-5700 for the closest branch office.

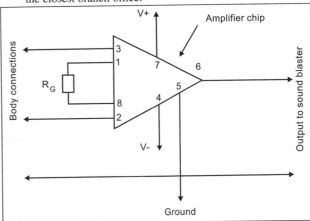

Fig. 1. Schematic of connections between subject, amplifier chip, and sound board for laboratory electrocardiogram.

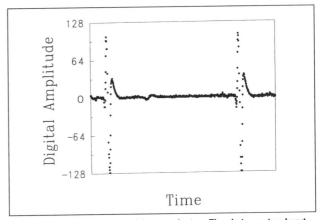

Fig. 2. Electrocardiogram signal from a volunteer. Time between two heartbeats is approximately one second. Vertical axis is the digitized signal from the sound board: port[$22a] – 127.

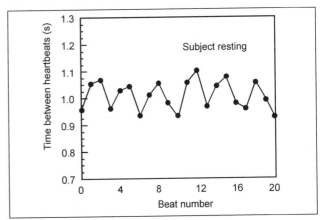

Fig. 3. Plot of time between heartbeats vs beat number for a volunteer at rest. Oscillations are due to breathing.

Building a Competition Buzzer Set

J.R. Dennison* and *Richard Davis, Physics Department, Utah State University, Logan, UT 84322-4415;
physjrd@cc.usu.edu

From the days of *The $64,000 Question, The College Bowl,* and *Jeopardy,* the quiz-show format has proven to be a highly entertaining and intellectual endeavor. Today, similar activities such as the *Science Bowl* and *Physics Olympiad,* or even simple in-class review sessions, provide physics students a chance for excitement, while fostering interest in the subject and honing the students' knowledge and skills.

Conducting such contests requires a buzzer set to determine which contestant is the first to "ring-in" with the answer. Commercial units are available, but the expense (from about $600 to $1000 per set) inhibits many schools from participating in contests or conducting in-class sessions. The Competition Buzzer Set described here provides an attractive, low-cost alternative that can easily be assembled by anyone familiar with building simple electronics projects. The set costs about $50 for all parts and requires about 10 hours for assembly, plus the time to fabricate the printed circuit board and program the logic chip.[1]

The set is comprised of a control box, a power supply, and handheld push-button switches (PBS) for two teams with four members each. The first button pushed sounds a buzzer and turns on a light that indicates which contestant pushed the button, the contestant's team, and position on the team. Buttons subsequently pushed will not activate the buzzer or additional indicator lights. This first light stays on until the judge pushes the reset button on the control unit; this clears the indicator lights and enables a new sequence to be initiated.

Circuit Description

A schematic of the circuit is shown in Fig. 1 and a complete parts list is given in Table I. The circuit comprises two integrated circuits (IC), a 556 dual timer[2] (U1), and a PLD, programmable logic device (U2).[3] One timer on the 556 is configured in an astable mode to provide a logic clock output for the PLD. The oscillator frequency is given by $v = 1.44/[(R_{19} + 2R_{20})C_3]$ (listed components yield 3300 Hz). The other timer is used in a monostable "oneshot" mode to

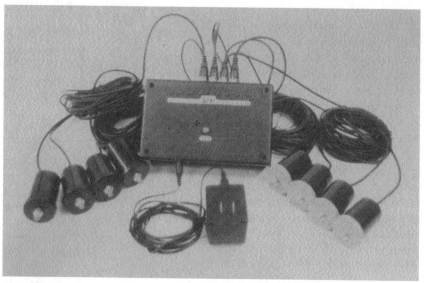
Competition Buzzer Set.

set the duration of the buzzer signal. The value of resistor R_{18} can be adjusted to modify the signal duration ($\approx C_1 R_{18}$; currently 1 s). A negative trigger pulse from one output of the PLD (pin 23) is fed into the 556 trigger (pin 8) of the second timer. The 556 output (pin 9) then goes high, starting the buzzer. After the preset signal duration, the output returns low, shutting off the buzzer.

The heart of the Competition Buzzer Set circuit is the PLD, which performs all logic functions for the circuit. A PLD is a user-configurable (programmable) IC that is capable of implementing digital logic functions.[3] The exact nature of the device logic is determined by the array gate and macrocell multiplexer connections assigned by using a PLD device programmer. A listing of the JEDEC programming file for this application is available on our Web site (see Ref. 1). The PLD in this circuit uses ten of twelve dedicated input ports; pins 3-10 are used for inputs from the eight PBS, pin 2 functions as the reset input, and pin 1 as the common clock input from the 556 timer to the edge-triggered D-type flip-flop of each output macrocell. Eight of the ten available macrocell outputs (pins 14–17 and 18–22) are used to drive the indicator light LED's (D1–D8). An additional output (pin 23) initiates the buzzer signal. Closing a PBS causes the corresponding PLD input and outputs for the corresponding indicator light and the buzzer to be asserted low (0 V). The outputs are latched by the D-type flipflops using the clock, which initiate the buzzer signal and cause the LED to remain lit. Subsequent input signals from other PBS do not affect the latched outputs, preventing two contestants from being latched in at the same time and two LED's to light. The reset button resets the D-type flipflops of the output macrocells and allows the PLD to be ready for another input.

Switch (S2) selects the power source, a 9-V battery (typical lifetime $\geq$ 15 hours) or an ac adaptor (P2), regulated with a +5 VDC voltage regulator (P1). An LED (D9) acts as a power-on indicator. Diode D10 is a reverse polarity protection device to prevent damage to the IC's.

Construction

The first step in assembly is to fabricate the printed circuit (pc) board shown in Fig. 2. The method chosen depends on availability of equipment, materials, and a darkroom, as well as your previous experience with pc boards. Mount all electronics components on the side of the pc board without copper traces, after drilling the mounting holes shown in Fig. 3. In order, solder the IC sockets (oriented with the notch in the socket corresponding to pin 1 of the chips), resistors (R1--21), capacitors (C1–4), three jumpers (A-A, B-B, and C-C in Fig. 3), voltage regulator (P1), diode (D10), reset switch (S1), power jack (P2), and buzzer to the pc board. Align the hole in the P1 heat-sink with the pc board mounting hole. Make sure the diode polarity is correct; if installed incorrectly, it will cause a virtual electrical short and may damage the power supply. Mount S1 so that the top edge just below the threads is ½ in above the pc board. The positive lead on the buzzer is connected to U1. Solder one lead on each LED, carefully line them up, then solder the other lead leaving ½ in between the top edge of the LED ring and the pc board.

Use Fig. 3 to locate and drill mounting holes for the reset button, LED's, the pc board mounting, and buzzer access holes in the control box lid (see Fig. 4). Cut out a square hole and drill mounting holes for the octal jack, the power switch (S2), and the power indicator LED (D9) on the side of the control box. On the opposite side of the control box, drill mounting holes for the battery clip. Use a 30-cm segment of 13-strand ribbon cable to connect the octal phone jack board, D9, S2, and the 9-V battery connector to the pc board, as indicated in Table II. Connect the octal jack shields together to a common ground. Mount the 9-V battery clip to the back of the box. Slip the ribbon cable into the square hole and mount the octal jack. Mount S2 to the box. Using LED mounting hardware, mount D9 to the box. Install the two IC's in their sockets on the pc board. Mount

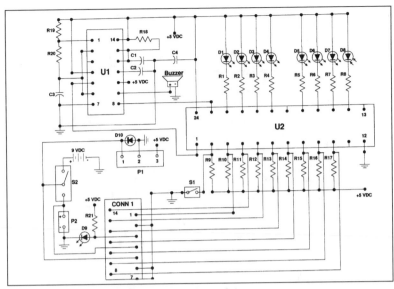

Fig. 1. Schematic diagram of the Competition Buzzer Set.

the pc board on the control box lid so that the LED's and S1 show through. Note that one mounting screw also secures the voltage regulator. With the board securely mounted to the lid, you can now drill the hole for the power jack on the side of the box.

Cut the RCA connector cables to make two leads each. Drill a small hole in the bottom of each film canister, just large enough for the cable wire. Drill a hole in each canister lid and mount the PBS. Solder the wires to the PBS leads, using heat-shrink tubing for insulation and reinforcement. Tie a knot in the cable to prevent it from being pulled out of the canister bottom. Color code the PBS, using grey lids for one team and black lids for the other team.

Acknowledgments

This work has been supported in part by a grant from the DOEd Dwight D. Eisenhower Professional Development Program and a project for the DOE Western Area Power Administration.

References

1. Two options are available from the Utah State University Physics Department: (1) a fully assembled and tested Competition Buzzer Set, or (2) a kit with some key parts (etched, undrilled pc board, programmed PLD and 556 timer integrated circuits, hardware, and detailed assembly manual). Details are available at our web site (http://www.physics.usu.edu/) or by contacting the authors.

2. For information see the manufacturers' specification sheets or standard electronics references, e.g., Forrest M. Mims III, *Engineer's Mini-Notebook: 555 Timer IC Circuits,* 2nd ed. (Radio Shack, Fort Worth, TX, 1989),

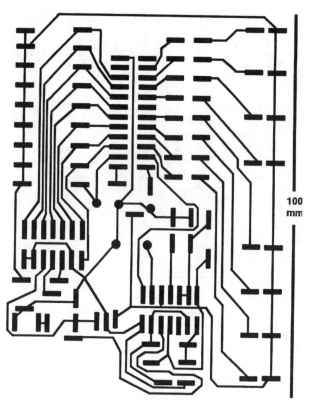

Fig. 2. Foil pattern for control box pc board.

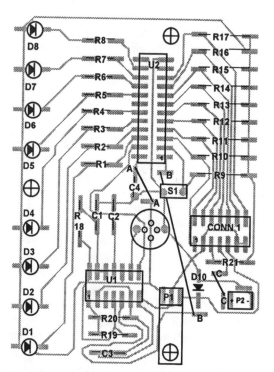

Fig. 3. Parts placement diagram. Diagram can be used as a template to drill mounting holes for the three pc board mounts (⊕), eight LED's (D1–8), four buzzer access holes (◎), and reset button (S1).

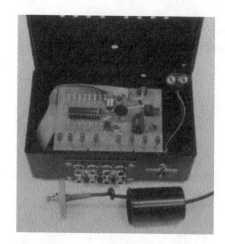

Fig. 4. Internal details of the control box and disassembled push-button switch.

pp. 6-7, or P. Horowitz and W. Hill, *The Art of Electronics*, 2nd ed. (Cambridge University Press, Cambridge, 1989), pp. 286-291.

3. A general discussion of PLD's is given in P. Horowitz and W. Hill, *The Art of Electronics*, 2nd ed. (Cambridge University Press, Cambridge, 1989), pp. 499-540. A much more extensive treatment, including specific details on the 22V10, is given in D. Pellerin and M. Holley, *Practical Design Using Programmable Logic* (Prentice Hall, Englewood Cliffs, NJ, 1991). Manufacturer's specification sheets also provide specific details on the device.

4. Possible suppliers include:
   Electronics Components
   All Electronics
   P.O. Box 567
   Van Nuys, CA 91408-0567
   818-781 -2653

   Jameco
   1355 Shoreway Road
   Belmont, CA 94002-4100
   800-831-4242

   Printed Circuit Board Kit
   Kepro Circuit Systems
   630 Axminister Drive
   Fenton, MO 63026-2992
   800-325-3878

   Hardware
   McMaster-Carr
   9630 Norwalk Boulevard
   Santa Fe Springs, CA 90670-2932

   Small Parts
   13980 NW 58th Court, P.O. Box 4650
   Miami Lakes, FL 33014-0650

   Radio Shack
   Consult your phone book for the nearest location.

Table I. Parts list. [4]

Label	Part Description	Quantity
Electronics Components		
U1	LM556N IC Timer	1
U2	22V10-25 Programmable Logic Device	1
PI	7805T +5 V Voltage Regulator (1 A)	1
D1-D9	Diffused T1-¾ LED's	9
D10	1N4003 Diode Rectifier	1
Buzzer	PC Mount Piezoelectric Audio Transducer (0–12 VDC)	1
C1	1 μF Ceramic Capacitor	1
C2, C4	0.01 μF Ceramic Capacitors	2
C3	0.0022 μF Ceramic Capacitor	1
R1-8, 21	270 Ω ¼–Watt Pull-up Resistors	9
R9–18	1 MΩ ¼-Watt Resistors (5%)	10
R19	1 KΩ ¼-Watt Resistors (5%)	1
R20	100 KΩ ¼-Watt Resistors (5%)	1
Other Electronics Parts		
SI	¼-in Momentary On Switch (¼ A 12 V)	9
S2	SPDT on-off-on Toggle Power Switch (1A 12 VDC)	1
	14-Pin Dip Solder Tail Socket	1
	24-Pin Dip Solder Tail Socket	1
	9-V Batter Clip Holder	1
	9-V Battery Connector	1
	9-V Battery	1
	9-V Power Supply 100 mA with 2.1x5.5 mm Female Plug	1
P2	DC Power Jack 2.1 mm	1
	28 AWG Flat Ribbon Cable ($\geq$ 13 wire)	1 ft.
	25 ft. Shielded Auto Cable-2 RCA Plugs	4
	Octal Phone Jack Board	1
	¼- to 1/8-in Heat-Shrink Tubing	1 ft.
	¼-in Red Heat-Shrink Tubing	2 ft.
	T1-¾ LED Mounting Hardware	1
Hardware		
	Round Head Machine Screw 2-56 x 3/8 in	4
	Round Head Machine Screw 2-56 x 5/16 in	2
	Round Head Machine Screw 2-56 x 7/8 in	3
	Hex Nut 2-56	11
	Washers #2	7
	Nylon Washers #2	2
	Nylon Spacer #2½ in long	2
	Rubber Feet	4
Miscellaneous Parts		
	Project Box (6" L x 3½' W x 1.88" H)	1
	35-mm Film Canisters	8
	3- x 4-in Printed Circuit Board	1
Estimated Total Cost		**$50**

Table II. Ribbon cable.

Cable Connection	Pin #
Octal Jack—Left PBS 1	11
Octal Jack—Left PBS 2	10
Octal Jack—Left PBS 3	9
Octal Jack—Left PBS 4	8
Octal Jack—Right PBS 1	1
Octal Jack—Right PBS 2	14
Octal Jack—Right PBS 3	13
Octal Jack—Right PBS 4	12
Octal Jack—Ground	2
+V to Power Indicator LED (D9)	3
Switch (S2)—left lead	4
Switch (S2)—middle lead	5
Battery—V (Gnd) and –V of D9	6

Magnets, Magnetic Fields

Measuring Magnetic Force and Magnetic Field of Small Permanent Magnets

J.L. Sandoval, A. Porta, and P. Segarra, Laboratorio de Acustica, Facultad de Ciencias, Universidad Nacional Autonoma de Mexico, 04510, Mexico, DF

Measurement of a magnetic field requires instruments that may not be available in some physics laboratories. However, students can measure the magnetic force and the magnetic B field produced at the surface of small permanent magnets and electromagnets by using a quite simple and inexpensive apparatus and implementing basic concepts learned in fundamental mechanics and electromagnetism courses.

This modest apparatus requires only three lucite plates [two squares (L_1 and L_2) and one circle (L_3)], a pair of

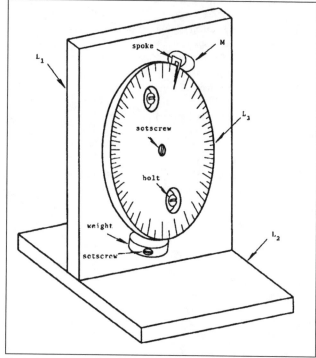

Fig. 2. Apparatus setup.

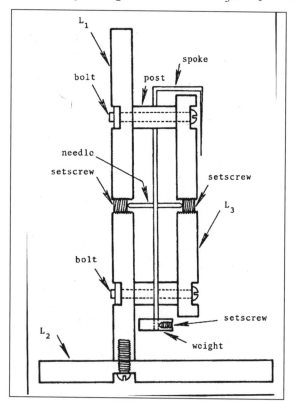

Fig. 1. Lateral view of the more relevant parts of the apparatus.

setscrews, a bicycle spoke, a polar sheet, a needle, and a set of known weights. Dimensions of the parts are irrelevant, although it is worthwhile to choose them according to the minimum scale division desired. For instance, if the minimum scale division required is 1°, the angular scale should be a polar sheet 16 cm in diam. The plates and the spoke may then be made about 3 cm larger.

Construction details are shown in Fig. 1. Setscrews are placed exactly in the centers of L_1 and L_3, and L_3 is held parallel and separate from L_1 by two lucite posts. The needle, which has pointed ends, serves as the axle at the middle of the spoke. This assembly is made by welding the axle

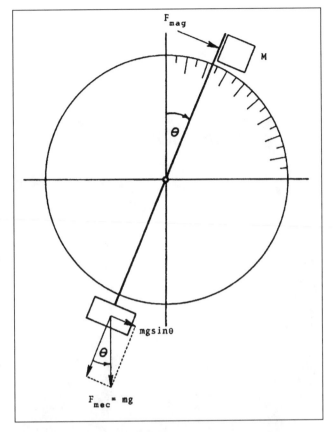

Fig. 3. Diagram of equilibrium forces.

into a hole drilled in the spoke. An angular scale of diameter equal to plate L_3 is cemented onto L_3. The pointed ends of the axle are held by setscrews, which are adjusted for free movement of the spoke. Plate L_2 serves as a support base for the system. Weights are made by cutting disks from a cylindrical bar, drilled so that they slide onto the spoke where they can be held by setscrews, as shown in Fig. 1.

When a magnetized body M is placed at the upper end of the spoke, the spoke is attracted (Fig. 2). When M is moved over the border of L_3, there will be a point at which the mechanical torque equals the magnetic torque. A small angular displacement of M therefore separates it from the spoke. As both arms of the spoke are made equal in length, the magnetic force (F_{mag}) equals the mechanical force (F_{mech}). Assuming the reference frame shown in Fig. 3, F_{mag} is given by

$$F_{mag} = F_{mech} = mg \sin \theta \qquad (1)$$

On the other hand, textbooks[1,2] on applied electromagnetics state that

$$F_{mag} = \frac{A B^2}{2\mu_o} \qquad (2)$$

where B is the magnetic field at the surface of the magnet and A is the contact area between the magnet and the iron spoke.

This is a mathematical expression that can be derived by dimensional analysis if $F_{mag} \equiv F_{mag} (B, A, \mu_o)$. Then, using Eqs. (1) and (2), B is written as

$$B = \left(\frac{2\mu_o \, mg \, \sin\theta}{A} \right) \qquad (3)$$

where m is the mass of the weight, μ_o the magnetic permeability, and A the contact area between the spoke and M, which is small but different from zero. In order to calculate A, we made the contact part of the spoke flat and 1-mm wide.

The uncertainties in F_{mag} and B, on the other hand, obviously depend on the minimum scale division. It is not difficult to show that their percent uncertainties are given by

$$\Delta F_{mag} \% = 100 \cot (\theta) \sin (\Delta \theta) \qquad (4)$$

and

$$\Delta B\% = \frac{\Delta F_{mag} \%}{2} \qquad (5)$$

Significantly, both uncertainties are functions not only of $\Delta \theta$, but also of θ. This implies that the apparatus is more precise for large angles.

Acknowledgment
We wish to thank Miss C. Miralrio for helpful revision.

Note: Readers interested in the details of the derivation of Eq. (4) or the derivation of Eq. (2), using dimensional analysis, should contact the authors. This information appeared in two unpublished appendices.

References
1. M.A. Plonus, *Applied Electromagnetics* (McGraw-Hill, New York, 1978).
2. I.S. Grant and W. R. Phillips, *Electromagnetism* (John Wiley & Sons, New York, 1976).

Oatmeal-Box Magnetometer

Thomas B. Gabrielson, Code 5031, Naval Air Development Center, Warminster, PA 18974

In the Spring of 1986, I built a portable magnetometer for a series of experiments on the polar ice cap north of Alaska. Because of severe restrictions on the amount of equipment that could be taken, the unit had to be small, easy to power, light, rugged, and self-contained. Also, since I did not have time to go through the Government procurement process, I had to build the unit at home; consequently, it had to be cheap. Fortunately, I needed to measure only the horizontal component of the Earth's field, which is very simple to measure.

The result was a magnetometer that easily met the design requirements and performed well in the Arctic. Over the next six months, I took the magnetometer to Nova Scotia, California, Hawaii, and Korea—collecting measurements along the way. The results were especially gratifying because they compared well with the model for the Earth's magnetic field used by geophysicists: the International Geomagnetic Reference Field.[1] Furthermore, I was able to locate and map a known magnetic anomaly a few miles away from my house. A subsequent error analysis of the magnetometer showed that the unit should have an absolute accuracy of better than two percent.

The project was simple, and it gave insight into a truly global phenomenon. Out of the conviction that this would make a good science project came the oatmeal-box magnetometer.

The principle of operation is simple: A compass needle aligns itself with the horizontal component of the Earth's field. (The direction of that component is magnetic North.) If a perpendicular field, still in the horizontal plane, is artificially generated, then the compass needle will rotate some angle away from magnetic North. If the artificial field is adjusted so that the deflection is 45°, then the artificial field is equal in strength to the Earth's horizontal field. In this design, a Helmholtz coil pair generates the artificial field. (A Helmholtz coil pair consists of two circular coils with the same number of turns and the same axis but separated along that axis by one coil radius.) The magnetic flux density generated by such a coil pair in free space is directly proportional to the current through the coils, and the proportionality constant is easy to calculate from the dimensions of the coil pair:

$$B = 64 \, \pi \, N \, i \, / \, (R \, 5^{\frac{1}{2}}),$$

where i is the coil current in milliamperes, R is the coil radius in centimeters, N is the number of turns in either of

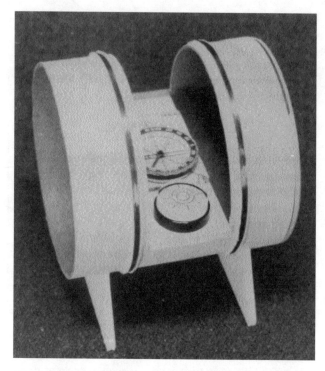

Fig. 1. A completed oatmeal-box magnetometer showing the Helmholtz coil pair, compass, and bubble level.

the two coils, and B is the magnetic flux density in nanoteslas.

The oatmeal-box magnetometer is shown in Fig. 1. Choice of materials is not critical except for the compass; use a good one with a jewel bearing (the Silva Polaris is inexpensive and easy to mount). In general, the construction is not critical either, but some care should be used to ensure that the coils are separated by a distance equal to their radius and to ensure that the compass (more specifically, the pivot point of the compass needle) is centered on the coil axis and the compass platform is perpendicular to the plane of either coil. Also, do not lose track of the number of turns in each coil as you wind them.

Glue coil guides to the oatmeal box for the first coil. I used 60 turns of #30 enameled wire for each coil fitted between 3 mm high guides spaced 3 mm apart. (To make the guides, I wrapped a loop of plastic tubing around the box, caulked along both sides of the tubing with bathtub caulk, and then removed the tubing.) Wind the first coil, then measure its diameter (mine was 13.7 cm) and position the second set of coil guides along the box a distance equal to the radius of the first coil. Wind the second coil. Cut out a semi-circular section of the box between the coils for the compass platform.

Using a piece of stiff cardboard or foam-core board, cut a platform for the compass. If the compass base is transparent, draw guidelines on the platform: Draw one set perpendicular to the coil axis and another set at 45° to the first set crossing at the coil axis. These guidelines will make aligning the compass needle easier. Glue the compass to the platform, centering it over the intersection of the guidelines. Although it is not necessary for demonstration purposes, if accurate measurements are required, glue a small, circular bubble-level to the platform. Glue the platform between the coils, making sure the compass is centered.

Connect the coils so that they are in series and their fields add. Connect a 1.5-V battery (AA size is fine) to the coil pair through a potentiometer (100-500 Ω), a switch, and an ammeter (expected currents will be less than 50 mA). Use enough wire so that the battery pack can be placed about one meter away from the compass and the ammeter can be placed well away.

To make a measurement, turn the switch off and level the assembly while aligning the unit so that the compass needle is perpendicular to the coil axis. With practice, holding it steady by hand works reasonably well. Next, turn the switch on and adjust the current until compass needle swings 45° away from original position. Read the current and convert to flux density. (The conversion factor for my unit was 787 nanotesla/milliamp.) If good measurements are required, level and align the unit on a firm, nonmetallic surface; take several readings and average the results. Stay away from all metal (keys, watches, belt buckles, cars, steel reinforcing in concrete). If you are interested in the Earth's field, take the measurements outside (even wood-frame houses have enough steel or stray currents to disturb the field significantly). Also, if you are using an ammeter with a needle and scale instead of a digital display, keep the meter at least 6 m away from the magnetometer—the d'Arsonval movement in these meters contains a permanent magnet.

Suggestions for Use

1. Examine the influence of nearby metal objects on the ambient field.

2. Find a local magnetic anomaly and map it. (At least 10% change in the total field will be required for a reasonable map.) Ask a university's geology department for help.

3. Take the magnetometer on long trips and measure the field.

4. Make a more rugged version, and mail it to other parts of the country or the world with instructions for making a measurement and returning it. For any substantial change in latitude, a correction for needle tilt will have to be made.

5. Compare measurements with the International Geomagnetic Reference Field (IGRF85) or recent magnetic maps. Send me a blank disk and a mailer to get an IBM-PC version of IGRF85.

There are, of course, many interesting issues connected with the study of the Earth's magnetic field, and this demonstration magnetometer can be used to stimulate a study. The field-balance method of measurement is easy to understand and gives an absolute measure of the field without complicated equipment. A more detailed investigation might involve an estimate of the instrument error or a consideration of the effects of needle tilt in the vertical plane. Several other approaches are also practical for introductory courses.[2,3,4]

References

1. For more information on IGRF85, write to National Space Science Data Center, World Data Center A for Rockets and Satellites, Code 630.2, Goddard Space Flight Center, Greenbelt, MD 20771.

2. J.E. Fredrickson. "Magnetic field of earth and magnetic dipole moment—an experiment," *Am. J. Phys.*, **43**, 186–187, 1975).

3. Paul A. Bender, "Measuring magnetic fields with an IC chip in the introductory lab," *Am. J. Phys.*, **54**, 89–90 (1986).

4. David T. Kagan, "Measuring the Earth's magnetic field in an introductory laboratory with a spinning coil," *Phys. Teach.* **24**, 423–424 (1986).

Charge Amplifier Type of Flux Meter

B.D. Sukheeja *and* **D.K. Kohli,** Department of Applied Physics, Regional Engineering College, Kurukshetra-132 119, India

Measurement of magnetic flux density between the pole pieces of an electromagnet is a common laboratory requirement, and for this purpose instruments based upon the search coil have long been used.[1] Such flux meters employ a fragile suspended coil, the angular throw of which measures the charge pulse. Recently, Hall-effect magnetometers have become available, which always require a fresh calibration because of a strong dependence of the Hall coefficient of semiconductors on temperature. There is also some difficulty in soldering contacts to the semiconductor. The authors have found that it may be useful to revert to the use of the search coil along with an integrated circuit operational amplifier as a charge amplifier[2] to measure the charge pulse.

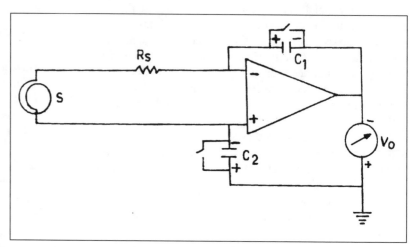

Fig. 1. Circuit diagram of the charge amplifier type of flux meter.

Consider the circuit shown in Fig. 1. The search coil, S, is held normal to the field and the capacitors C_1 and C_2 are discharged by a double-pole pushbutton. When the coil is taken out of the field, the induced emf brings about a circulation of charge, and charges the capacitors with the polarity shown in the figure. Assuming negligible current in the operational input terminals, the amount of charge, Q, which circulates and charges C_1 and C_2 to voltages V_1 and V_2, is given by $Q = BA\, n/R = C_1 V_1 = C_2 V_2$, where B = magnetic flux density, A = mean area of the search coil, n = number of turns in the same coil, and R = sum of the search coil resistance and the series resistance, R_s.

The output voltage is $V_o = V_1 + V_2$, as the two input terminals of the operational amplifier are virtually at the same potential. For convenience let $C_1 = C_2 = C$, giving $V_1 = V_2 = V$.

Thus $BA\, n/R = CV = \tfrac{1}{2}CV_o$ and $B = RCV_o/2An = KV_o$, where $K = RC/2An$.

There is a linear relationship between the meter reading and the flux density. The constant, K, can be obtained from the constants of the apparatus or by comparison with a standard flux meter, but frequent calibration is not required. The instrument can be made multirange by using different values of R_s.

In a conventional flux meter, the search coil has to be removed from the field quickly with a jerk. In the present instrument it can be removed smoothly, since the capacitors will hold the total integrated charge. The stability of the output voltage, V_o, depends on the difference between the two input bias currents of the operational amplifier and can be improved with the use of an FET input type.

The authors have assembled the apparatus using an operational amplifier (536) and the following components: R = 10 kΩ, $C_1 = C_2 = 100$ μF, the number of turns in the search coil = 1000 (AWG 40), and the mean area of the search coil = 9.62 cm^2. The resulting $K = 0.52$ T/V. For this arrangement the output voltage, V_o, was found to be 1.9 V/T of flux density.

Reference

1. S.G. Starling, *Electricity and Magnetism* (Longmans Green, London, 1962), p. 266.
2. J.G. Graeme and G.E. Tobey, *Operational Amplifiers, Design and Applications* (McGraw-Hill Kogakusha Ltd. Tokyo, 1971), pp. 233–235.

Measuring the Magnetic Force on a Current-Carrying Conductor

W. Herreman, Faculty of Science, K.U. Leuven Campus Kortrijk, 8500 Kortrijk, Belgium, *and*

R. Huysentruyt, Instituut O. L. Vr. van Bijstand, 8500 Kortrijk, Belgium

The magnetic force acting on a current-carrying conductor can be measured by means of a current balance, but depending on the type of balance, the experimental investigation is sometimes very time consuming. What follows is a fast and simple method for such measurement that makes use of an ordinary digital balance, which can register changes of 0.01 g, corresponding to a force of 0.1 mN.

Method

Place a wooden holder containing two small bar magnets[1] (10 x 15 x 75 mm) on the digital balance.[2] The bar magnets are parallel, with the opposite poles facing. The total mass is 205 g. Place a conducting wire between the poles (Fig. 1).

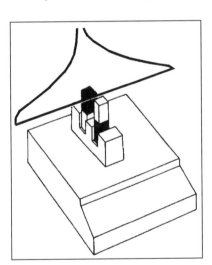

Fig. 1. Measuring the magnetic force by means of a digital balance.

By means of the tare key, bring the indicator on the balance to 0.00 g. The moment a current passes through the wire, the balance indicates a value different from zero. In fact the balance measures the reaction force opposite to the magnetic force. Indeed, a magnetic force is exerted on the wire, which in turn exerts a force on the magnets. This force is measured by the balance as an increase or decrease of mass depending on the direction of the current. In order to get the force in mN, the value indicated on the balance must be multiplied by 9.81 (in Belgium).

Results

I. Influence of current intensity

In a first experiment the distance between the magnetic poles was 10.5 mm and the length of the wire between the poles $\ell_1 = 15.1$ mm. The results are given in Table I. The magnetic force is directly proportional to the current intensity, as is also shown in Fig. 2.

The results of an analogous experiment with an identical pair of bar magnets are given in Table II. The distance between the poles was also 10.5 mm, but the length of the wire between the poles $\ell_2 = 15.3$ mm.

Results of both experiments are needed to investigate the influence of the length of the wire at a constant-current intensity.

II. Influence of wire length

Table I. Magnetic force on a wire (ℓ_1 = 15.1 mm) placed between the poles of a pair of bar magnets.

I (A)	Balance Reading (g)	F(mN)
1.0	0.26	2.6
2.0	0.52	5.1
4.0	1.05	10.3
6.0	1.57	15.4
8.0	2.07	20.3
10.0	2.60	25.5

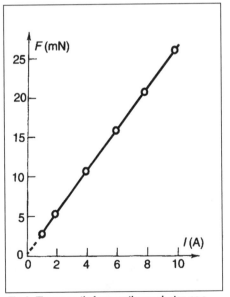

Fig. 2. The magnetic force on the conductor as a function of the current intensity.

Table II. Magnetic force on the wire ($\ell_2 = 15.3$ mm) using another pair of magnets identical with those used in Table I.

I (A)	Balance Reading (g)	F(mN)
1.0	0.24	2.4
2.0	0.48	4.7
4.0	0.98	9.6
6.0	1.45	14.2
8.0	1.93	18.9
10.0	2.39	23.4

Table III. Magnetic force on the wire with a total length $\ell = \ell_1 + \ell_2 = 30.4$ mm.

I (A)	Balance Reading (g)	F(exp) (mN)	F(calc) (mN)
1.0	0.50	4.9	4.9
2.0	1.01	9.9	9.8
4.0	1.99	19.5	19.9
6.0	2.98	29.2	29.6
8.0	3.91	38.4	39.2
10.0	4.90	48.1	49.0

Both pairs of magnets were then placed on the balance at a distance of about 10 cm from each other. This distance is necessary to avoid mutual influence of the magnetic fields of both pairs of magnets. Table III gives the results of the measured magnetic force (F_{exp}) and the sum of the results (F_{calc}) obtained in the previous experiments (Tables I and II). From Table III we can conclude that at any constant current the magnetic force on the wire is directly proportional to the length of the wire in the magnetic field.

Comments

It is possible to measure the magnetic force on a current-carrying conductor by means of this simple experimental setup. The influence of the direction of the current, as well as the direction of the magnetic field intensity on the direction of the exerted force is immediately known since the value indicated on the balance is preceded by a plus or a minus sign.

We have discussed the influence of I and ℓ in a constant magnetic field, and by changing the distance between the magnetic poles at constant I and ℓ investigated the influence of the magnetic field intensity on the value of the magnetic force. These data are not included in the text but can be obtained from the authors.

References

1. Alnico magnets from Eurofysica, 's Hertogenbosch, The Netherlands.
2. Balance from Sartorius, model BA 3100P, Göttingen, Germany.

Determine the Magnetic Induction of a Coil with a Hall Element

An Zhong, Eastern Illinois University, Charleston, IL 61020

In this experiment we use a Hall element to measure the magnetic induction along the axis of a cylindrical coil. The apparatus and setup are shown in Fig. 1.

When a current-carrying strip of material is placed in a magnetic field (B), a potential difference (V_H) is generated across two points in the material that lie on a line perpendicular to the current (I) and to the field. This potential can be expressed as $\vec{V}_H = R\,(\vec{I} \times \vec{B})$, where R is the Hall coefficient. The charge carriers in the material are directed by the Lorentz force to move perpendicular to the applied emf. An understanding of the Hall effect is necessary in the study of thermoelectricity and photoelectricity, and so the Hall element becomes as important a transducer as the thermo-couple and the photocell.

The potential difference across the crystal is proportional to the current passing through it. The current also produces joule heating at the junctions between electrodes and crystal. A potential difference between the junctions occurs when a temperature gradient is set up along the sample. These thermoelectric phenomena are known as the Peltier, the Seebeck, and the Thomson effects.[1] The Hall voltage V_H will include these other voltages. These subordinate voltages, however, are several orders of magnitude less than the Hall voltage and may be neglected under conditions of a weak field and room temperature.[2]

If the Hall probes are not exactly opposite each other, a

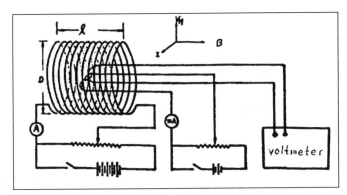

Fig. 1. A schematic of the experimental setup.

voltage V_o will be produced, which depends on the current only. This V_o may be measured before the magnetic field is established, and then V_H can be separated from V_{Ho} when the field is applied. Students are given the value of the Hall coefficient R of the crystal they are using. By placing the Hall element on the axis at the center and at the end of the cylindrical coil, the magnetic induction may be determined at these positions for a given current.

References

1. E.H. Putley, *The Hall Effect and Related Phenomena* (Butterworths, London, 1960), pp. 23–64, 99–101.
2. K. Seeger, *Semiconductor Physics* (Springer-Verlag, New York, 1982), pp. 58–61, 91–96.

Magnetic Fields in a Slinky™

Colin Terry, Physics Department, Ventura College, Ventura, CA 93003

The availability of inexpensive Hall effect magnetic field probes interfaced to a microcomputer provides students with a simple and direct method of investigating magnetic fields due to various configurations of electric currents. One of the most useful activities involves measuring the magnetic field in and around a solenoidal Slinky spring toy carrying a current of a few amps.

The advantage of a Slinky over a regular solenoid is that students can investigate the field within the coil by inserting the probe between adjacent turns. They can see how the field varies along the axis, how the field in the center compares with that at the ends, and how it varies across the width of the solenoid. A Slinky also provides a simple way to investigate how the field depends on the number of turns per unit length by "stretching" or "compressing" the coil. Plastic strips can be used to hold the Slinky in place as shown in Fig. 1.

Figure 2 shows some data obtained with a Vernier magnetic field sensor. About a 1-m length of the Slinky was used; current through the coil was about 6 amps, (enough to cause the coil to get quite hot if the current is left on for an extended period of time)! The upper diagram shows how uniform the field is across the width of the coil. The coil spacing was about 2 cm in this case. The lower graph illustrates how the field depends on the number of turns per meter of the Slinky coil. With the somewhat irregular coils of the Slinky, especially near the attachment points of the current connectors, it is a little more difficult to accurately position the probe at the end of the solenoid. Nevertheless,

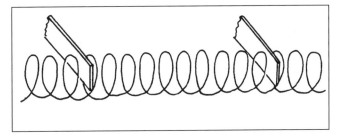

Fig. 1.

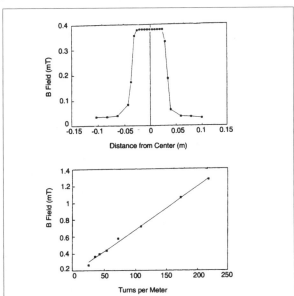

Fig. 2. Top: B field inside Slinky; Bottom: B field vs turns density.

with the configuration used, the probe reading at the end can be shown to be close to half the value deep inside the solenoid. The Vernier magnetic field sensor comes with a plastic protective cover, which we removed so that the Hall slice could be more easily oriented in appropriate directions.

Note: The magnetic field probe we used is available from Vernier Software, 8565 SW Beaverton-Hillsdale Highway, Portland, OR 97225-2429. 503–297-5317, FAX: 503-297-1760. Similar probes are available from PASCO, 10101 Foothills Boulevard, P.O. Box 619011, Roseville, CA 95678-9011. 916-786-3800 FAX: 916-786-8905.

Magnetohydrodynamics on a Tabletop

Esi Morgan, Germantown Friends School, Philadelphia, PA 19144

In a magnetohydrodynamics generator (MHD), a current is induced by a conducting fluid moving through a magnetic field. Conversely, a current may interact with a magnetic field to produce a force that acts on the fluid to create motion. If the current was in a wire, the force on the wire would be used for the motion of a motor. However, in a fluid this force creates an MHD pump. Large-scale models could be employed as coolers in nuclear reactors, with the conducting fluid a liquid metal such as mercury or a sodium-potassium alloy absorbing heat as it travels through the system. There are also experiments using the effect to propel ships and submarines.[1]

A demonstration model illustrating MHD is shown in Fig. 1. The following materials are required:

- salt solution (50 g/l of water works well)
- batteries (two 6-V lantern batteries or a power supply)
- large permanent or electro-magnet (horseshoe shaped)
- open circular trough (obtained by using the channel at the bottom of a cut-down plastic dog dish. The groove in some plastic container lids could be also used.)
- electrodes (see Fig. 2.) A 16-pin wire wrap socket (Radio Shack-Archer Cat. No. 276-1994) with a dip head (Radio Shack-Archer Cat. 26-1980) snapped to the top, so that the 8 pins on each side can be easily soldered to a wire lead. This has the advantage of keeping the electrodes nicely spaced, but there are other possibilities. Multistranded copper wires, with the ends fanned out, can be used as well.

To construct an MHD pump, place the electrodes in the circular plastic container, and position a magnet so that the magnetic field will be perpendicular to the electric field between the electrodes. Fill the trough to just below the top of the electrodes with the salt solution, and connect the electrodes to the power source. The potential difference causes the positive and negative ions in the solution to move toward opposite electrodes. The magnetic field acting on the moving ions creates a force which propels the fluid around the

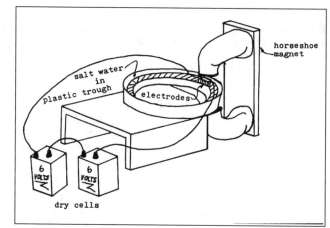

Fig. 1. Experimental setup for MHD pump.

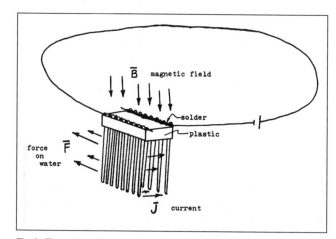

Fig. 2. Electrodes with interacting and resultant vectors.

trough.

Hydrogen gas is released from the cathode, and the hydroxide ions created react with this electrode to form a precipitate. This precipitate is actually beneficial as it highlights the motion of the solution.

This is a simple but clear way to demonstrate the natural principle of the production of a force from such an interaction as described in textbooks. Various combinations of voltages [current density $(\vec{J})$] and magnetic field strengths $(\vec{B})$ will produce predictable able changes in the force exerted and thus the speed of the fluid flow $(\vec{F} = \vec{J} \times \vec{B})$.

In the model constructed, movement was detected with as little as 6 V from a battery, and a large magnet (approx. 0.2 teslas). However, in switching to a smaller magnet (about 0.13 teslas), to get the same flow, a larger potential difference was required.

This model can be easily manipulated. Switching the positions of the poles of the magnet will reverse the flow of the fluid. Reversing the current while maintaining the position of the magnet will give the same effect. The students can predict these results with the right-hand rule.

This model takes minutes to assemble or disassemble and is well worth the effort to demonstrate very graphically and dramatically some important principles of physics.

The following demonstration is another version of this well-known phenomena. Rather than using a channel with a limited pump area of electrodes and magnet, others have used a flat circular dish with one electrode a strip of zinc[2] or copper[3] lined all the way around the inside of the dish. A second electrode is placed on the axis at the center of the dish. A conducting salt solution is placed in the region between the electrodes. A strong bar magnet is held vertically over or under the center of the dish, causing the fluid to rotate about the axial electrode when current is passed through the system. Some cork filings may be floated on the surface of the solution. The images of these bits of cork may be projected onto a screen by vertical projection.[4]

Acknowledgments

Allan Feldman, Germantown Friends School, Science Department Head, my physics teacher and project advisor.

James Drew, Montgomery County Community College, PA, for his assistance with the first models (mercury then salt water).

F. Jack Malone, Montgomery County Community College, PA, for consultation.

W.C. Connolly, editor of the TPT Apparatus Column, for bringing Ref. 2 and 3 to my attention.

References

1. John Langone, *Discover*, **6** (4), 42–48 (1985).
2. R.M. Sutton, *Demonstration Experiments in Physics* (McGraw-Hill, 1938), p. 330.
3. G.D. Freier and F.J. Anderson, *A Demonstration Handbook for Physics*, (University of Minnesota, 1971), p. 99.
4. Sutton, p. 330.

Induced emf, Lenz's Law

Using LED's To Demonstrate Induced Current

C. Lopez and *P. Gonzalo,* I.B. Lope de Vega, San Bernardo 60, Madrid, Spain

When studying Faraday's law, there are many demonstrations that can be used to show the existence of induced currents but not many of these indicate the current direction as given by Lenz's Law. Light emitting diodes (LEDs) can be used to indicate current direction.

Light emitting diodes are semiconductors that radiate light from their PN junction when a voltage is applied. LEDs emit red light if the diode is formed by a PN junction of gallium arsenide (GaAsP) and green light if the junction is of gallium phosphide (GaP).

Two LEDs, one red and the other green, a coil, and a permanent bar magnet are needed for this demonstration. First, the LEDs are connected parallel to one another as shown in Fig. 1. For our apparatus, the least number of turns needed in order to produce a detectable induced current (light from the LED) is about 500, and this depends on both the speed with which the magnet moves with respect to the coil and the field strength of the magnet.

Initially, the room should be darkened when the magnet is placed in the coil and then rapidly removed; a flash of either red or green light will be observed, the color depending on which magnet pole is removed from the field first. This indicated the induced-current direction.

The direction of the induced currents are thus indicated, and Lenz's law, which states that the induced current will be

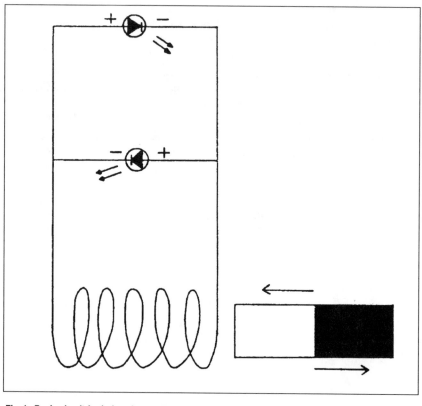

Fig. 1. Basic circuit for induced current.

in a direction so as to oppose the change in magnetic flux, may be verified.

By using a coil of N turns and varying the type of diode, the induced emf produced in each experiment can be estimated. The typical voltage needed to cause light emission from a red LED (GaAsP) is 1.6 V and for a green or yellow LED (GaP) is 3.5 V.

Lenz's Law Demonstration

Don Kangas and Haym Kruglak, Department of Physics, University of Arizona, Tucson, AZ 85721

There are a variety of apparatus setups for demonstrating Lenz's law. We have modified the simple but effective device suggested by T. Miner[1] so that the 18-cm-long magnet[2] is suspended from two string loops. The solid and the split rings are hung with their planes perpendicular to the magnet axis. The apparatus is shown in Fig. 1.

The four supporting string loops are hung from a frame made of wooden dowels. The dowel in the right-angle clamp is 1.9 cm in diameter and 35 cm long. The two dowels for the bifilar suspension are 1.25 cm in diam, 27 cm long, and 20 cm apart. The dimensions are not critical. The string loops should be long enough so that when the magnet is set in motion, its path of several centimeters will be approximately linear.

Allowing the magnet to oscillate will cause the solid ring to move but not the ring with the gap.

The magnetic brake action is demonstrated by allowing both rings to swing. The solid ring will come to rest after a few swings. The split ring will continue to oscillate after the solid ring has come to rest.

If rings of smaller internal diameter and greater thickness are used, the eddy currents are greater because of lower ring resistance. The resulting forces are greater, and their effects more pronounced. We made such rings from aluminum washers of 4.6 cm external diameter and 2.7 cm internal diameter. Three washers were put together with double-face tape.

By moving the solid ring back and forth, the magnet may be made to oscillate. This emphasizes the factor of relative motion. Obviously, the motion of the split ring will not have any effect.

The advantages of the apparatus are: (1) Simple and inexpensive construction, (2) quick setup, (3) convenient storage in a flat box, (4) simultaneous observation of both rings as the magnet approaches and recedes, (5) an aid to the instructor with poor vision and/or lack of eye-hand coordination, and (6) ease of shadow projection in a large lecture class.

References

1. Distributed by Sargent-Welch, Cat. No. 2341A.
2. Distributed by Sargent-Welch, Cat. No. S44371-20G.

Fig. 1. Apparatus for demonstrating Lenz's Law: (left) system at rest: (right) magnet in motion.

*[**Editor's Note:** The next two columns describe two different ways of seeing the position and speed of a magnet dropping through a copper tube. Each method can enhance the observation and analysis of this popular demonstration.]*

Lenz's Law Demonstration for a Large Class

R.C. Nicklin, Andrew Graham, and Robert Miller, Department of Physics and Astronomy, Appalachian State University, Boone, NC 28608

Arbor Scientific sells some very strong magnets made from neodymium.[1] In their catalog is a suggestion to "Drop a joined pair down a 3/4 inch copper tube and challenge your students to explain the resulting phenomenon." We did and were so impressed with the result that we decided to make a demonstration that would allow a large class to watch the magnets fall down the tube.

Figure 1 shows the apparatus. Two 3/4-in (inside diameter) tubes 110 cm long, one copper and one clear plastic, are clamped by three blocks (2 x 4-1/2 x 3/4 in) of PVC sheet.[2] A front-surface mirror is mounted on a pivoting plate of PVC beneath the copper tube. All fasteners are non-magnetic—nylon, brass, aluminum—of necessity because these magnets are so strong. A small flashlight with adjustable focus[3] is mounted above the copper tube in a pivoting 1/2-in CPVC tee bushed with three pieces of 1/2-in CPVC pipe. We cleaned the tube a bit by pulling steel wool through it.

To make one falling magnet visible to a large audience, we use a FlexCam[4] to look up the copper tube via the mirror and feed the video signal to a classroom monitor. We frequently use the FlexCam in demonstrations because it can see in faint light and will fill the screen with the image of anything down to 1 cm across.

For the demonstration, we first drop the magnet through the transparent tube to illustrate the time for free fall, about 0.5 s. An L-shaped piece of steel plate, visible in Fig. 2, catches the magnet and gives an audible click. Then we drop the magnet through the copper tube and wait, and wait, for 4.4 s. There is a click when a brass screw with a steel nut, also visible in Fig. 2, catches the magnet. We explain that the field from the falling magnet causes a flux change at the copper, which induces a current with its own magnetic field to oppose the original flux change—the essence of Lenz's Law.

Finally, we position the FlexCam so it points at the mirror where it catches the light reflecting down the tube and drop the magnet again. The audience sees it float slowly into view and gradually fill the screen, much like objects in those NASA zero-g films.

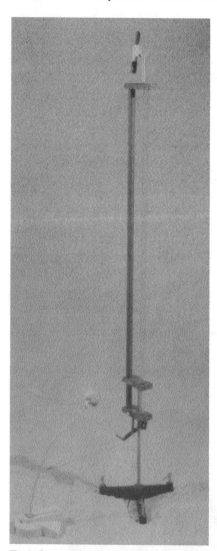

Fig. 1. Setup for Lenz Law demonstration, showing copper and transparent tubes for dropping neodymium magnets. Miniature video camera captures magnet's descent in illuminated copper tube by means of front-surface mirror that pivots for best view.

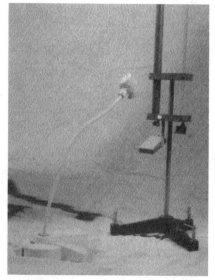

Fig. 2. Steel plate under transparent tube gives audible click as it catches falling magnet; steel nut (to allow better camera view) catches magnet falling down copper tube.

References

1. P8-1123 neodymium magnets, $20/pair from Arbor Scientific, Box 2750, Ann Arbor, MI 48106-2750.
2. #45023 3/4-in sheet PVC, $11.43 a square foot from US Plastic Corporation, 1390 Neubrecht Road, Lima, OH 45801.
3. Mini-Maglite (1/2 in diameter x 5 in long) available in hardware stores.
4. Standard FlexCam, a 1/3-in color CCD camera with 50:1 magnification, $395 from Videolabs, 10925 Bren Road East, Minneapolis, MN 55343. See *Phys. Teach.* **34**, 564 (December 1996) for evaluation of FlexCam.

A Dynamic Demonstration of Lenz's Law

Charles A. Sawicki, Physics Department, North Dakota State University, Fargo, ND 58105-5566;
sawicki@plains.nodak.edu

A standard demonstration involves dropping a metal cylinder and an apparently identical magnet through an aluminum or copper tube. The slower fall of the magnet demonstrates Lenz's law. One shortcoming of this demonstration is that the magnet is out of view while inside the tube. We use a more visible and dynamic variation of this demonstration that our students have found interesting.

Systems subjected to retarding forces proportional to velocity are often discussed in calculus-based physics classes, but students only rarely do experiments with these systems.[1] A dipole magnet moving along the central axis of a conducting cylinder is one such system.[2]

In our experiment, a rare-earth magnet[3] is dropped through a vertical 1-m length of cellulose acetate tubing[4] (inside diameter 2.54 cm and outside diameter 2.86 cm). We slide several short (4.8 cm) thick-wall copper-tube segments[5] (inside diameter 2.88 cm and outside diameter 4.6 cm) over the plastic tube and hold them in place with tight rubber bands. Initially, the magnet falls freely, but when it reaches a copper-tube segment the magnet decelerates rapidly and emerges from the bottom of the segment with a greatly reduced velocity. Dropping a plain metal cylinder prior to dropping the magnet dramatically demonstrates the contrasting behaviors. If students are to handle the apparatus, you might want to seal the magnet inside the tube by tightly packing high-density foam plugs into the tube ends. Figure 1 shows one end of the assembled tube with the magnet sealed inside.

Figure 2 shows the effect of currents induced in one copper-tube segment on the motion of the falling magnet. Magnet velocity was determined as a function of the distance fallen down the tube using a computer interfaced photogate[6] that measured the time, Δt, required for the magnet to fall through the light beam. Velocity was calculated as the length of the magnet divided by Δt. In passing through the copper-tube segment the velocity of the magnet decreases by a factor of about 90. In Fig. 2 crosses represent velocity data points while the solid curved line represents free-fall motion with an acceleration of 9.8 m/s². The position coordinate is the location of the center of the photogate infrared LED light beam[7] relative to the magnet starting position. This choice allows a clearer discussion of the relation between the magnet position and the force on the magnet due to induced current. The black rectangle represents the position and length of the copper tube. The top of the copper tube is located 0.792 m below the starting position for the magnet. Vertical solid lines are located 2.5 cm (the length of the magnet) on either side of the rectangle. Comparing the changes in velocity with the location of these vertical lines shows that the force due to the induced current is of very short range since it does not significantly affect magnet motion until the end of the magnet enters the copper tube. The large acceleration undergone by the magnet gives a dramatic demonstration of Lenz's law. Using initial and final data points at (0.772 m, 3.53 m/s) and (0.792 m, 2.03 m/s),

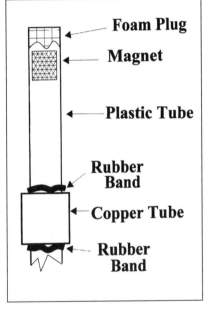

Fig. 1. Diagram at one end of experimental apparatus consisting of a plastic tube with magnet sealed inside and one thick-wall copper tube held in place with rubber bands.

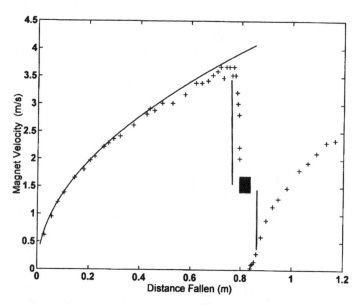

Fig. 2. Plot of magnet velocity vs distance fallen. Magnet starts at rest at $x = 0$. Crosses represent experimental measurements; solid curve is the velocity calculated for a constant acceleration of 9.8 m/s^2; solid rectangle shows location and length of thick-walled copper-tube segment relative to the horizontal axis. Vertical straight line segments are placed 2.5 cm on either side of the ends of the copper tube.

This result is in good agreement with the magnet velocity $V = 0.041$ m/s as it starts to exit the tube (smallest velocity point plotted in Fig. 2). The total impulse in Ns exerted on the magnet as it passes through the tube is constant independent of magnet velocity,[9] so the final magnet velocity after passing through the tube will be reduced to terminal velocity for any initial velocity less than the largest velocity shown in Fig. 2 (3.7 m/s).

When several short copper-tube segments are in place on the plastic tube, the magnet falls jerkily down the tube nearly stopping each time it encounters a copper segment. This demonstration also works well using pieces of thick aluminum tubing (5.1 cm long, 5.1 outside diameter, 3.88 cm inside diameter). The thicker tube wall partially compensates for the smaller induced currents resulting from the higher resistivity of aluminum (2.83, $\mu\Omega$/cm), as compared with that of copper (1.72 $\mu\Omega$/cm).[10]

respectively, Eq. (1) gives an average acceleration $a = -210 \pm 40$ m/s^2.

$$V_f^2 = V_i^2 + 2a\Delta x \qquad (1)$$

V_f and V_i are the final and initial velocities and Δx is the difference in location between the final and initial positions of the magnet. Velocities are assigned errors of $\pm 7\%$; position can be measured to about 0.2 cm. To within experimental error, the velocity of the magnet as it leaves the tube is the terminal velocity[8] for the falling magnet in this tube. We found the time for our magnet to fall through 0.167 m of the specified copper tubing to be 3.7 $\pm$ 0.3 s for ten measurements. We dropped the magnet from rest with its bottom end at the top of the copper tube and timed until it just began to emerge from the bottom end. The magnet reached terminal velocity, $V_{terminal}$, where weight force is balanced by the force on the magnet due to induced current, essentially as soon as it was released.

$$V_{terminal} = \frac{0.167 \text{m}}{3.7 \text{ s}} =$$

$$0.045 \pm 0.004 \frac{\text{m}}{\text{s}} \qquad (2)$$

References

1. J. Priest and B. Wade, *Phys Teach.* **30**, 106 (1992).
2. W.M. Saslow, *Am. J. Phys.* **60**, 693 (1992).
3. Arbor Scientific, P.O. Box 2750, Ann Arbor, MI 48106-2750; catalog #P81124. This neodymium-iron-boron magnet is 2.5 cm long, 2.2 cm in diameter, and polarized on the ends. This magnet is very powerful and should be handled with care to avoid pinching injuries.
4. Cellulose acetate tubing is cheaper and much less prone to fracture than either acrylic or polycarbonate tubing. Available from almost any supplier of plastics.
5. We machined copper-tube segments from a piece of scrap copper tubing (4.6 cm outside diameter, 2.5 cm inside diameter). Keep in mind that alloys (for example brass) have much higher resistivities and will not work in this demonstration.
6. PASCO scientific photogate (model #ME-9204A) attached to a PASCO 6500 interface (model #CI-6500).
7. The position of the infrared beam was determined with an infrared sensor card; Radio Shack catalog #276-1099).
8. P.A. Tipler, *Physics for Scientists and Engineers*, 3rd ed. (Worth Publishers, New York, 1991),p. 116.
9. C.A. Sawicki, *Phys. Teach.* **34**, 38 (1996).
10. *Handbook of Chemistry and Physics,* 42nd ed. (CRC Press, Boca Raton, FL, 1960), pp. 2589–2590.

Quantitative Demonstration of Lenz's Law

O. Romulo Ochoa and *Frank Kolp,* Department of Physics, The College of New Jersey, Ewing, NJ 08628-0718, and *Joel T. Handler,* Holmdel High School, Holmdel, NJ 07733

A popular and exciting demonstration of Lenz's law involves the dropping of a cylindrical magnet through a copper or aluminum tube. Recently, two articles in *TPT* showed different ways of enhancing this demonstration.[1,2] We present yet another method in which the position of the magnet within the tube is followed as a function of time and the motion is presented simultaneously on a computer screen.

In our demonstration we begin by dropping the magnet through a plastic tube. Students get a rough idea of the short time required for free fall. Then we drop the magnet through an aluminum tube with the same diameter as the plastic tube. Students react with surprise and curiosity to the relatively long time required for the magnet to drop in this case.

To prove that the magnet falls at essentially constant velocity, we have prepared a setup that provides the position of the magnet within the tube as a function of time. Figure 1 shows a schematic of the apparatus. The critical component in this method is the computer mouse. It is used to interface the motion of the falling magnet to the computer. The use of the mouse as an interface was described by Handler et al.[3] In addition to its applicability to a variety of laboratory activities and demonstrations referenced there, the mouse has the advantage over commercially available devices of being easily available and considerably less expensive. Access to the small cylindrical rollers that detect

the motion of the mouse is gained by removing the ball and bottom plate. Briefly stated, the roller motion is read by an onboard chip that sends this information to the computer. A software program written in PASCAL reads the motion information and converts it into appropriate units by using a predetermined conversion factor. In the setup shown, the pulley and counterweight are used to improve the coupling of the string holding the magnet to the mouse's roller. With a magnet mass of 100 grams and a counterweight of 80 grams, the string does not slip on the roller.

Figure 2 shows the position of the magnet with time as it falls through a 3/4-in diameter copper tube. The last few points correspond to the magnet exiting the bottom side of the tube. The data within the tube are fit to a straight line with slope of 4.18 ± 0.02 cm/s. Data outside the tube (at distances greater than 60 cm) indicate motion for which we found an acceleration of 58.3 ± 1.9 cm/s^2. A direct measurement of this acceleration under identical conditions yielded a value of 56.6 ± 5.5 cm/s^2. This last method involved the use of photogate timers to measure the time required by the magnet to fall a fixed distance. The friction of the mouse roller results in an acceleration lower than that obtained by a force analysis.

In addition, the apparatus shown in Fig. 1 can be used to demonstrate the difference in conductance between aluminum and copper tubes of the same diameter. The copper

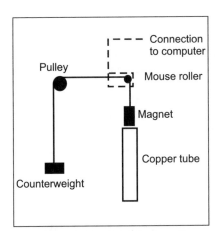

Fig. 1. Diagram of Lenz's law demonstration apparatus. Mouse roller conveys motion of magnet to computer. Counterweight reduces acceleration and provides a better contact between the string and mouse roller.

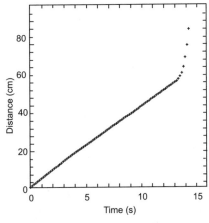

Fig. 2. Plot of distance traveled by the magnet vs time. Straight line corresponds to motion of the magnet within copper tube; last few points represent magnet's motion as it leaves tube.

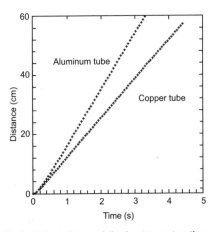

Fig. 3. Plots of distance fallen by a magnet vs time. Tubes have equal diameter but copper tube is thicker. Lower resistance of the copper tube results in higher induced currents and larger retarding force.

tube is thicker than the aluminum tube so it is expected to have lower resistance resulting in higher induced currents. In Fig. 3 we can clearly observe the different slopes with the magnet in the aluminum tube having a larger velocity. In this case we used a 60-g counterweight and found velocities of 18.2 $\pm$ 0.3 cm/s and 13.1 $\pm$ 0.1 cm/s for the aluminum and copper tubes, respectively.

References

1. R.C. Nicklin, Andrew Graham, and Robert Miller, *Phys. Teach.* **35**, 46 (Jan 1997).
2. Charles A. Sawicki, *Phys. Teach.* **35**, 47 (Jan 1997).
3. Joel T. Handler, O. Romulo Ochoa, and N. Franklin Kolp, *Phys. Teach.* **34,** 488 (Nov 1996).

The Rail Gun

Gay B. Stewart, Department of Physics, University of Arkansas, Fayetteville, AR 72701

A rail gun demonstration can address a broad group of educational goals in introductory electricity and magnetism. Our rail gun uses a battery-powered circuit consisting of a moveable conductor (projectile) placed across two conducting rails in a magnetic field. We use the rail gun to review mechanics, foster approximate reasoning and lateral class discussion, and demonstrate the use of physics in calculating properties of the universe.

Construction

Simple Model. Our original rail gun was two brass welding rods taped to a book and two aluminum spacers connected by a copper wire (total cost about $2). A broad magnet with narrowly spaced poles that will produce a strong, fairly uniform, field is required. This "bargain" rail gun is excellent for student familiarity and encourages the students to build their own, but requires constant adjustment.

More Dependable Model. An "upgraded" rail gun is also inexpensive, with only the magnet[1] being costly. Unlike the excellent set of experiments for $\vec{F} = q\vec{v} \times \vec{B}$ with an electron gun,[2] no elaborate support equipment is needed. The materials are familiar, and the force is something that can be felt as well as seen.

You will need two pieces of 1- x 4-in board an inch wider than the magnet, a piece of rectangular brass tubing (projectile) cut the same width as the magnet, two solid brass welding rods 10 in long, an ammeter, 6-V battery, meterstick, knife switch, and three alligator leads.

On a drill press, drill holes through the projectile that are 1/32 in larger than the rails. As shown in Fig. 1, the holes should be drilled through the broad side of the projectile. The rails should be inside the magnet, but close to the edge. Mark holes the same separation on the boards by using a

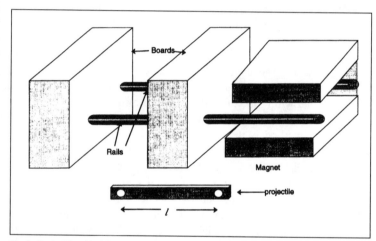

Fig. 1. Projectile with drilled holes and orientation of boards, rails, and magnet for rail gun apparatus.

nail to dimple the board through the projectile. The holes are positioned so that the rails run parallel through the center of the magnet, perpendicular to the field, and at a fixed separation so the projectile can pass between the magnet's poles. The rails must be smooth, with any corrosion removed so they conduct well, and the projectile must fall off the rail ends easily. Sliding the projectile along the rails repeatedly will improve contact. A properly constructed projectile rides freely along the rails.

Presentation

Introducing Force. There are several ways to introduce the topic of force on a current-carrying wire, including the traditional current balance and the more user-friendly method recently published in this magazine.[3] To prepare students for the rail gun, provide a wire, battery, and big magnet and tell them to observe what happens when they

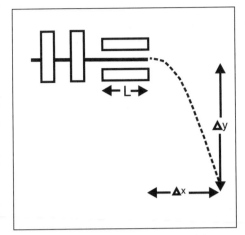

Fig. 2. Side view of rail gun showing some of the quantities to be measured: Δx, the horizontal distance traveled; Δy, the vertical distance traveled, and L, the distance the projectile is in the magnetic field.

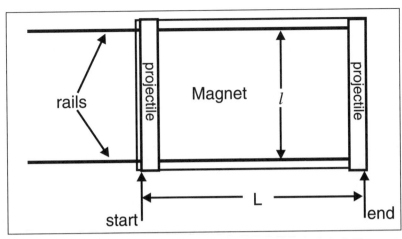

Fig. 3. Cutaway top view showing path of projectile through magnet.

put the wire through the magnet and connect it to the battery. They see the wire move and, more importantly, they feel it jump in their hands thereby gaining a tactile impression of the force on the wire.

Lorentz Force Demonstration. Give your students a list of apparatus that they can pick up at a hardware store. Ask them how to use the materials to measure the field strength of the magnet. Most students cannot find the force on the wire. As a group, with the instructor at the board, students find the Lorentz force for the rail gun, giving them real-life reinforcement of some mechanics. Reusing the same magnet used to feel the force on a current carrying wire gives students a tactile reference for the demonstration.

Carefully align the ends of the rails, magnet edge, and table edge. Place the projectile on the rails without the magnet. Connect the battery in series with the ammeter and switch to one rail. Connect the other rail to the other terminal of the battery. Measure the current, then open the switch. Draw attention to the fact that there is no force on the wire, and record the current. Replace the magnet. Place the projectile just inside the edge of the magnet farthest from the rail ends and close the switch. If aligned correctly, the projectile flies off the rails. Occasionally a slight tap is necessary to overcome static friction. Record the distance Δx from the end of the magnet to where the projectile lands (see Fig. 2). The students use this and other measurements to calculate the force:

$$\vec{F}_B = I\vec{l} \times \vec{B} = IlB\hat{x} \qquad (1)$$

where l is the length of the projectile between the holes.

Mechanics Review

A difficulty experienced by students in electricity and magnetism is lack of proficiency in mechanics. Reiterating

mechanics concepts in new contexts should improve understanding. The rail gun touches on a number of important topics.

Work = Force · Distance. Force on the projectile is constant, if we assume constant current and magnetic field. The difference in field strength between the two sides of the magnet where the rails pass averaged 4%, ranging from 0 to 11% for ten magnets. A lower difference leads to a better result, since difference in field causes a difference in force on the ends of the projectile, making it twist and bind.

The work done by the magnet on the projectile is

$$W_B = \int \vec{F}_B \cdot \vec{dl} = F_B L \qquad (2)$$

where L is the length of the magnet (see Fig. 3).

Conservation of Energy. The kinetic energy gained by the projectile is the work done. Once the projectile has left the magnet the kinetic energy is expressed as

$$K = \frac{1}{2} m v_{x0}^2 = W_B \qquad (3)$$

The velocity is all in the $\hat{x}$ direction since the force was purely horizontal.

Projectile Motion. Once the projectile leaves the magnet, the only force (neglecting air resistance) will be due to gravity. We can use this fact to calculate the velocity. We didn't list a stopwatch as equipment, so we calculate Δt from $\Delta y = 1/2 g \Delta t^2$. Substituting Eq. (1) into Eq. (2) and then into Eq. (3), rearranging, and substituting for v_{x0},

$$B = \frac{\frac{1}{2} m v_{x0}^2}{IlL} = \frac{m}{2IlL} \frac{\Delta x^2 g}{2\Delta y} \qquad (4)$$

A sample calculation for our setup, where $l = 0.04$ m, $L = 0.06$ m, $m = 0.004$ kg, $I = 7$A, $\Delta x = 0.38$ m, and $\Delta y = 0.78$

$$B = \frac{(0.004\ \text{kg})\ (0.38\ \text{m})^2\ (9.8\ \text{m/s}^2)}{2(7\ \text{A})\ (0.04\ \text{m})\ (0.06\ \text{m})\ 2(0.78\ \text{m})} = 0.1\ \text{T} \quad (5)$$

Compared with the measured value of 0.17 T, this result is remarkable considering that friction and back-emf were neglected.

Comments

We find the rail gun an effective means for introducing the Lorentz force and reviewing mechanics. Students use simple materials to calculate something about the universe, developing approximate reasoning skills.

Many students state that they take physics only because it is required. We teachers often assume that the utility of physics is obvious, but this is not always the case. The rail gun "draws them in." Students often pursue improvements to the rail gun, and in discussing their ideas become animated, debating among themselves, doing physics on their own time and enjoying it.

Acknowledgment

Thanks to J. Brad Shue, our laboratory curator, for fabrication advice and, above all, for his help in finding the perfect projectile.

References

1. PASCO scientific, 10101 Foothills Boulevard, Roseville, CA 95678, WA-9609A magnet for vibrating wires.
2. E.R. Huggins and J.J. Lelek, *Am. J. Phys.* **47**, 992 (1979).
3. W. Herreman and R. Huysentruyt, *Phys. Teach.* **33**, 288 (1995).

A "Relevant" Demonstration

G.R. Davies, Physics Department, University of Natal, Pietermaritzburg 3200, South Africa

Physics teachers are constantly on the lookout for demonstrations that illustrate the "relevance" of physics in day-to-day life. What could possibly be more relevant in the minds of at least some of our students than showing how an electric guitar pickup works?

Stretch a steel wire between bridges, sonometer fashion, to act as the "string." (We use a stainless steel wire of relatively low quality, which is therefore appreciably magnetic.) The pickup we use is simply a coil, along the axis of which is placed a bar magnet. The assembly is such that one end of the magnet is close to the wire (see figure).

Connect the coil to a power amplifier (*large* power, for even greater relevance) and loudspeaker.

The bar magnet magnetizes the portion of the steel string in its vicinity. As the string is plucked, it vibrates close to the coil and so changes the magnetic flux linking the coil. The vibratory motion thus produces an alternating voltage of similar frequency at the coil terminals,

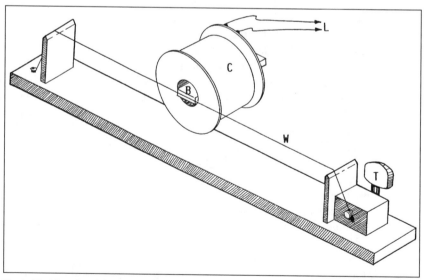

Fig. 1. Electric guitar pickup model. W: wire; C: coil; B: bar magnet; T: tensioner; L: leads from coil to power amplifier and loudspeaker.

which is then amplified and fed to the loudspeaker.

To generate a more interesting noise, a guitar-type tensioner can be fitted to one end of the stretched wire. This is then adjusted as the string is sounded.

Miniature Hydroelectric Power Demonstration

R.E. Benenson, Department of Physics, State University of New York, Albany, NY 12222; rayben@cnsvax.albany.edu

A small "turbine" connected to an electric motor and placed under a sink faucet makes an amusing demonstration of hydroelectric power. The motor generates enough voltage to light an LED. The pulley arrangement and turbine are useful at all levels, including in elementary-school discussions both of energy production and of simple machines.

The turbine is part of an air blower,[1] and a very small permanent-magnet dc motor[2] serves as the generator. An O-ring acts as the connecting belt between turbine and motor pulley. The ratio of diameters is such that the angular velocity of the latter permits the motor to generate a sufficient emf, just over 1.6 V. A small gap between the edge of the turbine blades and rim makes a convenient groove for the O-ring belt. A photograph of the apparatus under a stream of water from a faucet is shown in Fig. 1; relevant parameters are given below.

Fig. 1. Miniature hydroelectric power generator in action under a faucet running cold water. Bright spot above the motor is the glowing LED.

Some care is required to obtain a voltage above the LED threshold. In order to adjust belt tension, we attached the bottom of the motor bracket to the frame base by a screw that passed through a slot. Too tight a belt tension slows the turbine excessively. The motor pulley is mounted on a 1/4-20 threaded rod that was press-fit (or soldered, or cemented with epoxy resin) to the motor shaft by means of a small hole drilled in the rod. This arrangement makes it easy to try different pulley diameters and adjust the position of the pulley to match the edge of the turbine.

The turbine is mounted on a well-lubricated bolt acting as an axle, on which a number of washers are mounted as spacers to keep the turbine away from the supports. The faucet is most effective when it delivers a well-collimated stream as in Fig. 1. Spilling water from a can held above the turbine works only marginally.

Some approximate relevant dimensions of the apparatus are:

Motor pulley diameter	1.0 cm
Turbine diameter	9.6 cm
O-ring i.d.	11.4 cm (45 in)
Motor shaft-turbine axis separation	8.5 cm
Output voltage	1.6 to 1.7 at 1200 rpm

The angular velocity of the motor needed to light the LED connected to its terminals is obtained by inserting the motor shaft into a speed-calibrated drill press. Not every motor nor LED is satisfactory for this setup.[3]

We considered, but did not try, making a turbine by mounting buckets on a narrow pulley of a comparable or greater diameter than the one described here. The buckets could be made from plastic 35-mm film canisters and might be more efficient than the fan blades.

References

1. A surplus parts supplier (for example, Herbach and Rademan, 18 Canal Street, P.O. Box 122, Bristol, PA 19007-0122; 800-848-8001) would be the most sensible source for a centrifugal fan airblower similar to the one in Fig. 1. Electronics catalogs show such blowers, but they cost from $30 to more than $60, and it seems wasteful to tear one apart to get the fan. My source was our own laboratory, which stocks such blowers as pieces

worth saving from obsolete equipment.

2. The Radio Shack motor is rated at 1.5 to 3.0 V and costs less than a dollar. Its diameter in the rounded portions of the housing is 2.3 cm, and there are two flats.

Unfortunately, it is not in the latest catalog.

3. Likelihood of success is greatest with low-threshold voltage (1.6 V) LED's. We used one marked FLV 102 120, and Data Display Products HLMP D105 was also satisfactory, but others are available. Test motor and LED by the drill-press method.

Electromagnetic Shielding

Zhu E-qing, Ningbo Food College, Ningbo, China

To demonstrate the shielding of radio waves, slowly lower a small, playing transistor radio into a metal container (Fig. 1). Use any metal container, such as a gallon paint can, with an opening of sufficient size to receive the radio. As the radio, suspended from a string, is lowered into the can, the sound intensity will diminish, thus demonstrating the weakening of the electromagnetic signal caused by the shielding effect of the metal. The strength of the signal near the bottom of the can is near zero.

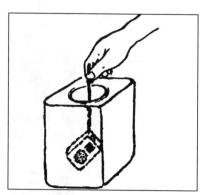

Fig. 1. A transistor radio is lowered into a metal container.

Light Rays, Reflection, Refraction

Making Laser Beams Visible

Michael E. Knotts, School of Physics, Georgia Institute of Technology, Atlanta, GA 30332-0430

To conduct classroom demonstrations in optics or to photograph experimental setups, it is often desirable to find a means of making a laser beam (or other intense light beam) visible. Several methods are commonly used to do this by dispersing a scattering material in the medium surrounding the beam. This column will briefly discuss a few of these methods, and then proceed to describe an easily constructed, inexpensive apparatus that produces a safe, controllable fog that is well suited for visualizing or photographing beams.

Banging chalkboard erasers together to dust the path of a beam is an ever-popular method useful for some quick, "gee whiz" demonstrations. However, even though chalk is cheap and students seem to

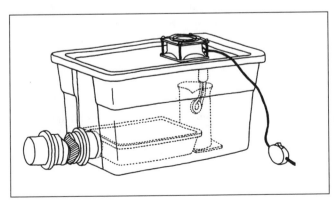

Fig. 1. A simple fog machine, constructed of inexpensive, commonly available parts, that is useful for demonstrations and photography.

Fig. 2. Darlene Hart, a Ph.D. candidate in physics at the Georgia Institute of Technology, demonstrates the homemade fog machine. She is working with a simple laser-light show apparatus used by members of the Georgia Tech student chapter of the Optical Society at America to conduct education outreach programs for schoolchildren.

Table I. Parts list for the homemade fog machine.

Item and source(s)	Cost
Large plastic box with resealable lid (Rubbermaid™ brand, dimensions 16 x 11 x 9 inches). Sources: grocery store or discount department store.	$ ~8.50
200-W immersion heater. Sources: grocery store, discount department store, or luggage store.	4.00
Small plastic tray (Paterson™ brand, polypropylene, dimensions 9 x 7 x 2 inches). Source: sold by photography stores for developing small 5 x 7-inch photographic prints.	2.75
400-ml glass beaker or measuring cup. Sources: chemistry lab supply house or grocery store.	2.00
Large flexible shop vacuum-cleaner hose (2½-inch diameter, with 2 ¼-inch diameter fittings). Sources: hardware store or home improvement center.	13.50
Small fan (dimensions 3 x 3 x 1½ inches, flow rate approximately 12 1/s ≈ 25 CFM) .Sources: salvaged equipment, surplus stores, local or mail-order	≤17.00

allergies!).

Fortunately, plenty of other techniques are available. For example, the optics can be placed in an aquarium-type tank containing a scattering suspension such as milk in water. Special scattering media and immersible optics are sold expressly for this purpose.[1] However, this method is not ideal for many demonstrations, since many optical setups cannot be immersed, and the refractive index of water (~1.33) causes angles of refraction to differ significantly from those in air. Demonstrating the effects of Rayleigh scattering on sunlight (polarization, blue sky, red sunset), using a mixture of sodium thiosulfate (photographic fixer) and dilute sulfuric acid, is a notable exception for which the aqueous technique is ideal.[2]

Another method uses a mist of droplets sprayed from an upside-down can of Dust-Off™ (sold for cleaning small parts), or from a product packaged specifically for the purpose.[3] The mist stays suspended longer than chalk dust (up to a few minutes if sprayed into an enclosed box), and it usually doesn't leave a residue after evaporation. Until recently, many of these products were unacceptable because they contained ozone-damaging ingredients; now, some of them claim to be harmless.

Smoke also works, and various means, such as a trained cigar smoker, can be devised to distribute it in the region of interest. But it has obvious health hazards, and it can be very damaging to precision optical surfaces (e.g., thin-film dielectric coatings). Commercial smoke/fog machines are available for theatrical and photographic application, but they tend to be quite expensive.[3–5] Most of them work by heating atomized fluids to produce smoke that is claimed to be "non-toxic." But testing to determine their compatibility with optical coatings and surfaces would still seem to be a good idea.

An inexpensive apparatus that works well for demonstrations or photography can be made with commonly available parts for less than $50. It uses liquid nitrogen to chill steam, creating a fine mist that is safe even around expensive, precision optics, because it evaporates leaving no residue. (To be extra safe, use distilled water.)

delight in observing the scintillating beam, the method has problems: the effect is short lived, the beam is visible as many little point-like specks of light rather than as a continuous distribution, and most important, the dust particles can be damaging to lasers and other optics (and bad for one's

The mist does not tend to condense on surfaces, presumably because it is significantly cooler than the surroundings. And since it's only water, it's environmentally inert. The apparatus can alternately be used (somewhat less effectively) with dry ice.

Figure 1 shows the device. A plastic storage box with a resealable lid is fitted with a large flexible shop vacuum-cleaner hose. A small fan mounted in the lid forces air to flow through the box at a modest rate (10 to 20 l/s). The box encloses a tray for the liquid nitrogen and a water-filled beaker containing an immersion heater of the type used by travelers to boil water for soup or coffee. The beaker rests on a small hot pad, which serves to protect the plastic box from the heat. Optional cord switches for the fan and immersion heater complete the assembly.

To use the apparatus, turn the heater on. When steam begins to rise from the beaker, fill the tray with liquid nitrogen and place the lid on the box. Switch the fan on and watch a stream of fog emerge from the hose (Fig. 2). The density of the fog can be changed by partially blocking the air flow through the fan. It can last for several minutes, which is sufficient time for extensive demonstrations or complicated time-exposure photographs. For visual use, the hose can simply be pointed toward the areas of interest. To make time-exposure photographs such as the example in Fig. 3, use the hose to control the exposure by adjusting the fogging time for each part of the scene. Figure 4 shows a sinusoidal diffraction grating simultaneously illuminated with two colinear laser beams (one red, one blue). Note that the beams (made visible by using the apparatus described here) remain colinear in the specular, or zeroth, diffraction order.

For use with dry ice, no immersion heater is necessary. Dropping small chunks of dry ice (cut from a larger block with a hacksaw) into a large bowl of warm water placed inside the plastic fan box gives better results. Some experimentation is required to obtain a good continuous stream of fog. The initial burst of fog with dry ice can be quite impressive, but the sustained output is less substantial than that obtained using the liquid nitrogen setup.

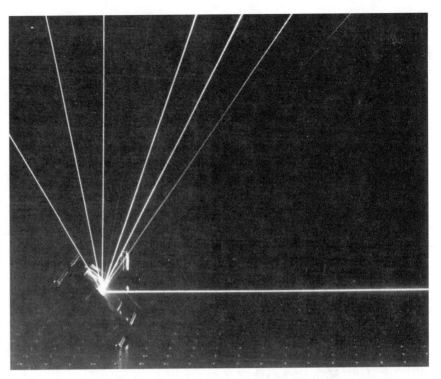

Fig. 3. Diffraction of a He-Ne laser beam (λ = 632.8 nm) by a reflective holographic grating. Incident laser power: 10 mW. Fog exposure: 20 seconds at f/5.6 using ISO 100 film with room lights off. Detail in optical table: 2 f stops underexposed with room lights on.

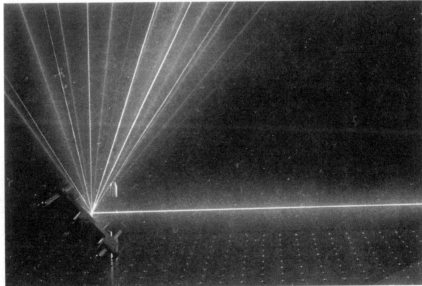

Fig. 4. Diffraction by the grating of Fig. 3. illuminated by colinear red and blue laser beams.

A parts list with approximate costs is shown in Table I. For the liquid nitrogen tray, it is best to avoid materials that become brittle at cryogenic temperatures (e.g., rubber or polyethylene); experimentation will turn up many suitable materials (e.g., Pyrex or polypropylene). An oversized computer fan can be adapted by partially blocking it to reduce the air flow. Liquid nitrogen is available on many campuses with active research programs, and a few liters, which is enough for several demonstrations, can often be "borrowed" (to be returned in gaseous form!). It may be purchased directly from local industrial gas and welding supply dealers (~\$ 1.40 per liter).[6] Alternately, dry ice can be purchased in small quantities (~\$2.50 per kilogram) from local ice houses or other sources.[7]

References

1. Edmund Scientific Co., 101 E. Gloucester Pike, Barrington, NJ 08007. Call 1-609-573-6879 to request a catalog.
2. Peter W. Milonni and Joseph H. Eberly, *Lasers* (Wiley, New York, 1988), p. 56.
3. Calumet Photographic, 890 Supreme Drive, Bensenville, IL 60106. Call toll-free 1-800-225-8638 to request a catalog.
4. Markertek Video Supply, 4 High Street, Box 397, Saugerties, NY 12477. Call toll-free 1-800-522-2025 to request a catalog.
5. In addition to mail order sources, fog machines can be purchased at stores that sell musical instruments and live entertainment performance equipment.
6. Since liquid nitrogen is cheapest to organizations that buy large quantities, a substantially discounted price (~25¢ per liter) may be available if it is purchased from a supplier having a state- or university-wide contract.
7. Look in the *Yellow Pages* under *Ice-Dry*.

Speed of Light Measurement with the Laser Pointer

John E. Carlson, Fox Lane High School, Bedford, NY 10506

A recent article in *The Physics Teacher*[1] explained how to modulate the Metrologic laser pointer with an audio signal, a technique that allows the teacher to demonstrate the information-carrying ability of laser light. Teachers can also use a laser pointer to measure the speed of light. Although the idea of measuring the speed of light by incorporating the phase delay between a modulated split beam of light is not new, the ability to do it at relatively low cost makes this technique attractive. In this application the laser pointer is modulated at a high frequency (1.0 MHz). You will need a "travel" distance of about 45 m one way.

On a homemade optical bench (Fig. 1)[2] the laser is connected to the modulating circuit and turned on. The exiting light passes through a beam splitter so that 30% of the light is directed immediately to a light detector while the other 70% travels down the hallway and back again. At the point of reflection, a plane mirror mounted on a gimbal mirror mount (Fig. 2) is aimed so that the reflected light hits a small convex mirror on the optical bench. The second light detector is positioned at the focal point of this lens. By feeding the outputs of these two detector circuits into a dual trace oscilloscope, the two sine wave patterns appear on the screen, but they are out of phase (Fig. 3). If the sine wave patterns are

Fig. 2.

Fig. 1.

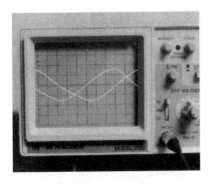

Fig. 3.

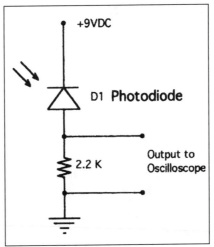

Fig. 5. Light-detection circuit (two required).

When I do the demonstration, the oscilloscope is on the 0.1 μs/cm scale and reads 3.2 cm. The round-trip distance down our hall and back is 87 m. Therefore, the speed of light as calculated is 87 m divided by 0.32 μs = 2.7 × 10^8 m/s. Circuit diagrams for the oscillator/modulator (Fig. 4) and detection circuits (Fig. 5) are shown; a source list is also provided.[3]

Readers who are interested in this apparatus but cautious about proceeding because of difficulty in obtaining the parts or lack of experience in building circuits should contact me (Phone: 914-241-6097; FAX: 914-241-6064; E-mail: JOCARL@delphi.com).

References

1. Dames J. Boire, *Phys. Teach.* **33**, 58 (1995).

2. The optical bench is constructed by screwing a piece of thin steel to a plywood base. Using stubby horseshoe magnets with predrilled holes on top, it is possible to mount wood blocks to a threaded post. This allows the mounting of objects to the wood which can move vertically and turn horizontally as the wood block is screwed into or out of the threaded post.

3. Sources for materials: Photodiode (#PN334PA-ND)
Digi-Key Corp., 701 Brooks Ave. South, P.O. Box 677, Thief River Falls, MN 56701-0677, 800-344-4539.

Beam Splitter (#E43,734)
Gimbal Mirror Mount (#E39,929)
Edmund Scientific, 101 E. Gloucester Pike, Barrington, NJ 08007-1380, 609-573-6295.

Function Generator Integrated Circuit (EXAR XR-2206)
JAMECO, 1355 Shoreway Road, Belmont, CA 94002-4100, 800-831-4242.

Laser Pointer
Metrologic Instruments, Inc., P.O. Box 307, Bellmawr, NJ 08099-0307, 800-436-3876.

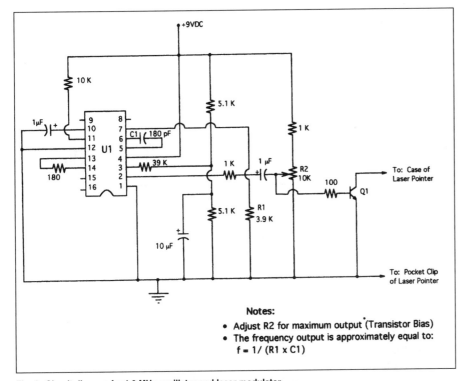

Notes:
- Adjust R2 for maximum output (Transistor Bias)
- The frequency output is approximately equal to:
  f = 1/ (R1 x C1)

Fig. 4. Circuit diagram for 1.0-MHz oscillator and laser modulator.

centered vertically, the ascending sine waves will cross the *x* axis at different positions, which correspond to a measurable time (using the calibrated time scales of the oscilloscope). Using this technique, the precise frequency of the modulating circuit is not critical to the success of the experiment. Finally, since the extra distance traveled by the light can be easily measured along the floor with a tape measure, the speed of light can be calculated ($v = d/t$).

Using a Standard Force Table to Verify Snell's Law

George Shellenberger, University of the Ozarks, Clarksville, AR 72830

A tank attachment to a standard force table will allow refraction measurements to be made on liquids (Fig. 1). The tank is approximately 2 cm deep, 14 cm long, and 9 cm wide. Cut a slot 1.5 cm wide and 1.7 cm deep near one edge to form an opening for a plastic window. Scribe the window, which is about 3 mm thick, 4 cm long, and 2 cm wide, with a sharp line and fill the line with black Lacquer-Stik® or black India ink. Cement the plastic window to the inside of the tank with a good quality adhesive, being careful to keep the window portion free of adhe-

Fig. 1. Photograph of force table and modifications to measure the index of refraction of liquids.

sive and the engraved line perpendicular to the bottom of the tank. Paint the back of the tank white so a metal indicator rod will be easier to see. The indicator rod is made out of steel spring material 0.5 mm in diam and 4 cm long. Friction fit the indicator into a hole drilled in a piece of aluminum 2 cm by 3 cm by 3 mm.

A movable arm pivoted at the center of the table serves as a pointer and sighting device. It is made of commercial aluminum (2.54-cm wide by 0.32-cm thick). We made a cardboard pattern first to insure proper shape. Rivet a short brass pin, machined for a slightly loose fit in the hole in the center of the force table, near one end of the arm.

As Fig. 1 shows, a central slot (about 0.8 by 5 cm) is cut at the other end of the arm to frame and support a sighting string. Hold the sight indicator in position either by threading it through two small holes drilled above and below the slot or by cementing it in place. Also, at the appropriate location, remove one-half the width of the arm for a 3.5-cm cutout to allow the viewing of the degree scale. Bend the arm 90° at a distance about 1 cm longer than the radius of the force table. It is important that the string and the other indicators be vertical. The angle pointer should be radial. Some judicious bending of the arm may be necessary for final adjustment. Figure 1 shows our prototype; subsequent angle indicators would be cut out in a manner illustrated in Fig. 2.

In use, the arm is attached and the tank is supported on thin plywood. The scribed line on the plastic window is placed directly over the pivot point and the degree arm is positioned to zero. A small mirror is held behind and against the window and the tank rotated, keeping the scribed line axial with the pivot point. Rotate the tank until reflections of

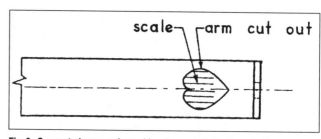

Fig. 2. Suggested manner for making the angle indicator cutout.

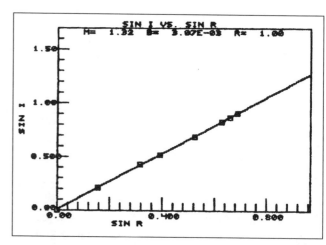

Fig. 3. A plot of sine of refraction vs angle of incidence for water using the modified force table.

the scribed line and the arm indicator string and the indicator string itself are all in the same plane. This insures that the scale reads zero when it is normal to the liquid-air interface. We used a small disk lying on top of the force table as a mirror. The refraction tank is attached to the force table with a C-clamp and filled about halfway with the selected liquid; the rear pointer is positioned along the rear of the tank.

Take readings of the incident and refracted angles for different positions of the rear pointer as it is moved along the rear of the tank. You can sight either through the water or above it. If the line of sight is above the surface, the indicator arm gives the direction the light travels in the liquid; when you sight through the liquid, the reading is the direction of light as it emerges from the tank. This is contrary to what many students expect. In order to make the measurements, the image of the rear indicator and the scribe on the window must be lined up. An easy way to do this is to move your head until the scribed line and rear indicator are lined up, and then swing the indicator arm around until the indicator thread is in coincidence with the other two images.

Sample recorded data appear in Table I. These data were plotted with the aid of Vernier Software's *Graphical Analysis III*. Snell's law applies, so plot the sine of the angle of incidence vs the sine of the angle of refraction. Such a plot is shown in Fig. 3. The slope is the index of refraction,

Table I. Typical data collected with the modified force table.

Angle of incidence (degrees)	Angle of refraction (degrees)
0.0	0.0
12.0	9.0
25.5	18.5
31.2	23.0
43.9	31.5
55.6	38.9
60.6	41.2
66.2	43.6
73.2	46.6

and a value of 1.32 was found with this particular liquid (water). The accepted value at normal room temperature is 1.33. An experimental procedure that is applicable to this type of apparatus is CENCO's "Refraction of Light by Liquids (Refraction Tank, #71990-535)," one in their series of *Selective Experiments in Physics*.

Simple Homemade Container for Measuring Refractive Index

Alfred F. Leung and *Simon George,* Department of Physics and Astronomy, California State University, Long Beach, CA 90840

Various methods have been devised to measure the refractive index of a transparent liquid.[1-6] Using the geometry of Fig. 1, Snell's law is

$$n_1 \sin \theta_1 = n_2 \sin \theta_2 \qquad (1)$$

If you know the refractive index of one of the media and measure the angles θ_1 and θ_2, you can calculate the refractive index of the other medium.

We describe here a simple homemade experimental chamber for measuring accurately the angles needed to measure the refractive index of a transparent liquid. It is basically a transparent rectangular box with one side slightly tilted against the vertical. The three-dimensional representation of the box is shown in Fig. 2. The planes, denoted by *adhe* and *bcgf*, are made of 0.32-cm (1/8 in) Plexiglas. To construct these planes, two identical Plexiglas plates with dimensions 2.54 x 7.62 x 0.32 cm (1.0 x 3.0 x 0.13 in) were

mounted together side by side on a vise attached to a milling machine. The plates were tilted slightly so that the length of the plates was at an angle of about 5° with the horizontal axis and the excess material of the plates milled away. As a result, the length *eh* or *fg* was still 2.54 cm (1.0 in), and *ad* or *bc* was 2.32 cm (0.91 in). (If you lack a milling machine, you can mount the Plexiglas plates in a vise and then file the excess material away. One way is to mount the plates on the vise so that only the excess material is accessible for filing and file the material until the filing tool just scrapes the top of the vise. This procedure will give a result as good as milling.) After the plates *adhe* and *bcgf* were made, they were glued to two ordinary microscope glass slides of dimensions 2.54 x 7.62 x 0.10 cm (1.0 x 3.0 x 0.04 in) with epoxy adhesives. After the epoxy dried the "rectangular" tube was glued to a Plexiglas base plate of dimensions 7.62 x 8.89 x 0.64 cm (3.0 x 3.5 x 0.25 in).

The principle of operation of the simple homemade

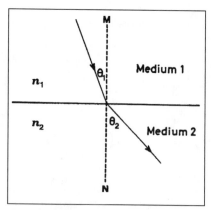

Fig. 1. Optical path of a monochromatic light beam traveling from Medium 1 to Medium 2. Dotted line *MN* is perpendicular to the interface of the two media; n_1 and n_2 are the refractive indices of the first and second media, respectively. In this example, n_1 is greater than n_2.

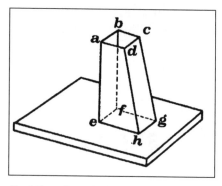

Fig. 2. Three-dimensional view of the experimental chamber. Faces *adhe* and *bcgf* are made of Plexiglas; *abfe* and *dcgh* are two ordinary microscope glass slides. The base plate is a piece of Plexiglas.

refractometer is as follows. With the experimental chamber empty, a He-Ne laser beam is aligned to illuminate the vertical face *abfe* of the chamber at normal incidence. The condition for normal incidence is achieved when the incident and reflected beams overlap. The aligned beam passes through the empty chamber with little deviation and strikes the viewing screen at P (Fig. 3). Make a mark on the screen where the laser beam strikes. Pour the liquid into the experimental chamber until the laser beam is below the liquid level. Now, as the beam exits the face *dcgh* at point O, it refracts and eventually illuminates the screen at a distance δ below the mark. The distance between O and P is L. For the discussion on how the refractive index of the liquid is evaluated it is assumed that the thickness of *dcgh* is negligible. The error induced by this assumption is small since the refractive indices of the liquid and the microscope slide are similar. If *dcgh* has no thickness, it essentially acts as the interface of the liquid and air. The incident angle of the laser beam at this interface is θ. According to Snell's law, the

refractive index (n) of the liquid can be expressed as

$$n = \sin \alpha / \sin \theta = \sin (\beta + \theta) / \sin \theta \qquad (2)$$

where

$$\beta = \arctan (\delta / L) \qquad (3)$$

The refractive index of air is taken to be unity. If θ and β are evaluated, n can be calculated with Eq. (2).

There are two simple ways to measure the angle θ. Both ways involve reflections from the tilted surface with the empty experimental chamber. The first way is illustrated in Fig. 4. The laser beam passes through a small hole on the screen. It is then aligned to illuminate the surface *abfe* at right angle. The alignment is achieved when the beam reflected from the surface *abfe* overlaps with the incident beam. This alignment is important because all subsequent measurements are taken when the incident beam is normal to the surface *abfe*. The reflection from *abfe* is projected onto a screen located at a distance L from *dcgh*. The reflection angle is equal to 2θ. Therefore,

$$\theta = 1/2 \arctan (S/L) \qquad (4)$$

A direct measure of S and L would provide θ. A larger L would yield a great accuracy in the determination of θ. The second way for evaluating θ is illustrated in Fig. 5. Again, the incident laser beam is aligned to illuminate the surface *abfe* at normal incidence. The major portion of the beam passes through *abfe* and *dcgh* with negligible deviation and then illuminates the screen at point P. A small portion is reflected by the surface *dcgh* and then reflected by *abfe*. Eventually the reflected light exits the experimental chamber and strikes the screen at a distance S below P. Since the laser beam illuminates the surface *dcgh* at an incident angle equal to θ, the angle $\angle ABC = \angle DCE = 2\theta$. Then

$$\tan (2\theta) = (S - AC)/(L + T) \qquad (5)$$

where

$$AC = T\tan (2\theta) \qquad (6)$$

Therefore

$$\theta = 1/2 \arctan [S/(L + 2T)] \qquad (7)$$

Clearly the second method for measuring θ is more complex than the first method. It requires an additional measurement of T [compare Eqs. (4) and (7)]. However, for the second method only one viewing screen is required, and it is

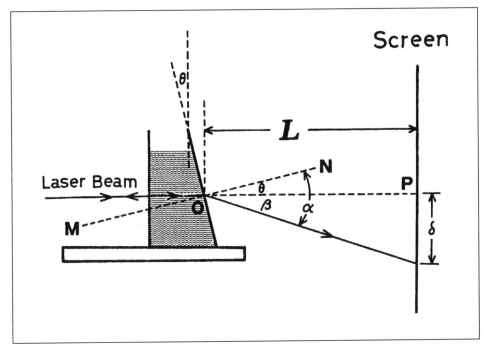

Fig. 3. Side view of the experimental chamber showing the optical path of the laser beam. The line *MN* is normal to the face *dcgh* (Fig. 2).

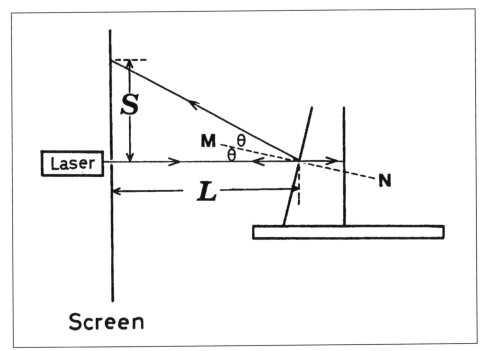

Fig. 4. Relationship between the reflection angle and the tilt (θ) of the face *dcgh*. The line *MN* is normal to the tilted face of the experimental chamber.

second method.

We have used the experimental chamber for a classroom demonstration. The laser and the chamber were placed on the lecture table with the chamber sitting on top of a lab jack. For the viewing screen we glued a large piece of graph paper on cardboard and positioned it 2.0 m from the chamber. Then about one-third of the chamber was filled with distilled water. Its height was adjusted so that the laser beam was about two centimeters above the water level. The beam was aligned perpendicular to the vertical face of the chamber. Its path length T (see Fig. 5) between the vertical and tilted faces of the chamber was measured to be 2.0 cm. With the room slightly darkened we saw two spots on the viewing screen. One spot was much brighter than the other. With a red pen we made a small dot on the graph paper to denote the location of the brighter spot and a small cross to denote the location of the dimmer spot. By measuring the distance between the red dot and cross, we determined S (see Fig. 5) to be 35.7 cm. Then the experimental chamber was raised so that the laser beam was below the water level. Again there were two laser spots on the viewing screen with one much brighter than the other. We used a green pen to mark the location of the brighter spot only. The distance between the red and green dots was measured to be 5.70 cm. The distance is δ (see Fig. 3). With these measurements

$$\theta = 1/2 \arctan [S/(L + 2T)] \tag{8}$$

$$= 1/2 \arctan [35.7/(200.0 + 4.0)] = 4.96°$$

according to Eq. (7), and

located to the right of the experimental chamber (see Figs. 5 and 3). For the first method one essentially needs to make two independent measurements, one for θ and one for β. After the θ measurement, the experimental chamber has to be rotated by 180° for the **β** measurement. We preferred the

$$\beta = \arctan(\delta/L) \qquad (9)$$
$$= \arctan[(5.70/200.0)] = 1.647°$$

according to Eq. (3). Accuracy of the distance measurements, and therefore of the angle measurements, is about 0.2 percent. Substituting these results into Eq. (2), we calculated n to be 1.331 ± 0.003. Using an Abbe refractometer and light from the He-Ne laser, we measured the refractive index of water to be 1.3315. We repeated the experiment for methanol and obtained 1.327 ± 0.003 with the experimental chamber and 1.328 with the Abbe refractometer. The results provided by the simple device described here are in excellent agreement with those found by using the commercial refractometer.

This device can be an excellent apparatus for classroom demonstration because students can visualize the laws of reflection and refraction. Furthermore, simple measurements with a graph paper can be made to produce precise values of refractive index. The largest refractive index that can be measured with the device is $1/\sin\theta = 11.57!$ This large upper limit seems unnecessary because most fluids have refractive indices less than 1.8. One can make a bigger θ to reduce the upper limit. The reason we chose $\theta \approx 5°$ is that $\sin\theta \approx \tan\theta \approx \theta$. Consequently, $\beta \approx \delta/L$ and $\theta \approx 1/2\ S/(L+2T)$ according to Eqs. (3) and (7). Then Eq. (2) can be simplified to

$$n \approx 1 + \beta/\theta = 1 + 2\delta(L + 2T)/LS \qquad (10)$$

Substituting $\delta = 5.70$ cm, $L = 200.0$ cm, $T = 2.0$ cm, and $S =$ 35.7 cm into Eq. (10), we obtained $n = 1.326$ for water. This value differs from that determined without approximations by only 0.4 percent.

The described apparatus has one defect. It requires a large amount of liquid. One obvious remedy is to scale down the dimension of the experimental chamber and inject liquid into the chamber with a syringe. For classroom demonstrations, however, a larger chamber should be used so that the audience can have a better view.

References

1. K. Tennekone, "A simple, sensitive method for measuring the refractive index of a liquid," *Am. J. Phys.* **44**, 303 (1976).
2. K. Hagenbuch and B. Scott, "Comment on the note 'A simple, sensitive method for measuring the refractive index of a liquid'," *Am. J. Phys.* **45**, 1004 (1977).
3. M.V.R.K. Murty and R.P. Shukla, "Simple method for measuring the refractive index of a liquid," *Opt. Eng.* **18**, 177 (1979).
4. M.V.R.K. Murty and R.P. Shukla, Simple method for measuring the refractive index of a liquid or glass wedge," *Opt. Eng.* **22**, 227 (1983).
5. B.P. Chandra and S.C. Bhaiya, "A simple, accurate alternative to the minimum deviation method of determining the refractive index of a liquid," *Am. J. Phys.* **51**, 160 (1983).
6. A.F. Leung, S. George, and R. Doebler, "Refractive index of a liquid measured with a He-Ne laser," *Phys. Teach.* **29**, 226 (1991).

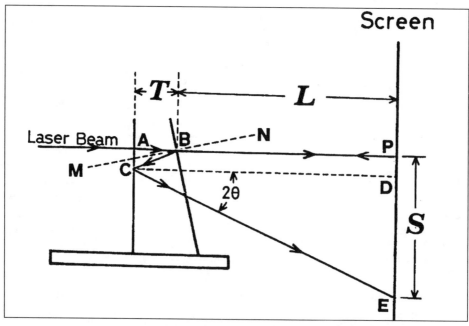

Fig. 5. Relevant optical paths of the laser beam illuminating the empty experimental chamber. The line *MN* is normal to the face *dcgh*. The line *CD* is parallel to the incident laser beam. The length of the line *AB* is *T*, and that of *BP* is *L*.

Measurement of Water's Refractive Index

P.M. Mejas, Departamento de Electricidad y Magnetismo (Optica), Universidad Nacional de Educacin a Distancia, 28040 Madrid, Spain

This note describes a simple experiment to determine the index of refraction of water. The experiment is based on the laws of reflection and refraction.[1]

Let us consider a linear object O, perpendicular to the water's surface (see Fig. 1). As observed from E, point B of the object's submerged part can be seen because ray 2 is refracted at the surface of the water. Point B appears to be in direction $\overrightarrow{EC}$, where C is the point where O intersects with the extension of ray 2 in the air. On the other hand, from E we can also see point A of the unsubmerged part of the object by the reflection of ray 1 on the water's surface. Point A also appears to coincide with C, and A's reflected image is actually found on C. Taking all of this into account, it is a matter of simply applying the aforementioned laws to demonstrate that water's refractive index can be obtained through the expression (neglecting dispersion)

$$n_w = [H^2(h+d)^2 + h^2D^2]^{1/2} [D^2 + (h+d)^2]^{-1/2} z^{-1} \quad (1)$$

where the quantities h, d, H, and D are shown in Fig. 1.

To obtain Eq. (1), note that $\tan\theta = (h+d)/D$ and $\tan\theta_r = \overrightarrow{PQ}/H = h/(H\tan\theta)$ (see Fig. 1). Then applying Snell's law: $\sin(\pi/2 - \theta) = n_w \sin\theta_r$.

Our experimental problem is thus to measure these distances. To do this, an opaque ruler with clearly marked divisions may be used for object O, submerged in a pan filled with water. To avoid error in measurement, we can observe the ruler through a hole ($\approx$ 1 mm in diam) in a piece of cardboard placed as is shown in Fig. 1. Through this hole we can see (below the surface of the water) two superimposed scales which correspond to the reflected and refracted images of the ruler's divisions: The refracted image will always be seen more clearly than the reflected one, but the latter may be made clearer by decreasing the angle θ. Once

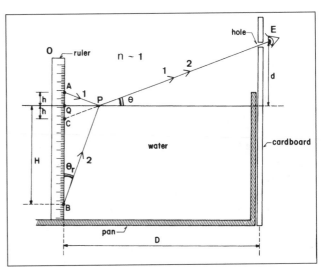

Fig. 1. Experimental setup.

this has been adequately adjusted, it is sufficient to note two coinciding divisions of both reflected and refracted scales, and to measure the distances d and D. Then, using these data, the value of n_w can be determined using Eq. (1).

Naturally, the water's surface should be kept absolutely still during measurements. Typical values for this experiment are d $\approx$ 70 mm, h $\approx$ 40 mm, D $\approx$ 250 mm, and H $\approx$ 100 mm.

Through the procedure just described, a mean value for n_w is found to be between 1.33 and 1.34 (ultimately depending on the observer, water temperature, etc.).

Reference

1. See, for example, F.A. Jenkins and H.E. White, *Fundamentals of Optics,* (McGraw-Hill, New York, 1981).

Refractive Index of a Liquid Measured with a He-Ne Laser

Alfred F. Leung, Simon George, *and* **Robert Doebler,** Department of Physics and Astronomy, California State University, Long Beach, CA 90840

Snell's law is usually used in the determination of the refractive index of a substance. This determination involves measurements of the incident and refraction angles of a light beam. When possible, the refraction angle is set at 90° to simplify the angle measurement.[1] The incident angle that gives rise to a refraction angle of 90° is called the critical angle. Consequently, a measurement of the critical angle yields the refractive index. To achieve a refraction angle of 90°, however, it is necessary to have the light beam travel from the denser medium to the rarer medium. We have constructed a simple refractometer that allows a He-Ne laser beam to travel from a liquid to air. By adjusting the incident angle of the laser beam at the liquid-air interface, we can easily set the refraction angle to 90° and obtain the critical angle. With the value of the critical angle, we obtain the refractive index of the liquid using Snell's law.

Our refractometer, which can provide a quick measurement of the refractive index to within one percent accuracy, is shown schematically in Fig. 1. A He-Ne laser is used as the light source, with its beam aligned to be horizontal. This horizontal beam first passes through a wall of a plastic chamber filled with a liquid, and then illuminates a small mirror[2] submerged in the liquid. The mirror is glued to one end of a shaft. The shaft, which is horizontal but perpendicular to the laser beam, passes through a hole in the wall of the chamber so that the free end is outside of the chamber. A shaft holder is necessary to prevent any liquid leaking out of the chamber through the cracks between the shaft and the wall of the chamber. The construction of such a shaft holder is shown in Fig. 2. After the shaft system has been constructed, including the mirror, a protractor is glued on the wall of the chamber (Fig. 3).

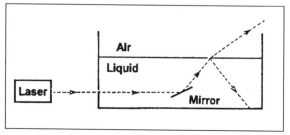

Fig. 1. Schematic of the refractometer. The incident light beam is first reflected by the mirror. The reflected beam is then reflected and refracted at the liquid-air interface.

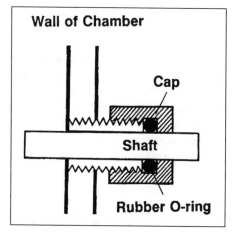

Fig. 2. Diagram of the shaft holder. The left end of the shaft is inside the chamber. The cap presses the rubber O-ring against the shaft so that liquid cannot leak out of the chamber along the shaft. Although the rubber ring is pressed hard against the shaft, the shaft can still be rotated easily if a small amount of silicone lubricant is put on the rubber ring. A simpler but less reliable method is to drill a small hole (= 0.3 cm) in a wall of the chamber so that a shaft can pass tightly through this hole. A small amount of silicone lubricant placed on the contact surface between the shaft and the chamber would prevent any liquid leakage.

By turning the free end of the shaft we can rotate the mirror submerged in the liquid. The amount of rotation of the mirror is monitored by the protractor. The mirror is first rotated to a position where its surface is at 45° from the horizontal. At this position, light reflected by the mirror is incident on the liquid-air interface at a right angle, and consequently the incident and reflected beams overlap each other. Under the overlapping condition the incident angle of the laser beam at the liquid-air interface is zero, and the protractor is adjusted to read zero. To find the critical angle associated with the liquid, the mirror is rotated toward the horizontal axis. As the mirror is rotated, the angle between the refracted beam and the liquid-air interface becomes smaller. Eventually the refracted beam lies on the interface. It is then scattered by the meniscus of the liquid at the wall of the chamber. This indicates that the refracted beam is on the liquid-air interface and the refraction angle is 90°. The

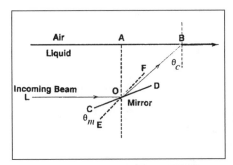

Fig. 4. Optical path of the laser beam. *EF* indicates the original position of the mirror. *CD* represents the new mirror position where the reflected light beam is at the critical angle relative to the liquid-air interface.

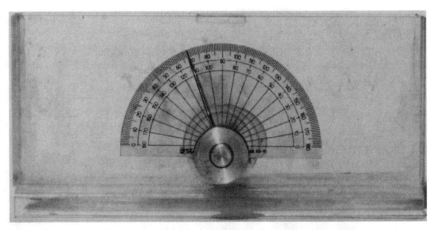

Fig. 3. A protractor is glued on the wall of the refractometer chamber. Any rotation of the shaft turns the needle. The amount of rotation is determined by the settings of the needle.

relationship between the critical angle (θ_c) and rotation angle (θ_m) of the mirror is shown in Fig. 4. The mirror is initially at *EF*, which is at 45° to the horizontal. Then it is rotated by angle θ_m to the position *CD*. At this mirror position the laser beam reflected from the mirror is incident on the liquid-air interface at the critical angle. According to Fig. 4, the angle $LOC + 90° + \theta_c + BOD = 180°$. The reflection angles are equal or $LOC = BOD$. Then, $2LOC + \theta_c = 90°$. $LOE - \theta_m = 45° - \theta_m = LOC$. Then, $2(45° - \theta_m) + \theta_c = 90°$ and $\theta_c = 2\theta_m$. Therefore, the critical angle is equal to twice the angle of rotation of the mirror. The refractive index, n, of the liquid is determined by

$$n = \frac{1}{\sin \theta_c} = \frac{1}{\sin (2\theta_m)} \tag{1}$$

To facilitate further refractive index measurements, the angular graduations of the protractor are converted to readings of refractive index value according to Eq. (1). In other

words, the amount of the mirror's rotation, which gives rise to the critical refraction, is expressed in terms of refractive index values.

We have used this simple refractometer as a classroom demonstration to measure the refractive index of water and anisole ($C_6H_5OCH_3$). The index values of these liquids were determined to be 1.32 and 1.51, respectively. Anisole can corrode a plastic chamber and therefore any measurement should be made as quickly as possible.

References

1. D.C. Giancoli, *Physics*, 2nd ed. (Prentice-Hall, Englewood Cliffs, NJ), p. 531.
2. First-surface mirror (9.4 x 26 x 3.2 mm) purchased from Edmund Scientific for $4.15.

"Colgate-Plus "— An Imperfect Light Pipe

P.J. Ouseph, Physics Department, University of Louisville, Louisville, KY 40292

Optical fibers have played a key role in the recent communications revolution and have helped in the development of several medical instruments capable of directly observing internal organs. Optical fibers use total internal reflections to transmit light from one end to the other.[1] These fibers can be bent to "pipe" light around corners. However, sharp bends (with radius of curvature less than 20 times the radius of the fiber) produce light loss at the bends through the surface. There are other causes that may contribute to the decrease in the intensity of transmitted light, including internal non-uniformity resulting from presence of other materials and surface irregularities such as

small protrusions. The transparent colorless Colgate-Plus toothbrush can be used to demonstrate the effects of these factors.

This particular toothbrush has several protrusions on the handle: the letters in Colgate-Plus and a few lines above the letters. Just above the lines there is a sharp bend and a sudden change in width and thickness. The bristles embedded in the toothbrush act as good light-scattering centers. When laser light is passed through the brush, light exits at the protrusions, at the sharp bend, and at the bristles, thereby producing a very impressive view of the brush. Because of these losses, the intensity of light coming through the other

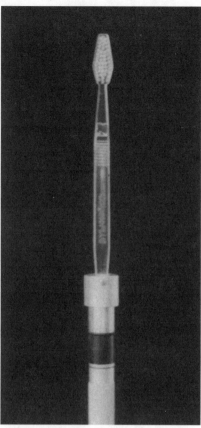

Fig. 1. The toothbrush is fixed to the laser with the help of an aluminum adapter and small screw.

Fig. 2. Front (left) and back (right) views of the brush with laser light going through it.

Figure 2 shows the front and back views of the toothbrush. The light seen at the letters, at the lines, and at the bend is similar in both views. However, there is a significant difference in the light intensity distribution at the bristles in the two views. In the front view the outer bristles appear brighter than the central bristles; in the back view all bristles appear equally bright. In the back, light is scattered equally by all bristles; in the front view we see mainly the light transmitted through the bristles. The outer bristles are transparent and therefore "pipe" more light to the front; the inner bristles are translucent (milky white) and hence block the light. This demonstration using an inexpensive toothbrush generates a lot of interest in my general physics class.

References

1. Amon Yarev, *Sci. Am.* **240** (1), 64 (1979). This article also contains the details of a system where a flowing jet of water is used as an optical pipe.
2. Laser available from Jenovation Optoelectronics, 672 Broadway Street, Suite 5, San Francisco, CA 94133. Price: $120.00

end of the brush is small. Hence the title: imperfect light pipe.

Figure 1 shows the arrangement we use for this demonstration. The handle of the toothbrush is in contact with the glass cover of the laser, and the toothbrush is held in position with the help of an inch-long aluminum adapter that goes tightly over the tube covering the laser. Note that the end of the brush in contact with the laser is not smoothened by sanding or machining. A screw in the adapter holds the brush in position. The laser (a diode laser used as a pointer for an overhead projector screen) has a beam output power of 5 mW.[2]

On Teaching Why a Rainbow Is Bowshaped

Paul G. Hewitt, City College of San Francisco, San Francisco, CA 94112

I have always had trouble explaining the bow shape of the rainbow, but have recently discovered that three colored dowels stuck in a wooden ball helps me to succeed. The dowels are about a meter long, and the ball is about 6 cm in diam, large enough for drilled holes to hold the dowels. The ball may be painted light greenish blue to represent a water drop, and a white dowel stuck in it represents an incoming ray of white sunlight. Violet and red dowels stuck in the ball, as shown in Fig. 1, represent rays of refracted violet and red light. For accuracy, the angle between the white and violet would properly be 40° and between the white and red 42°. (I use 43° between white and red so I have a visible 3° between the violet and red dowels—approximations to these angles do the job quite well.)

After an explanation of refraction and reflection in raindrops, this apparatus helps to explain why the rainbow has its bow shape. Enlist a student volunteer to crouch about a meter in front of the chalkboard. Hold the ball very near the board, above the student's head, with the white dowel perpendicular to the board. This position represents light from a rising or setting sun. I've found this perpendicular orientation of the white dowel most handy because it makes scribing a bow on the board easier and also provides an easy-to-follow reference when placing the ball at other locations.

Place the ball where the free end of the violet dowel nearly meets the student's eye. State that a drop of water at the location of the ball will refract violet light to the student's eye. The question follows: "Are there other locations that will also refract violet light to the student's eye?" Move the "drop" to other locations along the board, while keeping the white dowel perpendicular to the board, and show that

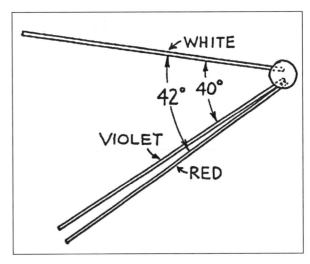

Fig. 1. Dowels used to show why a rainbow is bow-shaped.

refracted violet from drops farther away miss the eye altogether. It is easy to see that the only other locations that will send violet light to the student's eye are along a bow, which you trace on the board with violet or blue chalk. This is easy to accomplish if the student holds the end of the violet dowel near his or her eye while you scribe the arc in compass fashion (Fig. 2).

Then position the drop at the top of the arc, above and in front of the student's head, and ask where he or she must look to see red light. The answer is, a bit higher (2° higher, to be exact). Move the drop higher until the red dowel lines up with the student's eye. While your student holds the end of the red dowel near his or her eye, sweep the slightly wider arc along the board with red chalk to represent the outer border of the visible bow. So we see the outer part is red and the inner part violet.

We see the rainbow as an arc rather than a full circle only because the ground is in the way. From an airplane, full-circle rainbows are seen.

There's more. Have another student come forward and get near your first student. Ask the class if the second student is in a position to see the rainbow seen by the first student. You then have established the interesting fact that we all see our own personal rainbows. You may do as Marshall Ellenstein does and quip that when one person says to another, "Look at the beautiful rainbow," an appropriate response is, "Move over and let me see!"

Fig. 2. Part of a cone is scribed with the eye at the apex.

Mirrors, Lenses

Multiple Reflections from Common Mirrors

Jay S. Huebner, Physics Section, Department of Natural Sciences, University of North Florida, Jacksonville, FL 32216

The differences between front- and rear-surface mirrors are well known to physics and astronomy teachers. The number of images produced by rear-surface mirrors seems to be less well known, however. Fig. 1 was made by placing two mirrors in front of a Commodore SX-64 computer screen. The left mirror was glass-side-up: the right mirror was metal-side-up. Both mirrors were # 31578, Edmund Scientific, Barrington, NJ 08007, which are 9 x 50 x 110 mm each, and reflect from both sides.

An alternative arrangement that we use in our first physics lab covering optics is to place a 6V lamp (# 47, General Electric) close to the mirror. One clear image is seen from the metal side. Seven images of the filament may be clearly seen from the glass side, but they do not photograph as well as the computer-generated image shown in Fig. 1. A toothpick, needle. or pencil point held near a conventional household mirror will illustrate the effect, showing three clear images when the angle of incidence is greater than 45°. A dark background helps make the images easier to see. Four or five images can be seen at 70° with normal room lighting. The ray diagram shown in Fig. 2 is useful for explaining the origin of the multiple images and their relative brightness. The distance between the images increases with the angle of incidence as well as the thickness of the glass. Two images are also easily seen with common window glass.

Fig. 1 shows that all of the images are inverted. This inversion results since they are each produced by an odd number of reflections. In sequence, down the left side of the photograph: 1 reflection for an air-glass reflection; 1 for glass-metal; 3 for glass-metal, glass-air, and glass-metal; 5 etc.

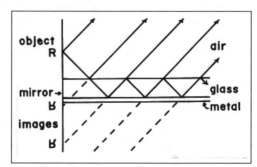

Fig. 2. Ray diagram illustrating how reflections from the two surfaces of a rear-surface mirror produce multiple images.

Many students are surprised by the fact that they have used mirrors for many years in grooming, yet were not aware of the multiple images. This is probably due to the fact that in grooming, the light is reflected close to the normal, placing the images on top of each other, while multiple images are most apparent when angles far from normal are used.

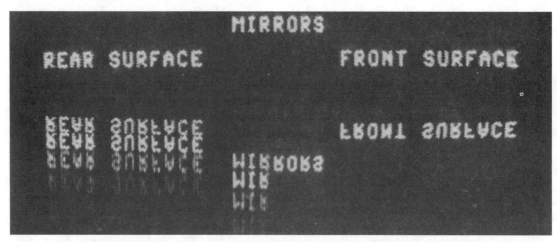

Fig. 1. Photograph of a computer-generated image (top) reflected in a rear surface mirror (left) and front-surface mirror (right).

Low-cost Cylindrical Mirrors

Se-yuen Mak, Department of Curriculum and Instruction, Faculty of Education, The Chinese University of Hong Kong, Shatin, N. T. Hong Kong

Cylindrical mirrors are valuable for studying ray optics, but since such glass cylindrical mirrors are easily broken, they must be handled with caution. However, we have found a way to replace these breakable glass cylindrical mirrors with homemade plastic ones. Our simple recipe for making plastic cylindrical mirrors requires no special skill or equipment and can be carried out even at home.

Procedure

(1) Obtain Plexiglas plane mirror strips of width 1.5 cm and at least 0.5 m long from your local plastics supplier. The length (ℓ) of the strip depends on the choice of the focal length (f) of the product and is determined by the simple formula $\ell = 2\pi r = 4\pi f$. Since an exact dimension is not required, scrap materials may be used. This both reduces costs and saves cutting time.

(2) Bend the strip into a closed loop and bind the ends together with string or a piece of waterproof adhesive tape. The silvered surface should be on the outside for convex mirrors, and the inside for concave mirrors. Since a fairly even stress is developed in the loop, its shape is very close to a perfect circle (Fig. 1).

(3) Immerse the loop in boiling water for three minutes, then allow it to set firm in cold water for one to two minutes. Direct heating of the mirror strip in a flame is not recommended since this may cause the metal film to detach from the plastic.

(4) Cut the circle into segments of desired length. Discard the distorted portion near the joint. Figure 2 shows a few sample products, and Fig. 3 shows a typical experimental result using one such mirror.

Comments

A small-scale production project of such cylindrical mirrors sponsored by the Hong Kong Association of Science and Mathematics Education was carried out in 1980. About 200 Hong Kong high schools benefited from the project and many of the schools are still using these mirrors. According to my own experience, a production rate of 2000 pieces of cylindrical mirrors per person-day is possible. Projects of a similar kind could be carried out by local education authorities or science teachers' associations almost anywhere in the world.

Fig. 1. The plastic loop forms an almost perfect circle.

Fig. 2. A few finished products.

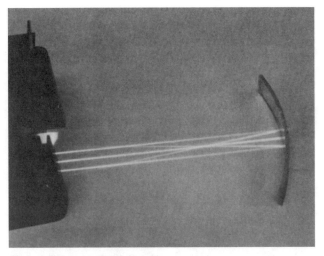
Fig. 3. A sample experimental result.

Heat-Wave Focusing by Concave Reflectors

Richard E. Berg, University of Maryland, College Park, MD 20742

Because radiant heat waves are electromagnetic waves with properties similar to light waves, heat waves from a distant source can be focused to a point by a parabolic reflector. A pair of polished metal parabolic reflectors (30-cm diameter, 8-cm focal length) are commercially available for this purpose.[1] Freier and Anderson used such a reflector to light a cigarette with a carbon arc lamp from a distance of 30 feet.[2]

We have developed a somewhat different demonstration sequence using two such parabolic reflectors, a match, and a homemade heat source. The heat source, shown in Fig. 1, was constructed from a coil of nichrome wire[3] wound on a fired-lava base.[4] The lava was first machined and then fired for electrical resistance, mechanical strength, and resistance to heat and abrasion. After that preparation, we mounted the nichrome coil in position using screws threaded into the lava before firing. Our heat source is about 7 cm in diameter and does not use a full 110-V coil of nichrome wire; we use a variac to run it at about 80 V.

The demonstration is done very effectively in three stages, with the equipment arranged as shown in the second figure.

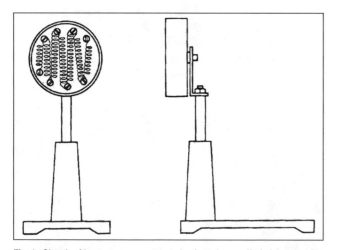

Fig. 1. Sketch of heat source constructed using a long coil of nichrome wire wound on a fired-lava base.

1. Place the heat source about one meter from the match. Heat waves spread out as they propagate away from the source; therefore, the intensity is insufficient to ignite the match [Fig. 2(a)].

2. Position one parabolic reflector behind the match so that it focuses the heat waves onto the match head. The

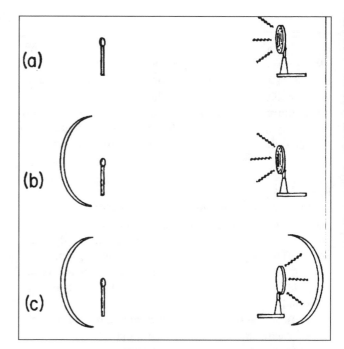

Fig. 2. The three sequential setups in our demonstration of lighting a match with a heater using focusing mirrors. In (a) the match does not light, in (b) the match lights after a moderate time interval, and in (c) the match lights more quickly.

match almost immediately begins to smoke and lights in about 15 s [Fig. 2(b)].

3. With the match and first reflector kept in the same position, rotate the heat source 180° so that it faces away from the match and position the second reflector with the heat source at its focal point. The second mirror reflects heat waves diverging from the source to produce a beam of heat waves aimed at the first reflector, which in turn focuses them onto the match head. The match ignites in less than 10 s [Fig. 2(c)].

Note that the focal point of the first mirror is slightly different in cases (b) and (c) because the rays from the source are not coming in parallel in (b). This nearly negligible effect is due to the large size of the source. Compensation for this can be made by a small adjustment of the position of either mirror. Focusing the heat waves onto the match head can be done in a few seconds using parallax between the match head and the image of the heater.

The time difference between the two setups for igniting the match is clearly due to the increase in the amount of heat on the match head. This results from increasing the solid angle of collection of heat by placing the second mirror close to the source.

This demonstration excites people of all ages and experience levels and surprises many knowledgeable individuals who have not thought about the effect of solid angle in such a context.

References

1. Sargent-Welch Parabolic Reflectors, Catalog Number 1737.

2. G.D. Freier and F.J. Anderson, *A Demonstration Handbook for Physics*, 2nd ed. (American Association of Physics Teachers, College Park, MD, 1981), Demonstration Oc-9, Lighting a Cigarette.

3. 115-V, 1000-W nichrome coils are available from JEM, 4111 Primrose Ave., Baltimore, MD 21215.

4. Machinable Grade A Lava is available from General Electric Ceramics, Inc., P.O. Box 89, Laurens, SC 29360.

The 70-mm Kaleidoscope

Terrence P. Toepker, Physics Department, Xavier University, Cincinnati, OH 45207-4111

For ten years we've been using homemade kaleidoscopes such as described here. When I saw such a device being passed out during a recent AAPT meeting, it occurred to me that it might be useful to pull together for *TPT* readers some ideas on how to construct and use this little apparatus. The "toy" is inexpensive to make, fascinating to use, and has educational value.

Warning: If you start this project, be sure to have a source of film canisters. You will be surprised by the number of kaleidoscopes you can "make and take" over a school year!

Construction

For each kaleidoscope you will need two *plastic* 35-mm film canisters and three microscope slides. (Experience has taught us that glass slides can easily be broken when trying to fit them into the canisters. Especially when working with young children, we recommend using 3- x 1-in plastic slides, even though they are a bit more expensive than glass ones.[1] Also, the plastic slides have a slightly looser fit than glass ones, so the canisters can be rotated relative to one another, just as in commercial kaleidoscopes.)

Discard the canister tops. Drill a quarter-inch hole in the end of each film canister. Figure 1 shows how the three slides are fitted snugly into one canister to make an equilateral triangle. Slide the open ends of the canisters together, covering the slides. Look into one hole; you will clearly see the hole on the other end *and* 12 clear reflections from the three glass surfaces. Since the angle of incidence for the incoming light is rather large (almost grazing), the percentage of reflected light is high. (Of course commercial kaleidoscopes use front surface mirrors, which are quite expensive.)

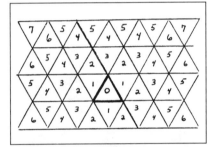

Fig. 2a. Equilateral triangle array with the number of reflections that make the image. Zero is the hole in the kaleidoscope.

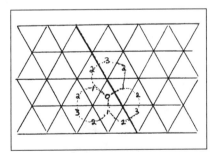

Fig. 2b. Equilateral array with dotted lines to emphasize symmetry of pattern seen in the kaleidoscope.

Comments

The fascination with multiple images from mirrors has been treated in many texts and articles.[2,3] The diagram by Jearl Walker[4] for an equilateral triangle array is particularly instructive, as seen in Fig. 2. The number of reflections is represented by the number in the array.

With these inexpensive kaleidoscopes, 12 images are easily seen (and the hole in the center, of course). From Fig.

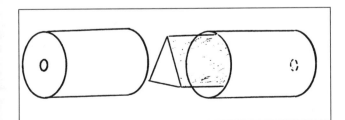

Fig. 1. Microscope slides fitted into two 35-mm film canisters.

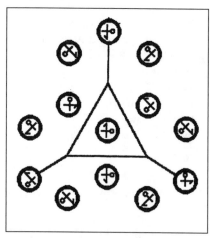

Fig. 3. "Oriented object" with the appropriate reflections, as seen in kaleidoscope.

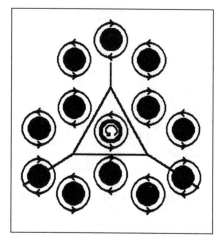

Fig. 4. Observe rotations of a six-sided pencil placed in hole of kaleidoscope.

Fig. 5. Put the figure together using the three single reflections and the center hole. The "body" should just fill the center hole.

2, all of the first reflections (marked 1), all of the second reflections (2), and the closest third reflections (3) are seen. Figure 2b shows the pattern with a dotted line connecting the images about each vertex. If you look through the hole and farther off to the side, more of the third reflections and some of the fourth reflections can be seen.

If you shine the bright light of a slide projector through the hole in the kaleidoscope, it is possible to observe the reflected light images. This works best if the kaleidoscope is tilted off-axis.

Figure 3 shows an "object" with a definite pattern for observing and identifying the various reflections. You can easily see this for yourself by making a small copy of the "object" on tracing paper. Tape this over one of the holes of your kaleidoscope. By referring to Figs. 2 and 3 at the same time, you can ver-

ify that a (2) reflection is a reflection of a (1) reflection, and a (3) reflection comes from a (2) reflection.

Figure 4 and a six-sided pencil provide another interesting observation. Insert the tip of the pencil in the hole of your kaleidoscope to partially restrict the light. Then spin the pencil to track the movement in reflections, like gears alternating direction at each cog. (It helps to make the hole slightly larger than the pencil.)

Using Fig. 5 and all of the (1) reflections, you can create the Xavier University (or something more local) figure! This may take a little practice, moving toward or away from the diagram.

Other Ideas

- Hold a colored marble over one end of the kaleidoscope; rotate it.
- Use pieces of colored filters for color mixing or partial covering of the hole.
- Cover the hole with a clear piece of tape and fit a slightly larger translucent "pill bottle" over the end. Put small pieces of colored filter paper in the pill bottle and rotate it.
- Look through the kaleidoscope with only one film canister on the slides. (Keep the open end away from your eye!)
- Try that idea again, looking in a mirror.
- Put your finger over the hole and see "red dots" as some light gets filtered through your fingers.

Acknowledgments

The film-canister kaleidoscopes Andria Erzberger was passing out at the 1995 winter meeting in Orlando during the "Dirty Demos" and "High-School Sharathon" were the motivation for this note. Thanks to my students P.J. McCarthy for Figs. 3 and 4, and Kristin Schmidt for Fig. 5.

References

1. Available from Sargent-Welch, 911 Commerce Court, Buffalo Grove, IL 60089; 800-727-4368; Catalog #S58810-50.
2. D. Falk, D. Brill, and D. Stork, *Seeing the Light* (Wiley, New York, 1986), p. 74.
3. R.K. Carpenter, "A favorite experiment," *Phys. Teach.* **11,** 428-430 (1973).
4. J. Walker, *Sci. Am.* **253**, 134-145 (1985).

A Technique for Making Brighter Rays

J.C. Martinez-Antón, Departamento de Óptica, Universidad Complutense de Madrid, Escuela Universitaria de Óptica, Arcos de Jalón s/n, 28037 Madrid, Spain

Geometrical optics in a student lab is often introduced by means of ray-tracing techniques. A common setup consists of a collimated light source and one or more slits on a slide, which permits passage of parallel, thin beams of light. These narrow vertical beams, when striking a slightly tilted table or board, produce what appears to be a one-dimensional ray. If we place a cylindrical lens in the path of the beams, we observe how the lens focuses the rays.

In practice, however, such a system is a little cumbersome. The width of the rays spreads, and since they are not very luminous, we have to work in virtual darkness.

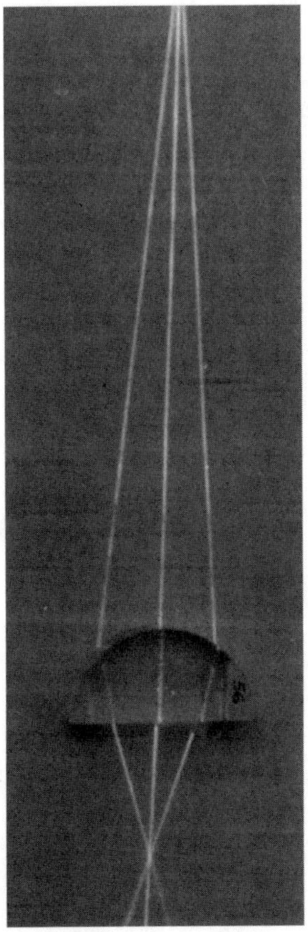

We have developed a simple system for our student laboratory that requires no special optical components, but vastly improves the luminous efficiency and sharpness of the projected rays. We find it possible to generate thinner (1 mm) and more luminous rays without resorting to a commercial ray box, but just by using common optical components available in most school labs (Fig. 1). The basic idea is to form the image of a thin slit on the work table or a board placed at grazing incidence. We make use of a Köhler illumination scheme, as is utilized in a standard slide projector. In this apparatus a condenser lens forms the image of the light source onto a second lens (the objective lens), which captures all the light that comes from the condenser. A slide is placed close to the condenser, allowing for its uniform illumination, and the objective lens then forms the image of the slide on a screen. In our modification (shown in Fig. 2), we use one or more thin slits instead of a slide, and for a screen we place a table in grazing incidence.

The condenser lens may be any one with a small focal

Fig. 1. The rays remain thin over a long distance.

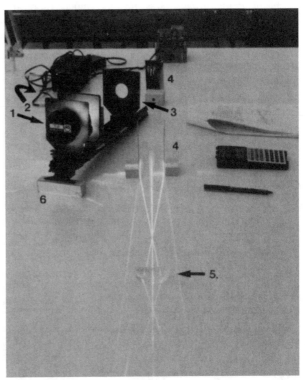

Fig. 2. Setup with component identification numbers: 1—light source; 2—condenser lens and slits; 3—objective lens; 4—mirror and glass plates to redirect light; 5—acrylic lens; 6—elevator to tilt optical bench and increase grazing incidence.

length (we use a 5-cm lens for the setup discussed here; all our lenses are of 36-mm diameter and are biconvex[1]). The objective lens used depends on how large (thin and short) and bright we intend to have the projected ray. We use a lens with 20-cm focal length; there is approximately 1 m between the lens and where the rays are being used. The light source is a 20-W halogen lamp with a filament measuring approximately 1 x 3 mm, and oriented parallel to the slits. We've found that slits that are between 0.1 and 0.2 mm thick work most successfully. We make them the easy way, by sticking some metal strips with straight and clean edges up on a flat glass support. To achieve a uniform and thin slit, we join two strips together while holding a sheet of paper between them, which gives a slit of about 0.1 mm. We use a simple mirror to redirect rays, thereby conserving space. Although the beams projected on the table are not parallel, we redirect the rays by reflecting them off glass plates at grazing incidence. Having the mirror at nearly normal incidence and the thin glass plates at grazing incidence avoids the visualization of multiple reflections. A more flexible choice is to use first-surface mirrors to redirect rays, but that is more expensive.

The experimental possibilities of this optical setup are greater than expected. Demonstrating Snell's law is more precise due to the narrowness of the beam. Also, other aspects of geometrical optics become much more discernible, including dispersion, the limit angle, multiple reflection, the chromatic and spherical aberration, and coma. Now we can control the width of the light beams, and

we don't have to work in the dark, which means that our students can keep notebooks and guides handy during the demonstration.

Acknowledgment

I want to thank E. Bernabeu, A. González-Cano, and M. Antón for suggestions and help in the development of this technique.

Reference

1. Our lenses, mounts, and bench are from Leybold-Heraeus GMBH, Köln—Werk 2, Leybold-Heraeus Strasse 1, Postfach 3250, 5030 Hürth, Germany.

Ray Tracing for a Few $

Harry D. Downing and *Walter L. Trikosko,* Department of Physics and Astronomy, Stephen F. Austin State University, Box 13044 SFA Station, Nacogdoches, TX 75692-3044, *and Paula Lovell,* Klein High School, 16715 Steubner Airline, Houston, TX 77379

There are kits[1] available that physically demonstrate light passing through thin lenses, but they can be very expensive for those teachers who have lean budgets. With this budgetary constraint in mind, we thought that it would be beneficial to design an inexpensive model with moving parts to show how the image formed by a positive thin lens changes as the object is moved. After designing and constructing several variations over a four-week period, we settled on a model for doing thin-lens ray diagramming (see Figs. 1 and 2).

We present here some general instructions only because readers may wish to modify the design once they understand the basic construction of the model. Detailed construction plans are available by writing or calling (409/568-2290) the authors.

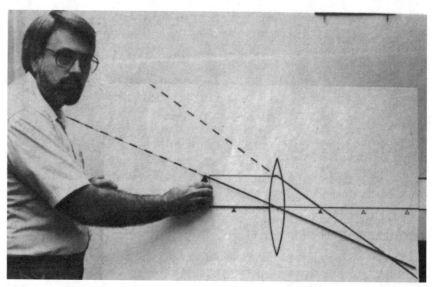

Fig. 1. Inexpensive ray tracer in use.

The base, spacers, and top shown in Fig. 2 are sandwiched and glued together so that a space for the slider exists between the top and base. The arrow, which serves as the object for the lens, is glued to the slider. The dowel, which represents the ray that passes through the center of the lens, is glued to a screw that passes through the arrow. The screw must be able to swivel so that the dowel can change positions as the "object" is moved closer to or far-

ther away from the lens. A T-pin or similar support is placed in the middle of the lens to support the wooden dowel. (The dowel rests on top of the pin and is not attached to it.) Felt markers are used to outline or highlight the lens, the arrow, the dowel, the optical axis and focal points, and the parallel-axis ray and its "dashed" extension for virtual images (see Fig. 1). To operate the model, one slides the slider in and out of the space between the top and the base of the model (see

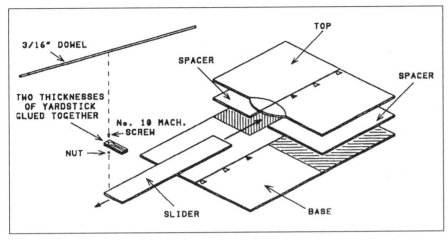

Fig. 2. Construction details.

State University. This model was well received by teachers at the 1989 fall meeting of the Texas section of AAPT and also at the 1990 AAPT summer meeting. At the latter meeting, the model shown in the photograph won first prize in the low-cost apparatus competition. A smaller version of this model proved very popular at two recent Texas section AAPT teacher workshops.

The model is simple, inexpensive, and easily modified;[2] it should fit the budget of any teacher. It should also provide ideas for other similar projects.

Fig. 1). The dowel will change position with this motion, and its intersection with the parallel-axis ray will identify the image location.

Working models made with foam board (Foamcore or Foamboard brands) have been constructed and tested, and they work admirably. The total expense should be under $20, and the time for constructing each model is approximately three hours. Even less expensive models made with poster board have been constructed by teachers taking our summer in-service teacher courses at Stephen F. Austin

References
1. Central Scientific Company Magnetic Blackboard Optics Kit, Catalog Number 30650-01.
2. Bill Franklin, physics teacher at Memorial High School in Houston, Texas, has already constructed similar models for concave lenses and convex and concave mirrors.

The Sloooow Camera

Charlotte Farrell, Vestal Central High School, Vestal, NY 13850

Teacher: This is a slow camera. This camera is *sloooow*.

Students: How slow is that camera?

Teacher: Let me put it this way. You know how camera shutters usually open and close in a few thousandths of a second? Well, this camera takes half an hour to get a picture of a 200 W light bulb.

So, who would want such a camera? Maybe you could use one. If optics is your students' least favorite physics topic, or if your students draw beautiful ray diagrams and then seem unable to relate the diagrams to any physical reality, this inexpensive piece of demonstration equipment could be just what you need.

The advantage of the slow camera as a demonstration is that, while it operates essentially like any other camera, the studio proof paper used as film allows the class to observe the image forming in the camera. The finished picture then

may be passed around the class for students to inspect closely without the usual darkroom steps. The camera and photographic processes have been reduced to the absolute basics. This allows the class to discuss the object, image, lens, and light rays of the diagram with a handy physical reference that is not too far removed from student experience.

The camera is a cardboard box with a lens at one end and a ground glass or waxed paper window at the other end. Any grocery carton works fine. Light leaks are no problem since the film is so slow. I've operated mine with the cover completely off on cloudy days. The one specification that matters is that the lens and ground glass be separated by approximately two and a half times the focal length of the lens. Even this dimension is not critical. Any box with close to the correct length will do.

The lens need not be special either. I am currently using

Fig. 1. The slow camera, cover removed, showing the object (200 W bulb with foil silhouette), lens (taped to one side of box), and ground glass window with "film" taped to the opposite side. In use, the silhouette faces the lens and the distance is adjusted to focus the image on the ground glass. The "film" and glass are transparent enough that the class can watch the image turn magenta as the exposure occurs.

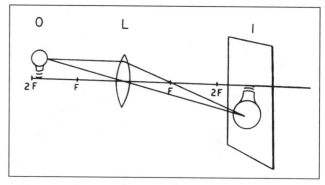

Fig. 2. A typical ray diagram of the situation illustrated by the camera. O = object, L = lens, I = image.

an inexpensive magnifying glass with a 6 cm diameter ($2.90 at the local museum gift shop). The paper is so slow that a large diameter lens is more important than a high quality lens.

The "film" in this slow camera is studio proof paper.[1] At $17 for an envelope of 25 sheets, this is the most expensive part of the camera, but the sheets may be cut into quarters, giving enough paper for 100 demonstrations. I have had the paper for 3 years now, using some each year, so that over the long term, the price seems reasonable in terms of the resulting student understanding. I cut the paper in the dark-room and slip the pieces needed for the day's demonstrations into a manilla envelope which stays in a drawer in the demonstration desk until needed. [*Editor's note:* We recently learned that this "film" is no longer available. We publish this note in the belief that some ingenious reader will come up with a usable substitute and will share this information with *TPT* readers.]

We use a 200-W light bulb with an aluminum foil silhouette of the school's mascot taped to the glass. I set up the camera with the ground glass facing the class and focus the image of the light bulb on the glass by adjusting the distance from light bulb to front of camera. On sunny days the shades should be drawn, but no other concessions to the paper are needed. I remove the paper from the envelope in front of the class and tape it to the inside of the ground glass window, then turn on the light bulb object. The paper and

ground glass are transparent enough that the class can watch the reddish color appear as the image builds.

Since it takes about half an hour, this is a good time to discuss what is happening. Usual topics that come up during the class discussions are: the parallels between the parts of the camera and a typical ray diagram, the functions of the parts of this camera as compared to the students' more familiar cameras, what a lens does to the light that passes through it, and how film works.

From the "aha" expressions that occur, I can only conclude that students get so hung up with the mechanisms of shutter, film advance, and focus on modern cameras that the connection between the familiar camera at home, thin lens experiments, and ray diagrams gets lost.

Toward the end of class I remove the picture and allow the class to examine it at close range. The whole experience seems worthwhile in terms of increased student understanding.

References

1. The toll-free Kodak customer service number is (800)242-2424. The person who answers has computer files available and can give the calling teacher the names of dealers in their home city with authority to special order the proof paper (cat. 143 3150) from Kodak's stock of discontinued items. The pictures can be preserved with Kodak fixer (cat. 197 1720) to prevent darkening over time. Directions are printed on the package. The ground glass (approx. 18 cm x 18 cm, $6.05) is available from Edmund Scientific, 101 E. Glouster Pike, Barrington, NJ 08007. It provides a stable surface on which to tape the paper. Waxed paper, while somewhat flimsy, works almost as well.

Locating Images Formed by Diverging Lenses

D.A. Crandles and *R.P. Kauffman,* Department of Physics and Astronomy, Franklin and Marshall College, Lancaster, PA 17604-3003; d_crandles@acad.fandm.edu; r_kauffman@acad.fandm.edu

One of the goals in a geometrical optics lab is for students to measure the focal length of a lens. The procedure is quite simple for positive lenses where a real image of an object is formed at the focal point on a screen if the object is placed very far from the lens. Diverging lenses, however, do not produce real images, and measuring the focal length in this instance is not so easy. We have developed a simple apparatus that allows students to determine the position of the virtual image by means of parallax and thereby locate the focal point for a lens.

As illustrated in Fig. 1, the method of parallax is often used to locate virtual images formed by plane mirrors. Students consider the line of sight (perpendicular to the mirror) joining the object to its image. They place an image position-finder (perhaps a pin on a cork) along this line at a certain position behind the mirror and simultaneously observe the relative positions of image position-finder and the virtual image as they change their line of sight. When students find the point at which pin and image do not move relative to each other, even as they move their eyes between the two lines of sight, they have located the position of the virtual image.

A simple design for an image position-finder that works for diverging lenses (with PASCO's optics bench, # OS-9103) is illustrated in Fig. 2. Cut a 3/4-in slice of 6-in-diameter PVC pipe and slit the pipe section so that it will fit over the optical bench as shown in the bottom sketch of Fig. 2. (The polyvinyl chloride material is flexible and rugged enough to withstand rough treatment without breaking.) Tap a hole for a screw opposite the slit made in the PVC and machine a point at the screw tip. As the bottom diagram shows, the lens must not obstruct the screw tip.

To use the apparatus, place the position-finder between the object and the lens and view the object through the lens (Fig. 2, top sketch). Locating the position of the virtual image is accomplished by considering the relative positions of the image viewed through the lens and an imaginary line that extends downward from the screw. Typically, students can locate the focal point of an $f = -15$-cm lens to within the nearest centimeter.

The apparatus can also be used, of course, as a second way to locate the real images formed by converging lenses if the lens is placed between the object and the position-finder.

Acknowledgment

The authors would like to thank S. Spadafore for suggesting the use of PVC pipe for the image-finder.

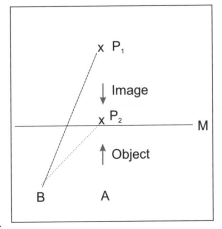

Fig. 1. Method of parallax in locating position of virtual image (I) formed by plane mirror (M). User compares relative positions of image and image position-finder X (e.g., a pin) when moving eye from observation point A to observation point B. If position-finder is at an incorrect position (e.g., P_1 or P_2), it will move relative to the image as viewer changes line of sight. When image and position-finder do not move relative to each other, the position-finder is at the location of the virtual image.

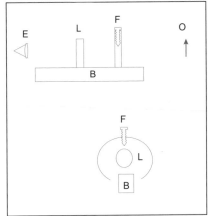

Fig. 2. Method of parallax in locating position of virtual image formed by diverging lens. Position-finder (F) fits over optical bench (B) and slides along bench between object (O) and lens (L). Observer (E) views object through lens and sees virtual image. Position-finder is in correct position when the virtual image viewed through lens and an imaginary line extending vertically downward from the screw do not move relative to each other.

A Biconvex Diverging Lens

R.H. Stinson, Department of Physics, University of Guelph, Guelph, ONT N1G 2W1 Canada

Students learn that a positive (biconvex) lens is a converging lens. They can easily lose sight of the fact that this is so because the lens is in air—a medium with an index of refraction less than that of the lens. A simple demonstration shows that having the lens in a medium with a higher index of refraction will make the biconvex lens a diverging (negative) lens.

We obtained two fish bowls with flat sides and convex ends. One is filled with water (with air outside), and a laser beam shone through it. As the laser is moved up and down to shine through the top or bottom halves, it is quite obvious that there is conventional behavior. The usual tricks of chalk dust in the air and a drop of milk in the water make the beams more visible.

The other fishbowl (empty) is placed in a rectangular

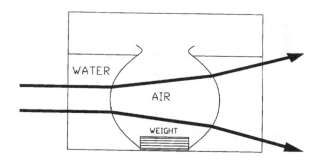

aquarium (see diagram). The bowl is weighted down and the aquarium filled with water. The procedure used with the first bowl is repeated; it is immediately obvious that the lens is now diverging the light rays.

Fluid Lenses

Roger E. Malcom, Kewanee High School, Kewanee, IL 61443

When teaching optics, I observe my students readily comprehending that the shape of a lens is important for the formation of images, but I have difficulty convincing them of the importance of the content of a lens. I tried using curved bottles filled with various fluids,

immersing them in water, holding them up in the air, etc., but it wasn't convincing because the bottles did not look like lenses.

Fig. 1. The components for constructing a fluid lens.

Fig. 2. Two convex lenses.

After considering the problem, I arrived at the following solution. Each lens requires two 65-mm chemical watch glasses, one 6.35-cm (2.5-in) PVC pipe joint, and a "00" rubber stopper (Fig. 1). Drill a hole into the side of the PVC pipe joint large enough for the stopper to fit snugly, and with aquarium cement fasten the watch glasses to the ends of the joint, curved to the inside to make a concave lens and curved to the outside to make a convex lens. I made two sets of each so I could demonstrate as shown in Figs. 2 and 3. Figure 2 shows two convex lenses, the one on the right filled with water and held normally. But the convex lens on the left contains air and is immersed in water, giving the visible characteristics of most *concave* lenses. Figure 3 is two concave lenses used as in Fig. 2. Note that this time the left concave lens gives an image as if it were the usual *convex* lens.

Fig. 3. Two concave lenses.

Low-Cost Homemade Liquid-Lens Refractometer

V. Anantha Narayanan, Drew-Griffith Building, Savannah State College, Savannah, GA 31404, *and*

Radha Narayanan, Windsor Forest High School, Savannah, GA 31499

W e describe here the experimental and theoretical details for constructing and calibrating an inexpensive, homemade liquid-lens refractometer. The cost is next to nothing, and the project can be done by high-school and college physics students, perhaps as a take-home experiment. Figure 1 diagrams details of the setup.

Construction and Operation

We fashioned the container for the various liquid lenses we studied from the convex transparent plastic cap of a can of Clearasil Face Wash (wall thickness about 1 mm, flat face diameter 3.8 cm). With a cutting lathe we shortened the container to 1.6 cm. By filling the cap to the brim with various liquids of known refractive indices and covering the open top with a thin microscope slide, we were able to produce a variety of plano-convex liquid lenses. The ceiling lamp served as the object; our screen was a sheet of white paper on a clipboard lying on the floor directly under the lamp. In our case, this distance measured 249.5 cm, which represents the sum of the object and image distances of the thin-lens equation and is constant throughout.

After marking the middle of the lens, we held the lens between the lamp and the screen on the floor, adjusting position until a small well-defined image appeared on the paper. The distance from the middle of the lens to the screen (q) was measured (correct to 1 mm) by means of a metal ruler (calibrated to 1/2 mm) fixed vertically and firmly to

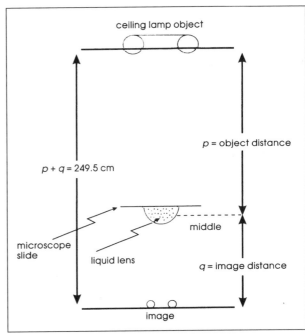

Fig. 1. Schematic for homemade liquid-lens refractometer.

the floor by a wedge in a wooden block. Using a simple magnifier to avoid parallax, we read the distance against the ruler, repeating the procedure three times. We found the average value of q in cm and rounded off to the nearest mm. The distance from the object to the middle of the lens (p) was found by subtracting q from 249.5 cm. We successive-

Table I. Focal-length values (in cm) for homemade lens

Liquid	Object Distance P	Thin-Lens Case Image Distance q	Focal Length f $pq/(p + q)$ Eq. (6)	Thick-Lens Case Focal Length f' $f' = (p + 0.3)(q - 0.8)/249$ Eq. (7)	Focal Length f' $f' = r/(n_L - 1)$ Eq. (8)*
Water	222.8	26.7	23.8	23.2	23.8
6½% salt solution	223.8	25.7	23.1	22.4	23.1
13% salt solution	223.9	25.6	23.0	22.3	22.3
40% sugar solution	227.2	22.3	20.3	19.6	19.9
50% sugar solution	228.1	21.4	19.6	18.9	18.9
Peanut oil	231.1	18.4	17.0	16.4	16.9
Castor oil	231.4	18.1	16.8	16.1	16.6
25% sugar solution	225.6	23.9	21.6	21.0	21.3
26% salt solution	226.0	23.5	21.3	20.6	20.9

*r = 7.94 cm; n_L = literature values of refractive indices.

ly filled the lens with nine liquids (see Table I), cleaning and drying the lens after each measurement, collecting and tabulating data for p and q.

We restricted our study to liquids within a very narrow range of values of n (between 1.3 and 1.5). The liquids we used can be handled safely by high-school students and are readily available. Now we derive the necessary formulas to use this refractometer.

Thin-Lens Formulas

The lensmakers' formula[1,2] for the focal length of a thin lens is given by

$$1/f = [(n_2/n_1) - 1] (1/r_1 + 1/r_2) \qquad (1)$$

where r_1 and r_2 are the radii of curvatures of the two faces of the lens; n_2 is the refractive index of the lens material; and n_1 is the refractive index of the medium that surrounds the lens. For a thin plano-convex liquid lens surrounded by air, the formula is

$$1/f (n_{liquid} - 1) (1/r) \qquad (2)$$

where r is the radius of curvature of the lens cap. Therefore,

$$f = r/(n - 1) \qquad (3)$$

and

$$n = 1 + r/f \qquad (4)$$

The focal length of the thin-liquid lens can also be directly measured from the thin-lens equation[1,3]

$$1/f = 1/p + 1/q \qquad (5)$$

which gives

$$f = pq/(p + q) \qquad (6)$$

In our project the value of $(p + q)$ remained constant since the distance of the ceiling light to the floor didn't change. We measured the r of the cap, which was used throughout, with a precision spherometer. The value was 7.94 cm ± 1%.

After experimentally determining the q value for nine liquids, we calculated the f values using thin-lens Eq. (6). These are listed in Table I.

Thick-Lens Formula

For a lens to be considered thin, the thickness of the lens at its thickest midsection (t) should be very small compared with r_1, r_2, f, p, and q values. The object and image distances are measured from the midsection of the lens.

The liquid lens we used in this refractometer has $t = 1.6$ cm, still small compared with r_1, r_2, f, p, and q values, and so using the thin-lens equations is a good approximation in this instance. Even if we treat it as a thick lens, which is a more appropriate way, Eqs. 1-6 can still be used as given, with the following changes.[4,5]

The principal plane inside the lens from which the object distance, p', for the thick lens must be measured will be $(1.6/n_L)$ cm from the plane face of the lens. Here we have to use n_L = the literature value of the refractive index of the liquid in the cap. We assume the planoconvex thick lens is held with plane side facing the ceiling light. For liquids listed in Table I, $(1.6/n_L)$cm works out to be 1.1 to 1.2 cm. It is obvious from the geometry of Fig. 1 that the average corrected values of the object distances, p', for thick lenses will be about 0.3 cm more than the reported values of p, for thin lenses, in Table I.

The second principal plane for a plano-convex lens will coincide with the convex face of the lens itself.[4] Thus the corrected values of the image distances, q', for the thick plano-convex lens must be measured from the convex face. So the q' values for the thick-lens case must be 0.8 cm less than the q values in Table I.

Also, due to the geometry of the principal planes of the thick lens, the $p' + q'$ value for the thick-lens case will always be 249 cm for our experimental setup. When such corrected values of object and image distances are used, the focal lengths of the thick lenses can be calculated by

$$f' = (p + 0.3)(q - 0.8)/249 \qquad (7)$$

The calculated f' values of the thick lenses work out to be 0.6 to 0.7 cm less than the respective f values of the thin lenses. Table I gives the calculated f and f' values, using Eq. (6) and (7), respectively.

Sources of Error

The measured values of p' and q' have an uncertainty of 3 mm. By using the extreme values of p', q', $p' + q'$, and $p'q'$, the % error in $n_{experimental}$ values was calculated to be about 2%, if we assume all the absolute values of the errors add.

The errors due to temperature variation of refractive indices from the values cited in the literature (given for 20°C) were minimized by performing the experiments in a climate-controlled room kept at 20° ± 1°C. The weighings were done to ±0.01 g and volumes were measured to ± 1 cc. The error in refractive indices values due to temperature variation or concentration determination will be around 0.6%. Assuming $n_{air} \approx 1$, whereas $n_{air} = 1.00028$, will introduce an uncertainty of about 0.03% in refractive indices values. In addition, our project uses composite white light, whereas the literature values of the refractive indices are for sodium yellow light. The mean wavelength for visible light is not far off from yellow light. The error due to such approximation can amount to about 0.5% in our range of n_E values. The total error due to all these causes is about 2%.

Results

Table I charts focal lengths for the nine liquids we used, measuring distances by both thin-lens and thick-lens formulas. The last two columns of Table I display focal lengths for thick lenses, f', calculated from Eq. (7) and f' from literature values:

$$f' = r/(n_L - 1) \qquad (8)$$

Table II. Refractive indices for thick-lens case.

Liquid	Calculated values $n_E = 1 = (r/f')$ $r = 7.94$ cm; $f' =$ focal length from Eq. (7) as in Table I.	Literature values n_L
Water	1.342	1.3334
6½% salt solution	1.354	1.3444
13% salt solution	1.356	1.3558
40% sugar solution	1.405	1.3997
50% sugar solution	1.420	1.42
Peanut oil	1.484	1.4691
Castor oil	1.493	1.477
25% sugar solution	1.378	1.3723
26% salt solution	1.385	1.3795

Comparing values in the last two columns of Table I is another way of estimating the discrepancy.

Table II charts the experimental refractive indices for liquid thick lenses, n_E, as calculated from

$$n_E = 1 + (r/f') \qquad (9)$$

The refractive indices collected from the literature, n_L, are given for comparison purposes.

Comments

Students can repeat these experiments with a homemade liquid-lens refractometer by varying the $p + q$ distance, using caps of different r, and using a variety of liquids. They can generate their own tables and graphs. The activity gives valuable experience in geometric optics and critical analyses of various sources of error in a research project. In addition, it can be used as a learning project in using thin-lens formula calculations and its modification for a plano-convex thick-lens case. The liquid-lens refractometer we designed measures refractive indices that are within the experimental errors discussed, close to the literature values.

References

1. F. Miller and D. Schroeer, *College Physics*, 5th ed. (Harcourt Brace Jovanovich, Atlanta, 1982), pp. 634–635, 650.
2. "Plano-Convex Optical Glass Lenses," *Newport 1990 Catalog* (Fountain Valley, CA, 1990), pp. N-6, N-43.
3. E. Jones and R.H. Childers, *Contemporary College Physics*, 1st ed. (Addison-Wesley, Reading, MA, 1990), pp. 616, 621.
4. E. Hausmann and E.P. Slack, *Physics*, 3rd ed. (Van Nostrand, New York, 1953), pp. 694–696.
5. E. Hecht, *Optics*, Schaum Outline Series (McGraw-Hill, New York, 1975), pp. 72–74.

Wave Optics, Diffraction, Interference

Giant Newton's Rings

Kai-yin Cheung *and* **Se-yuen Mak,** Department of Curriculum and Instruction, The Chinese University of Hong Kong, Shatin, NT, Hong Kong

The classic demonstration of Newton's rings (the pattern of concentric colored circles seen when thin films are bound together) is a popular one in introductory physics courses.[1] Usually a plano-convex lens of large radius is placed on a sheet of plane plate glass and light from a monochromatic source falls on the arrangement at right angles to its surface (Fig. 1). When the light is reflected into an observer's eye, the point of contact of the lens appears as a dark spot surrounded by a series of circles. These circular "interference fringes" are produced by the circular symmetry of the air film sandwiched between the curved surface of the lens and the upper surface of the glass plate. Unfortunately the rings produced in this manner are only barely observable to the unaided eye. For instance,

with a lens of $R = 1$ m, the radius of the fringe pattern is of the order of 1 mm. Observation and measurement are usually done with the help of a traveling microscope mounted directly above the fringes.

We describe here a simple modification of the traditional setup that magnifies the scale of the interference pattern so the demonstration can be used for the whole class or for semiquantitative measurements in any high-school laboratory. A set of fairly clear Newton's rings of up to 2 cm in diameter can be produced (Fig. 2) without need for precision instruments. Also, not only are the fringe patterns observable from almost any direction above the glass plate, but their size and shape are independent of the position of the observer.

To the best of our knowledge, although the method of the formation of giant Newton's rings was published in Chinese in 1988,[2] this column contains the first discussion of the theory involved.

Arrangement

Support a piece of white and smooth Plexiglas (about 30 x 30 cm, 3 mm thick) on a coin at its center of mass.

Bend the Plexiglas slightly convex upward by placing 1-kg standard weights at the four corners. Place a smaller piece of glass on top of the Plexiglas at its center point. Direct white or filtered colored light (from a 100-W bulb or overhead projector) onto the plates at near-grazing angles. With a partial blackout, students from all directions can observe Newton's rings above the plates of glass (Fig. 3).

Theory and Sample Experimental Result

The choice of a suitable white Plexiglas plate and a large angle of incidence for the incoming light are two crucial factors leading to a successful demonstration.

Like most opaque dielectrics, the white Plexiglas produces partial regular reflection on the smooth surface but diffuse reflection by impurities inside the material. From Maxwell's equations,[3] or by a simple experiment, we can show that the percentage of partially and regularly

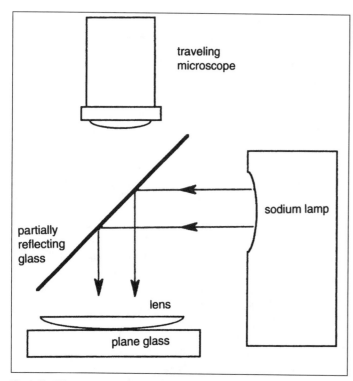

Fig. 1. Traditional setup for showing Newton's rings.

traveling microscope

sodium lamp

partially reflecting glass

lens

plane glass

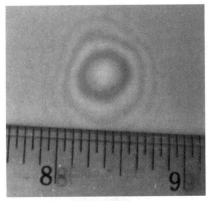

Fig. 2. Set of giant Newton's rings.

Table I. Radii of giant Newton's rings.

	measured r	calculated r
1st bright ring	7 mm	6.6 mm
1st dark ring	8.5 mm	8.1 mm
2nd bright ring	10 mm	9.3 mm
2nd dark ring	11 mm	10.5 mm
3rd bright ring	12 mm	11.5 mm

reflected light to the incident light increases as the angle of incidence is increased (Fig. 4). For a small angle of incidence, i, most of the incoming light passes through the surface and suffers diffuse reflection. However, the percentage of partially reflected light increases drastically when $i > 70°$ and becomes 100% when i approaches 90°.

The shape and the size of these circular fringes, like that of a real image caught on a white screen in geometrical optics experiments, are independent of the position of the observer. This suggests that the interference pattern is first formed on the upper surface of the white Plexiglas plate and then reaches the eye through diffuse reflection. This conjecture is further supported by an ad hoc change of the arrangement. When the white Plexiglas is replaced with clear Plexiglas, we find that the giant fringes almost completely disappear. However, if we place a piece of white paper under the Plexiglas plate, the fringes reappear on the white paper. The image gets blurred and finally disappears as we move the paper down to a lower position. No doubt these fringes are formed by transmitted light rays through the air film and caught on the white paper that acts as a projection screen. For this reason, we can consider the white Plexiglas plate as a combination of clear Plexiglas and a white screen.

Consider two light rays, 1 and 2, traveling from a point on the light source to a point P on the upper surface of the white Plexiglas plate (Fig. 5). Since the lower Plexiglas plate is bent by force, the variation in thickness of the upper glass plate is much smaller than that of the air film. Under this approximation, the glass plate introduces the same lateral displacement to both light rays and is used solely to provide a boundary to split the amplitude of the incoming light.

Although ray 2 suffers two more regular reflections (at A and B) than ray 1, they are still of comparable amplitudes because the angles of incidence of the incoming rays are close to 90° The rays that follow the paths shown are seen by the eye to interfere at P.

The path difference between these two light rays is

$$l_2 - l_1 = \frac{2d}{\cos\phi} - 2d \tan\phi \sin\phi$$

$$= \frac{2d(1 - \sin^2\phi)}{\cos\phi} = 2d \cos\phi$$

Since reflections at both A and B occur on the air-to-glass boundary, there will be no phase change in these reflections; a white spot will be observed at the point of contact. The conditions for constructive interference are simply

$$n\lambda = 2d \cos\phi, \qquad n = 0, 1, 2, ...(1)$$

From the sagitta theorem[4] (Fig. 6), let r be the radius of a Newton's ring, $(2R - d)$ $d = r^2$.

For $d << R$,

$$r^2 = 2Rd \qquad (2)$$

From the path-difference formula, the radius of the nth bright ring is

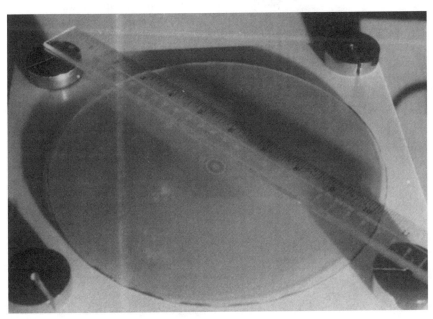

Fig. 3. Arrangement for producing giant Newton's Rings.

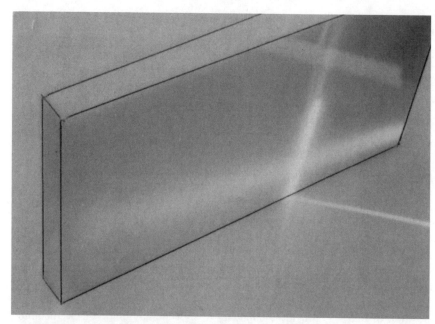

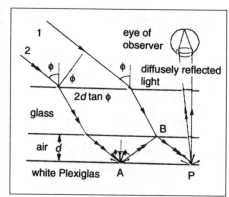

Fig. 5. Interference in the thin air film.

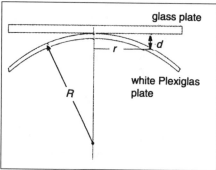

Fig. 6. Exaggerated scale geometry of arrangement for giant Newton's rings.

with one another with an understanding that an error of slightly over 10% is assumed in each column.

Comments

Under most circumstances, the rings obtained by bending a piece of white Plexiglas are not perfectly circular. However, they can be reshaped easily and made "circular" by trial and error through adding or removing weights from the corners. Nevertheless, as far as order of magnitude is concerned, a distorted circle is good enough for showing the wavelength of visible light at this level.

The errors in all measurements can be made less than ten percent except for R. This could be improved if a thick plastic plate with an accurate curvature were manufactured especially for this purpose.

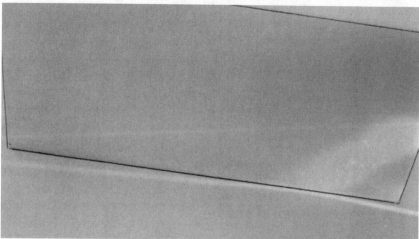

Fig. 4. Partial reflection by a white Plexiglas plate. Top: small angle of incidence. Bottom: large angle of incidence.

$$(r_n)^2 = \frac{n\lambda R}{\cos \phi} \qquad (3a)$$

and the radius of the $(n + 1)$th dark ring is

$$(r'_n)^2 = \frac{(2n + 1)\lambda R}{2 \cos\phi} \qquad (3b)$$

By using an ordinary meter rule and a thickness gauge, we find that when $d = 0.3$ mm, $r = 6.5 \pm 0.5$ cm. Substituting these values into Eq. (2), the radius of curvature of Plexiglas plate is $R = 6.5 \pm 0.6$ m.

In a typical experiment, we use filtered red light with $\lambda = 0.7 \times 10^{-6}$ m derived from an overhead projector. The angle of incidence is fixed at $\phi = 84°$. The radii of rings are measured directly and calculated using Eq. (3). The measured and calculated results (Table I) are in good agreement

References

1. R. Resnick and D. Halliday, *Physics* (Wiley, New York, 1966), pp. 1088–1089.
2. S.Y. Mak and K.Y. Wong, "Jumbo Newton's rings," *Wuli Jiaoxue* (Oct. 1988), p. 25.
3. Ref. 1, pp. 1027–1028.
4. Our derivation closely follows that of B. Rossi, *Optics* (Addison-Wesley, Reading, MA, 1956), pp.123–128.

Wedding PC Interfaces to Interference and Diffraction Experiments

Joe L. Ferguson, Department of Physics, Mississippi State University, Mississippi State, MS 39762

Simple inexpensive modifications to existing equipment have allowed us to computerize the interference and diffraction experiments done in two of our introductory laboratory courses. The modifications facilitate the use of computer interfaces from PASCO,[1] Vernier,[2] and other companies with the single- and multiple-slit experiments done with PASCO's Advanced or Intermediate Optics System or similar apparatus. The key to computerization is the use of the voltage on the moving contact of a potentiometer as a measure of position. While one analog-to-digital channel of the interface is detecting position in the interference pattern, another channel is monitoring the output of the photometer,[3] which is receiving light from that part of the pattern. Although similar ideas could be used with other equipment, our particular method involves adding an O-ring-belt-driven potentiometer to PASCO's linear translator.[4] Bennett[5] and Dodds[6] have described the use of potentiometer position transducers in experiments for advanced laboratories.

Figure 1 gives a schematic of the experiment in which data are collected by the computer as the student turns the linear translator screw to move the light-collecting fiber-optic probe across the diffraction pattern. Our position transducer is a linear ten-turn 5-kΩ potentiometer connected between the 5 V and ground of the computer. The voltage on the moving contact is monitored by one of the interface's analog channels. The calibration feature of the Vernier *Data Monitor* software used with the interface allows us to prepare the computer to read and record position (in millimeters) of the fiber-optic probe carried by the PASCO linear translator. The translator moves the probe 1 mm for each turn of a driving screw. An O-ring belt on the ¼-in-diameter unthreaded portion of this screw drives the potentiometer by means of a pulley [1¼-(in-the-groove) diameter] on the potentiometer shaft. This diameter ratio was chosen to allow the potentiometer's ten turns to accommodate the roughly 50 screw turns between extreme positions.[7] To make it easier to turn the screw of the linear translator smoothly we glued onto the drive screw knob a small

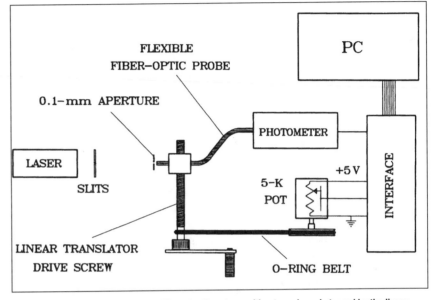

Fig. 1. Schematic of the experiment. The potentiometer position transducer is turned by the linear translator by means of an O-ring belt.

crank consisting of a flat aluminum crank arm and a banana-plug-insulator handle.

A 0.1-mm-wide slit (one of PASCO's photometer apertures) at the end of the fiber-optic probe limits the width of the interference pattern sampled at any instant. The fiber-optic probe carries the light to the photometer. The output voltage of the photometer is the input of another of the interface's analog channels.

The solid curve in Fig. 2 graphs some typical three-slit data collected by this apparatus. The dotted curve is the theoretical intensity pattern adjusted to match the intensity of the central peak. The slits were 0.04 mm wide, slit separation was 0.125 mm, and the pattern was detected 0.50 m from the slits. The wavelength was 633 nm.

For those who already have the computer interface and the PASCO linear translator and photometer, the modifications described here are quite inexpensive. A suitable potentiometer[8] costs about $11. The $7 voltage-measurement lead from Vernier is very convenient for connecting the potentiometer to the interface because it has a 5-V supply wire and the other two wires needed in addition to the DIN connector required by PASCO and Vernier interfaces. To connect the photometer to the interface we added an appro-

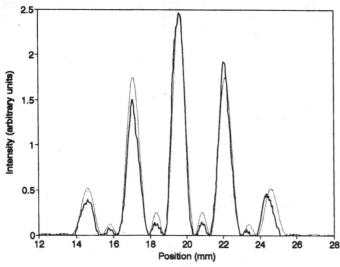

Fig. 2. Solid curve is typical three-slit data; dotted curve is theoretical.

priate DIN connector to a cable that already had the miniature phone plug needed for the output of our PASCO photometer. Both parts came from Radio Shack at a total cost for the finished cable of about $4. We machined our potentiometer pulley from aluminum, but suitable plastic pulleys

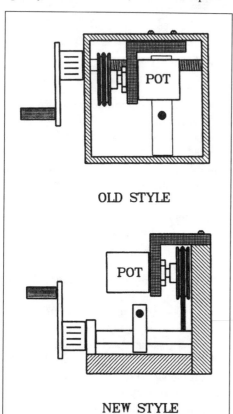

OLD STYLE

NEW STYLE

Fig. 3. Rear views showing attachment of potentiometer and pulley to both styles of PASCO linear translators.

are available from Small Parts[9] for less than $2 each. Figure 3 indicates how we attach the potentiometer and pulley to each type of PASCO linear translator by means of a small bracket cut from 1¼-in aluminum angle.

For those who neither have nor wish to purchase the PASCO linear translator or photometer, it should be straightforward to create a device that positions a detector or fiber-optic probe by means of a screw drive. A potentiometer, either driven directly by the screw or by means of a belt, would serve as a position transducer.

References

1. PASCO scientific, 10101 Foothills Boulevard, Roseville, CA 95678-9011. Phone: 800-772-8700.
2. Vernier Software, 8565 SW Beaverton-Hillsdale Highway, Portland, OR 97225-2429. Phone: 503-297-5317.
3. Our PASCO Intermediate Optics System includes the student photometer (Catalog #OS-9152B), which includes the fiber optic probe (003-01383). PASCO's Advanced and Complete Optics Systems have a more sensitive photometer (OS8020).
4. We have the older linear translators (OS9104A) that have an aluminum box housing. The new model (OS-9104B) has a housing consisting of two perpendicular steel plates. See Fig. 3.
5. C.A. Bennett, *Am. J. Phys.* **58**, 75 (1990).
6. S.A. Dodds, *Am. J. Phys.* **58**, 663 (1990).
7. PASCO's new linear translator has no unthreaded section on its drive screw. On our one new translator we added a short plastic sleeve over the threads. With a sleeve of about 0.3-in diameter, the ten-turn pot can accommodate about 40 turns of the screw. This is more than adequate to scan the interference patterns.
8. Our potentiometer came from Allied Electronics, Inc., 7410 Pebble Drive, Fort Worth, TX 76118. Phone: 800-433-5700.
9. Small Parts Inc., 13980 NW 58th Court, Miami Lakes, FL 33014-0650. Phone: 305-557-8222.

Low-Cost Diffraction Experiment

V. Anantha Narayanan, Department of Physics, Savannah State College, Savannah, GA 31404

I have been using circular holes salvaged from non-aerosol hair-spray bottles to produce spectacular circular interference fringes. The extremely uniform circular hole is in the base of a small hollow cylindrical cup of 4 mm length with a circular base diameter of about 4 mm. Since the wall thickness of the plastic cup is about 1 mm, the hole is sturdy and gives distortion-free circular fringes. This "equipment" can be salvaged as needed, involving no expenditure. Merely cut away the surrounding plastic cap to free the small plastic cup that contains the hole.

When using a HeNe 1-mW laser red line at 6328 Angstrom to form the circular interference pattern, I make the hole-to-screen distance 645 cm. Five well-defined dark circular fringes can be traced on a sheet of 8½ x 11-in white paper in a well-darkened room. We calculate the average diameter of the hole from the formula:

$$d = N_n \times 6328 \times 10^{-8} \text{ cm} \times 645 \text{ cm}/R_n \text{ (in cm)} \quad (1)$$

where d = diameter of the hole; R = radius of the dark circular interference pattern; n = 1,2,3,4,5; and N_n = 1.22; 2.233, 3.238, 4.241, or 5.243 for the dark circular fringes.[1,2] In one experiment the calculated average value of d was 0.028 cm. Using a comparator microscope of least count 0.001 cm, the average typical hole diameter measured 0.031 ± 0.001 cm. Because such a microscope may not be readily available, and because students like to confirm values independently, you can also try the following optical method of verifying the value of d. Fasten the cup with the hole on a sturdy stand with beeswax or gum and illuminate it with a 100-W lamp. With a convex lens you can achieve magnification of 6 to 13 to form a real image of the hole on the screen. Have your students measure the image distance (q), the object distance (p), the image size (I), and calculate the diameter of the hole: $d = p \times I/q$. Adjust I to be exactly 2, 3, or 4 mm to minimize error in visually estimating fractional parts of a millimeter. Our students calculate the d value to be 0.031 cm ± 4%.

This "hands-on, recycling" approach to a physics experiment that readily produces results is popular with students even though the experimental uncertainty is about 10%.

References

1. Jerry B. Marion and William F. Hornyak, *Physics for Science and Engineering* (Saunders, Philadelphia, 1982), pp. 1142–1143.
2. Hugh D. Young, *University Physics*, 8th ed. (Addison-Wesley, Reading, MA, 1992), pp. 1061–1062.

Linear Polarization Demonstration/Puzzle

Peter N. Henriksen, Department of Physics, The University of Akron, Akron, OH 44325-4001

A pair of "new," recently invented, linear polarizers are illustrated in Fig. 1. They have the unusual property that when either polarizer A or polarizer B is rotated 180° about its *x*- or *z*-axis, or 90° about the *y*-axis, transmission changes from maximum to minimum or vice versa.

I find it effective to use these polarizers in class following an introduction to linear polarization. After the students have worked with linear polarizers, I show them the "new" polarizers and ask them, as a written assignment for the next meeting, to record their observations and provide a hypothesis of how the polarizers are made to produce the observed effects. For most students the assignment is easy; it is designed to improve communication skills as well as develop a better understanding of a physical concept.

I use this and similar written assignments to help students improve their verbal skills, an aspect of education frequently neglected when teaching physics.

What is your solution to this puzzle?

Answer: The axis of polarization of each polarizer is diagonal to its square shape.

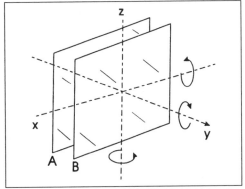

Fig. 1. Two linear polarizers with incident light shining along *y*-axis.

Microwave Interferometer

Mario Capitolo, Science Department, Bellarmine College Preparatory, San Jose, CA 95126-1899; marioc@bcp.org
and William Lonc, Astronomy and Physics Deptartment, Saint Mary's University, Halifax, NS, Canada, B3H 3C3; william.lonc@stmarys.ca

We present here the construction and performance of a small x-band (3-cm wavelength) interferometer quite suitable for the high-school or college physics laboratory. The apparatus (Fig. 1) can be built fairly easily from items available from the local hardware store. Dubbed "the Plumber's Delight" in the Bellarmine lab, this particular version was designed to work with 10.5-GHz (2.9-cm) microwaves.

As a preliminary venture, your class may want to try a no-funnel version; the system will work sufficiently well enough with no funnels at the two interferometer inputs, since the microwaves will enter the elbows directly.

To provide for several values of D, you will need several pairs of straight copper pipe to fit in the arms of the interferometer. Each pair should be equal in length. Since the copper tubing pieces fit snugly together, it is not necessary to solder anything except the funnels to the elbows; simply make sure that the arm lengths are symmetrical to within a couple of millimeters.

The combined output of the interferometer appears at the central branch and is butted up against the waveguide input of the typical microwave detector. To prevent any appreciable microwave radiation from reaching the detector horn before going through the interferometer, we simply packed some aluminum foil around the central section as indicated. Presumably, steel wool or other reflecting or absorbing material would be quite satisfactory. The interferometer is attached to the receiving horn with masking tape.

Mount the assembly (see Fig. 2) on a rotating base (such as a Lazy Susan); the rotation axis is vertical. It is rather

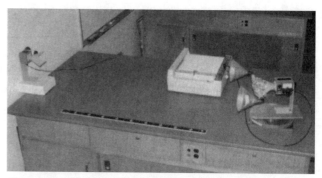

Fig. 2. Experimental configuration. Left to right: microwave source, strip-chart recorder (if used), receiver assembly on rotating base. Note metric tape on edge of rotator and aluminum foil wrapped around receiver horn. Recorder must be placed well outside space between microwave source and interferometer.

important to have the rotation axis coincide with the intersection of the interferometer's symmetry axis and a line representing its "front,"—point "c" in Fig. 1. We attached a short piece (about 25 cm) of metric tape along the periphery of the rotating table to enable measurement of $\Delta\theta$, using the expression $\Delta\theta = (\Delta s/R) \times 57.3°$, where R is the radius (in cm) of the rotating table and Δs is the distance (in cm) along the periphery associated with rotation between two adjacent maxima or minima indications on the receiver module. Experimental uncertainty could be reduced by measuring Δs for several consecutive maxima or minima. The distance between the microwave source and the interferometer should be much larger than D: our distance was approximately three meters.

We chose three values for D: 36.5, 25, and 20 cm, for which the expected fringe spacings were 4.4, 6.7, and 8.6 degrees respectively. Obviously, D is arbitrary, but if made too large, the resulting decrease in fringe-spacing becomes rather difficult to measure with any accuracy in a typical school lab.

In actual operation, the expected value for the angular separation $\Delta\theta$ between minima or maxima is calculated from the relation $(\lambda/D)57.3°$, where λ is the wavelength of the microwaves and D is the baseline length. Caution: this relationship assumes that the microwave source and interferometer are in the same plane. Observed values will be within a few percent of the expected values (see Table I).

If a recording system (such as a strip-chart recorder) is

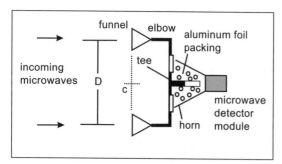

Fig. 1. Top view of interferometer. Thick lines represent elbows and tees (more curved than shown) connected by straight sections of copper tubing. c = center of rotation.

Table I.

D (cm)	Expected Δθ (deg)	Observed Δθ (deg)
20	8.3	8.6
25	6.4	6.5
36.5	4.4	4.4

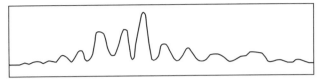

Fig. 3. Typical interferogram obtained by manually rotating the interferometer.

available, your students could obtain an interferogram such as shown in Fig. 3. The pattern will not be symmetrical, mainly because it is very difficult to maintain uniform motion while the output of the receiver is being fed to the recorder. Another source of non-symmetry could be spurious reflections of microwaves in the room entering the interferometer.

The first-time user of microwave apparatus should keep in mind that the microwave source and microwave detector should have the same polarization. Typical classroom apparatus is vertically polarized. This means that the broad dimension of the rectangular waveguide is along the horizontal. Or, if you look inside the waveguide of the source, there will be a little quarter-wave antenna (like a small nail), which should be vertical. If you look inside the waveguide of the detector module, there should be a somewhat similar structure (but it will usually be the crystal detector) and it too should be aligned vertically.

In addition, readings should be taken when the interferometer is facing more or less directly at the microwave source. Otherwise, the effective value of D is no longer the measured value. For example, if the angle between the interferometer axis and the line from the source to the center of the interferometer is 15°, then the effective value of D is $D\cos(15)$ = 0.97D. introducing an error of about 3% in the calculation

of Δθ.

In a typical laboratory session, the class could be divided into several teams, each team being responsible for cutting two equal lengths of pipe. Each team would announce to the class what the expected value of Δθ should be for their value of D and the experiment run to see what happens. The innate spirit of good-natured rivalry should provide for a relatively dynamic lab session.

Note: The microwave source and detector are part of the Basic Microwave Optics System, model WA-9314B, from PASCO scientific. The transmitter and receiver may be purchased separately, part numbers are 003-04319 ($300) and 003-04313 ($225) respectively.

Reference

Additional discussions of basic radio astronomy concepts and projects suitable for senior high-school and college undergraduate students will be found in the book ($20 + $3 shipping) *Radio Astronomy Projects,* (by W. Lonc) available from Radio-Sky Publishing, P.O. Box 3552, Louisville, KY, 40201; e-mail: radiosky@radiosky.win.net; also available from Radar, Inc., 168 Western Ave., Seattle, WA 98119, and its branches, as well as from the University Bookstore, Saint Mary's University, Halifax, NS, Canada B3H 3C3.

Spectra, Color Mixing

A Real Spectrum Chart

R.B. Knollenberg, III, Department of Physics, University of Louisville, Louisville, KY 40292

Introductory physics textbooks frequently have a color plate showing the spectra of a number of different gases. Here is a simple way to show your class the real thing.

Take four or five spectrum tubes, each of a different gas, and connect them in series with paper clips. Hang the chain of spectrum tubes vertically with a piece of string. Light the tubes simultaneously by using a neon sign transformer (such as a GE Luminous Tube Transformer model #9761Yll having a 120 VAC primary and a 15,000 VAC secondary) and a variac to control intensity. (Alternatively, a spectrum tube power supply such as those sold by CENCO, Sargent-Welch, and others, may be used.)

Connect the transformer (or power supply) to the ends of the spectrum tube chain with alligator clip leads. Give each person in the class a 2- by 2-in card-mounted diffraction grating (13,400 lines/in). When the students look at the chain of lit spectrum tubes through the grating, which should be held close to the eye, they will see a real spectrum chart like the ones printed in textbooks.

Film-Canister Spectroscope

Edwin Paul Heideman, Pleasantville High School, Pleasantville, NY 10570

Generate student interest and parent curiosity and pique inquisitive peers with an inexpensive take-home, film-canister spectroscope. With a number 2 cork bore, make a hole centered in the bottom of an opaque film canister. Remove the plastic cap and with an Exacto knife cut a slit approximately 0.2-cm wide by 1.5-cm long near the cap's center. From a sheet of acetate film diffraction material (available from most scientific supply companies), cut a square approximately 1.5 x 1.5 cm. Place the square of grating film over the hole made in the bottom of the plastic canister and mount it with two small pieces of Scotch tape on either side of the hole (Fig. 1). Look at the light reflected from the grating material covering the hole. It should have the appearance of fine scratches. Before snapping the cap in place, orient the slit so that it is in line with the grooves on the diffraction material. The spectroscope is now ready for use with gas-filled spectral tubes, incandescent lamps and other light sources.

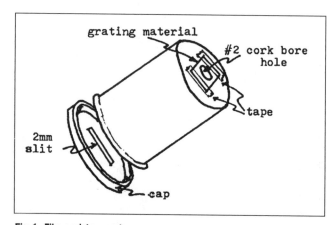

Fig. 1. Film-canister spectroscope.

Overhead Spectroscopy

George A. Burman, Tranquillity High School, Tranquillity, CA 93668

When first presenting the subject of bright-line spectra to my high-school chemistry class, I found that the concept of a color spectrum, not to mention the use of a spectroscope, was unfamiliar to the majority of students. I also found that physics students had some difficulty relating primary color addition concepts to what they had experienced with spectra generated by prisms and diffraction gratings. The overhead spectroscope described here introduces my chemistry students to the concept of spectrography and is also a useful demonstration tool for color analysis in my physics class.

Holographic diffraction gratings[1] produce brilliant spectra with wide dispersion. An ordinary overhead projector equipped with such a diffraction grating makes an excellent classroom tool for demonstrations and investigations of visible light spectra. Hand-held student spectroscopes employ a diffraction grating (although this might not be apparent to the student), so introducing the class to color spectra with a projection spectroscope employing similar materials eases the transition to student use of the hand-held spectroscope.

Construction is simple; the method described here is only one of several possible approaches to making a classroom spectral projector. In addition to the overhead projector and the holographic diffraction grating, all that is required is a cardboard mask for the projector, as shown in Fig. 1. Start with a good quality overhead projector. (Now is the time to clean the projection lenses and the Fresnel lens that have been collecting grime over the past few years.) Almost any projector except for the top-illuminated, reflecting type will provide satisfactory results. The special diffraction grating film designed for this purpose that I use[2] comes in a 12- x 23-cm sheet. I cut a piece 11 x 11.5 cm, mount it in a cardboard frame, and attach it to the front of the projection lens with masking tape. A smaller piece of film can be used, such as the type commonly mounted in a 35-mm slide mount,[3] but the best results are obtained when as much of the projection lens as possible is covered with the film. I make the mask from a piece of thin cardboard large enough to cover the top of the overhead projector's Fresnel lens, with a slit about 8 mm wide and 22 cm long cut in it with a sharp knife. I tape the mask to the top of the projector to reduce glare. A wider slit will increase the intensity of the spectral display, but the spectrum "smears"; a narrower slit reduces the smearing but also reduces the intensity. You can experiment with slit widths to match the projector's lamp intensity, room illumination, and projection screen quality.

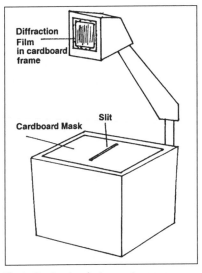

Fig. 1. Overhead projector spectroscope.

For an introduction to spectroscopy, present the class with the view of the vertical slit on the screen without the diffraction film in place. Then put the film over the projection lens; brilliant spectra will appear on either side of the white line. After explaining that their hand-held spectroscopes have a similar piece of diffraction film in the eyepiece, have the students observe the projected white line with their spectroscopes. After they have learned to orient their spectroscopes, they will be better prepared for observing gas-tube discharges or flame tests.

To observe color composition with the overhead spectroscope, place one or more primary color slides[4] over the slit of the mask. If desired, the length of the slit can be reduced by masking, and one primary color slide viewed at a time. Alternatively, several slides can be viewed simultaneously along with a section of the unfiltered slit. In this way a comparison of the primary color spectra along with the white spectrum can be made. This helps to reinforce the relationship of color and wavelength. As Sadler describes,[5] not all primary color filters are monochromatic. Finally, slides of mixed colors (yellow, cyan, magenta) can be presented and their primary constituents observed. This makes a nice counterpoint to viewing color addition with a light box.

References

1. Philip Sadler, "Projecting spectra for classroom investigations," *Phys. Teach.* **29**, 423 (1991).
2. Available from Learning Technologies, Inc., 59 Walden St., Cambridge, MA 02140. Stock #PS-08A.
3. Central Scientific Co. Stock #86252.
4. Central Scientific Co. Stock #32510; Sargent Welch Stock #3662.
5. Ref. 1.

Recycle Outmoded Air-Track Components

Gary Kessler, Physics Department, Illinois Wesleyan University, Bloomington, IL 61702-2900

Most physics departments, if they are like ours, began using air tracks in the general physics laboratory in the late 1960s. Measurements were taken using a progression of ever more electrically sensitive paper taped together with some type of spark timer.

In the early to mid-eighties when infrared photocell gates became commonly available along with on-line data acquisition, the spark timers were relegated to storage-room shelves. Since air tracks are still in general use in the laboratory and there is a wide choice of measurement techniques, including photocell gates, sonic rangers, and stop-frame camcorders, there has been no need to use the older technology. Our spark timers had been gathering dust for over a decade.

Recently, however, we needed a few power supplies to run Geissler tubes for relatively short periods during spectroscopy experiments in the basic astronomy course. It occurred to us that perhaps the old spark timers might be suitable, since they produced a high enough voltage. Moreover, the Daedalon EM-01 spark timers came equipped with a push-button control to turn the unit on and off. To our surprise these spark timers worked very well indeed, did not overheat the spectrum tubes, and were easily controlled by the students (all of whom were non-science majors). Figure 1

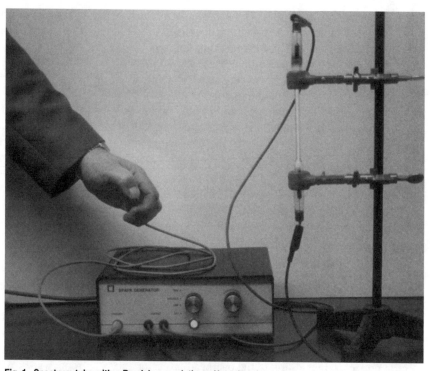

Fig. 1. Spectrum tube with a Daedalon spark timer. Note that the central region of the Geissler tube glows with an unexpected uniform brightness.

shows the experimental arrangement.

In short, recycling older equipment saved us hundreds of dollars and the controls provided the added advantage of using the spectrum tubes only when needed instead of having them operating for the entire laboratory session.

Color Mixing Using a Single Projector

Marinus G. Luttikhuizen, Hudsonville High School, Hudsonville, MI 49426

It is often difficult to demonstrate color mixing because you need three slide projectors. The following describes a method of color mixing, using a single slide projector and mirrors. The materials are inexpensive, and the apparatus is easy to construct.

To construct the apparatus, you will need: 3.8 cm x 3.8 cm lumber (1.5 in. x 1.5 in.); mirror tile cut into 3.8 cm x 3.8 cm squares; and Lee filter materials #106 Red, #139 Green,

and #119 Blue. The mirror tile can be found at builder supply stores, and the filter materials can be purchased at theatrical supply stores. You may want to check with your school's drama department as a source for the filters, since you need so little of it. The filter materials come in large sheets (50 cm x 60 cm). I purchased mine from Ringold Theatre Equipment Co., 6504 28th Street S.E., Grand Rapids, MI 49506 at $4.25 per sheet.

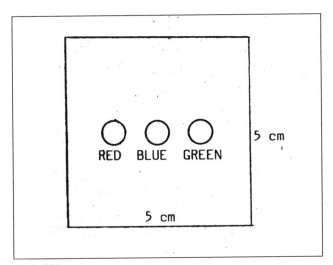

Fig. 1. Slide.

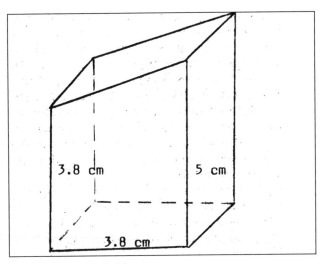

Fig. 3. Mirror mount pedestal.

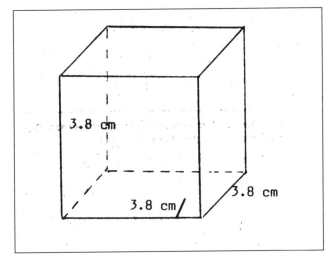

Fig. 2. Mirror mount.

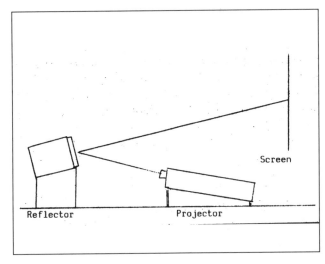

Fig. 4. Operational mode.

First you need to make your slide. Cut two 5 cm x 5 cm squares from construction paper and punch three holes that line up in each of these squares using a paper punch. Next, cement small pieces of each color of the filter materials over the three holes, respectively, and then cement the squares together to form a single slide that will have the three different colors (Fig. 1).

From the 3.8 cm x 3.8 cm lumber, cut three cubes (Fig. 2) and mount a mirror tile on each cube; also cut three blocks as shown in Fig. 3. The cubes with the mirrors mounted on them rest on top of the blocks (Fig. 3 and Fig. 4) and can be directionally adjusted manually.

To operate, place the slide into a projector facing away from the screen. Place the three mirrors at a convenient distance in front of the projector with one mirror in the red beam, one in the green beam, and one in the blue beam, and reflect these back onto the screen (Fig. 4). Manually adjust the mirrors to mix the colors as desired.

Tinkertoy® Color-Addition Device

Joe L. Ferguson, Department of Physics, Mississippi State University, Mississippi State, MS 39762

A demonstration of the addition of various combinations of red, green, and blue light is useful in connection with discussions of color, color vision, or color television. Some methods of performing such a demonstration can be time consuming and/or expensive. Luttikhuizen[1] has described an inexpensive method that requires only one slide projector. I use a simple homebuilt device that can be set up on a single overhead projector in about a minute and costs less than $20.

Figures 1 and 2 show drawings of side and top views, respectively, of this color-addition device, and Fig. 3 is a photograph of it in use. The apparatus sits on an overhead projector that is aimed away from the screen. Three mirrors intercept light that passes through three holes, each of which is covered by a red, green, or blue color filter. The articulated mirror mounts are assembled from a child's construction toy.[2] (I used Tinkertoy® rods and connector spools, but similar Fiddlestix® pieces would work as well.) These mounts allow the middle mirror to be rotated about a vertical axis and the other two mirrors to be adjusted about two axes, thereby making it possible to give the colored-dot images on the screen the desired overlap. The larger parts of the device were cut from scrap 1 x 12 pine lumber. Hinges allow the apparatus to fold up for storage with the mirrors inside a box for protection. For the demonstration the box lid folds out to serve as a counterweight for the mirror arm.

Most dimensions are not extremely critical, but two that work well with our 3M projectors are shown in Fig. 1. I cut the three (approximately 5 cm by 8 cm) mirrors from a single plastic locker mirror. I cut the magnetic tape backing from the original mirror into six pieces and reused it to attach the mirrors to the faces of the connector spools. Glue or double-sided tape would probably have worked just as well. The spacing between two adjacent mirrors is about 8.5 cm, and the three holes in the base have approximately 7.6 cm between centers.

The hole diameters are not critical. I used 1-in holes through the base with 2-in counterbore-holes part way through. The color filters sit on the shoulders at the bottoms of the larger holes.

Many variations on this basic idea are possible. For example, a simpler, and perhaps better, design for the filter holes would be to have the larger holes go all the way through and then have the colored filters attached to a metal or cardboard mask with somewhat smaller holes. This would give the colored-disk images sharper boundaries than

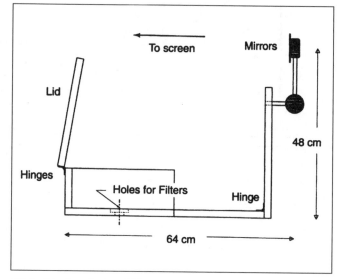

Fig. 1. Side view of color-addition apparatus.

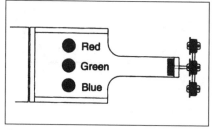

Fig. 2. Top view showing placement of color filters.

I get with a rough wooden border. It certainly isn't necessary to incorporate a storage box or to use the construction toys. My first model had glass mirrors glued to vertical wooden dowels that were held by drilled wooden blocks. The blocks fitted onto a horizontal dowel that was supported by a test-tube clamp attached to a tall ring stand. The color filters fitted over holes in a piece of cardboard I placed on the overhead projector. With a slide projector, construction-toy mirror mounts could provide an alternative to those described by Luttikhuizen.

Inexpensive plastic color filters are available from several of the scientific supply houses. Luttikhuizen suggests a source of theatrical filters.[1] I have bought both small and large sheets of filter material from Edmund Scientific.[3] Of the many colors available from Edmund, three that work well are Light Medium Blue, Medium Green, and Light Red.

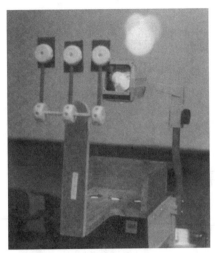

Fig. 3. Color addition device in use.

References

1. Marinus G. Luttikhuizen, *Phys. Teach.* **26**, 296 (1988).
2. Tinkertoy® is a trademark of Playskool, Inc., Pawtucket, RI 02862, a subsidiary of Hasbro, Inc. Physics teachers who have not encountered Tinkertoys since childhood may be shocked to find that the pieces are now made of plastic rather than wood. Fiddlestix® pieces are still made of wood. Fiddlestix is a product of Toys-N-Things International, Inc., 3208 Greenleaf Drive, Waco, TX 76710.
3. Edmund Scientific Company, 101 E. Gloucester Pike, Barrington, NJ 08007. Edmund also has higher quality, and more expensive, filters consisting of multilayer coatings on glass substrate.

A Simple Colorimeter

J.C. Martínez-Antón, M. Antón, and *A. González-Cano,* Departamento de Óptica, Universidad Complutense de Madrid, Escuela Universitaria de Óptica, Arcos de Jalón s/n, 28037 Madrid, Spain

The device we describe here resulted from our interest in providing some practical calorimetry experiences for our students. We wanted a system that would demonstrate, in an understandable way, how a color may be generated and specified in mathematical terms. Our device illustrates the mixing of additive primary colors as well as the concepts of saturation, luminance, and illumination. The device is inexpensive (materials cost about $25), easy to construct, and straightforward to use.

The Device

The system consists of three LED sources of different colors (taken as primaries), an integrating sphere, and a detector system. The primary colors are mixed to generate the desired color and a photodiode detector is used to measure the contribution of each primary.

Figure 1 shows the external appearance of the colorimeter along with a number of color samples that have been studied by our students. Figure 2 shows the heart of the device: an integrating sphere in which light from LEDs of three different "primary" colors is mixed. A hole in the integrating sphere allows the color mixture to be viewed. We use four LEDs: one red, one green, and two (because of

Fig. 1. Colorimeter with "baffle" and colored papers.

their lower luminance) blue. These are mounted on a small piece of electronic circuit board. A photodiode detector (such as a Siemens BPW34B) is placed on the board between the LEDs so that it receives some of the light emitted by each. It is important that the detector be sensitive to wavelengths throughout the visible range (400 to 700 nm).

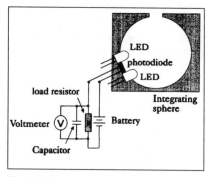

Fig. 2. Detail of the integrating sphere, including the detector electronics.

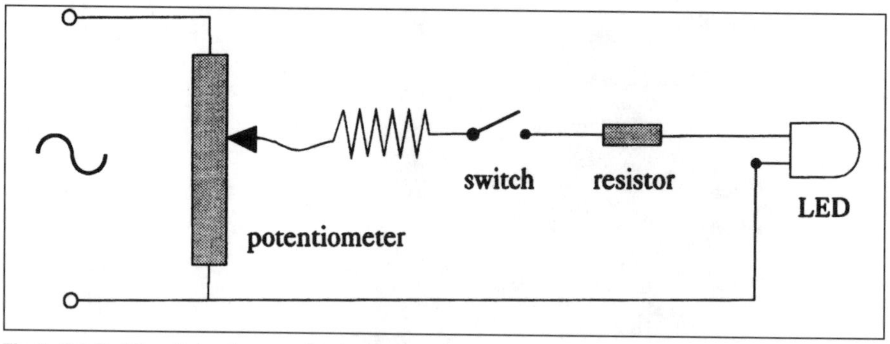

Fig. 3. Detail of the electronics associated with the LEDs.

The light source/detector board is attached to the wall of the integrating sphere as shown in Fig. 2.

Light Sources

Three switches (see Fig. 1) allow the three colors to be turned on and off independently. In addition, there are three potentiometers (Fig. 3), acting as voltage dividers, which control the amount of each color in the mixture. Logarithmic potentiometers (three-quarter turn, 100 Ω) are used since the light output from an LED varies approximately exponentially with applied voltage. All of the connecting wires leave the device at the bottom. The LEDs are powered by a simple ac supply of at least 4 V, connected through the switch and potentiometer. A resistor is also placed in series with each LED in order to limit the maximum current (and hence the maximum light output) when the full voltage is applied. Rectification of the current is not necessary since an LED behaves as a diode. The 60-Hz oscillation of the light output is not apparent to the eye. A dc supply with about half the ac voltage (and with proper polarity) may be used instead. The total light output of the blue LEDs is usually less than that of the other two sources. It is convenient to select the resistor for the blue pair first and then choose the resistances for the other two LEDs; that way, when all three are at maximum emission, the resulting light mixture is nearly white. The resistance values required will depend on the specific LEDs used. Of course the resistors (and potentiometers) must be able to withstand the power dissipated. Because this power is relatively large, we suggest that batteries not be used as the power source for the LEDs.

Light Detector

The photodiode detector circuit is shown in Fig. 2. A battery ($\epsilon = 1.5$ to 15 V) is connected with reverse bias to the photodiode so that very little current flows through it when it is in complete darkness. Light falling on the photodiode surface generates the electron-hole pairs resulting in a current, i, which is proportional to the amount of light collected. This current flows through a load resistance R. The

potential difference ($V = iR$) across the resistor is read with a voltmeter. Since V is proportional to current i, it is also nearly proportional to the amount of light received. This relation is quite linear for values of V much less than ϵ, the voltage of the battery. It becomes nonlinear as V approaches ϵ. In the linear region, V is nearly independent of the battery voltage. The value of R should be much smaller than the impedance of the voltmeter and yet large enough to give easily measurable potential differences. The capacitor is used to filter out the oscillations in the current when an ac supply is used to power the LEDs. (A possible improvement in our design is to use a single do power supply for both the LEDs and the detector.) We find a time constant (RC) of 0.5 s to be adequate. Our device uses a 1-MΩ resistor and a 500-nF capacitor.

Integrating Sphere

The integrating sphere should be large enough to accommodate the required electronic components without significant loss of uniformity in color mixing. At the same time, it should be small enough to provide sufficient luminosity. Ours is made of plaster (see Fig. 4) and constructed in the following way.

A ball with a diameter of 2.4 cm is placed in an appropriate mold box. (We use a plastic ball from a roll-on deodorant in which we fixed a screw.) Plaster is poured into the box until it just covers half the ball. After the plaster is set, the board holding the LEDs, detector, and connecting wires is attached to the uncovered side of the ball. Plaster is then poured over the rest of the ball. After the plaster has hardened sufficiently, it is taken out of the mold (box) and separated into two halves. The ball is removed, and the plaster cleaned off the LEDs and photodiode. When the plaster has completely hardened, a small viewing hole is made in the sphere half that does not contain the LEDs (see Fig. 4). The insides of the sphere halves are then painted with white matte paint. After sanding the outsides to the desired size and wall thickness, the two halves are placed together and wrapped with aluminum adhesive tape. The tape prevents unwanted light from entering the (translucent) sphere when the device is in use. After all of the electrical connections have been made and operation of the LEDS and photodiode checked, the components are placed in the colorimeter case, thus completing the assembly of the device (see Fig. 5).

Use of the Calorimeter

Our students work two to a colorimeter. The "unknown" colored samples they study are squares of colored matte paper, each with a hole in its center slightly smaller than the viewing hole in the integrating sphere.

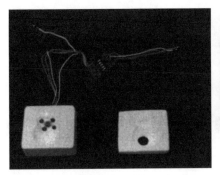

Fig. 4. Interior of integrating sphere, showing LEDs and viewing holes.

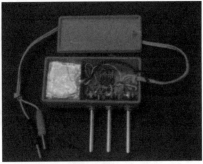

Fig. 5. Completed assembly.

The paper is placed against the integrating sphere with the holes aligned. The students view simultaneously the paper (illuminated with ambient light) and the light mixture emanating from the sphere through the hole. The ambient light level may be adjusted by using a piece of translucent white paper as a baffle (see Fig. 1). The color of the sample is measured by adjusting the amounts of light emitted by the LEDs until the hole appears identical to the surrounding paper. This requires adjustment of four variables: the relative light output of the three sources as well as the total brightness. With some practice, this can be done without difficulty. Once the color has been closely matched, it is easier to match the brightness by varying the ambient light falling on the sample rather than readjusting the levels of the primary sources.

After the unknown color sample has been matched in both color and brightness, all of the LEDs are turned off and the "zero signal" measured. (This signal is the minimum current that flows when the detector is in complete darkness.) Next, each LED is turned on separately and the voltage corresponding to each color measured. The zero signal is then subtracted from each of these readings. The resulting numbers are multiplied by scale factors.

The scale factor for every primary is the ratio between the photometric quantity (luminance of LED) and the detector response. A proper calibration requires turning on each LED separately and reading the detector's response in volts and luminance in photometric units such as lux. For example: red LED turned on—photodiode response: 103 mV; luxmeter reading: 20

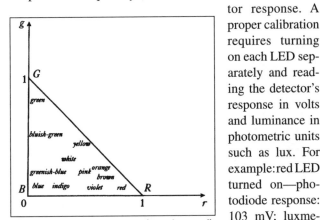

Fig. 6. Maxwell triangle representing color coordinates.

lux. Then the scaling factor for red is

$$f_R = \frac{20}{103} \text{ lux/mV, and so on with the other primaries.}$$

Important: the scaling factors are arbitrary, but they must remain proportional; that is, calibration for all three primaries must be performed under the same conditions.

The unknown color is represented by the three scaled values (coordinates) obtained by the above procedure. This set of numbers may be thought of as a vector whose direction represents the color and whose length is related to the luminance. The final step is to normalize the coordinates so that their sum $(r + b + g)$ is equal to unity. This set of coordinates is dimensionless and does not contain information about the luminance of the sample. The normalized coordinates may be used to represent the unknown color on the Maxwell triangle shown in Fig. 6. Taking the red contribution (r) as the abscissa and green (g) as the ordinate, the blue contribution is indicated by the color's proximity to the origin. The locations of the "pure" colors (red, blue, and green) are marked R, B, and G, respectively.

It is possible to find colors that cannot be generated with our colorimeter. Such colors fall outside the Maxwell triangle[1,2] defined by the three primaries. In such a case, the sample must be illuminated with colored light in order to make the resulting perceived color fall into the triangle.

Finally, with this colorimeter, it is possible to detect color vision anomalies or simply differences in color vision among students. We have found that in a number of cases students agree on measured brightnesses but not on location within the Maxwell triangle, so they perceive colors in a slightly different way.

References

1. G. Wyszecki and W.S. Stiles, *Color Science: Concepts and Methods, Quantitative Data and Formulae*, 2nd ed. (Wiley, New York, 1982), p. 121.
2. G.A. Agoston, *Color Theory and Its Application in Art and Design* (SpringerVerlag, NY, 1987), pp. 47–53.

Other Optics Apparatus

Equipment for an Inexpensive Introductory Optics Lab

H.E. Siefken and H.E. Tomaschke, Department of Physics, Greenville College, Greenville, IL 62246

The application of basic physical optics to the behavior of photons, electrons, and ions has led to various devices and materials that amaze and attract the consumer, provide new and exciting applications for those teaching optics, and create enthusiasm among students who like to produce laser shows and experiment with various light effects. The great commercial and industrial growth in the field is supported by related areas such as vacuum technology and photometry.

In our schools, however, even though introductory physics courses may have an optics laboratory component, many teachers cannot introduce experiments that use lasers and the associated apparatus because of the high costs involved. Summarized here is an inexpensive (less than $125) set of equipment items that enable the user to perform several basic optics experiments. We demonstrated this equipment at a recent workshop for secondary-school teachers, and they found our ideas very useful. We would be pleased to send a complete list of sources for parts and supplies to any teacher who writes us.

The starting point is the construction of an inexpensive instrumented laser diode light source. Laser diodes emitting in the visible region are now available at electronic supply centers at relatively low cost (about $50). Since the current-vs-voltage characteristic curve is very steep in the lasing region of operation, it is necessary to monitor and carefully control the current. Figure 1 shows a circuit that allows smooth adjustment of the diode current. In constructing the circuit, attach the T05 diode housing to a brass plate, which will serve as a heat sink. Before attaching the diode, solder the plate to a half-inch copper waterpipe coupling. Mount the diode so it is concentric with the coupling to achieve proper focusing of the beam.

The 670-nm light emitted by the diode used here is plane polarized[1] and highly divergent, so a lens system must be used. A simple system can be made by cementing a lens (13-mm diameter, 9-mm focal length) to the end of a short length of half-inch PVC tubing. The plastic tubing fits nicely inside the coupling, allowing for easy adjustment of the lens. A photograph of the completed light source is shown in Fig. 2.

A device for producing multiple parallel beams can be made from a piece of ordinary one-way mirror plate glass and a front-surface mirror, each about 1 x 4 in. The two pieces are glued to a pair of 3/4-in Plexiglas blocks, which serve as spacers. The path of the beams can be seen by passing them through water or chalk dust. This technique can be used to measure the focal points of lenses or flexible curved acrylic mirrors.[2]

The third inexpensive item is a light meter, which is easily constructed using two silicon photocells, each one mounted at opposite ends of a chassis box and selectable by a switch. A large PN-junc-

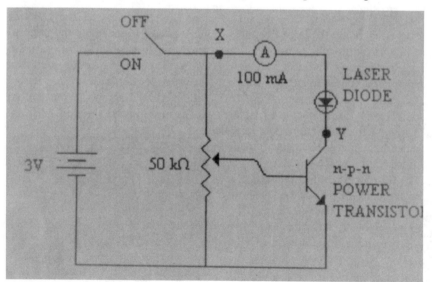

Fig. 1. Circuit used to control current to laser diode. Power is supplied by two C- or D-size batteries.

Fig. 2. Laser-diode light source showing the sliding lens assembly, ammeter, and potentiometer for current adjustments.

tion amorphous silicon cell is used for diffuse light sources, while a small PIN silicon cell is used with the laser. A 500-µA meter monitors the generated current from either photocell. For the current from a PN-junction photocell to respond linearly with light intensity, a small parallel resistance must be seen by the photocell. Unfortunately most inexpensive ammeters in this current range possess a significant resistance (which renders the light meter unsuitable for accurately demonstrating the inverse-square law from a point source) when using the large PN-junction silicon photocell. However, the small PIN silicon cell is linear with light intensity, so it is used to measure transmitted and reflected light intensities from various translucent materials. Knowing the fraction of transmitted and reflected light, a user can then calculate the fraction of absorbed light.

The fourth part of the optics kit is a polarizer/analyzer. This is used to show students how to produce polarized light from an unpolarized light source. It is also easy to use with the laser diode light source. A 1½-in PVC coupling (available at most hardware stores) is used to hold a circular piece of polarizing plastic film that is cut from a larger sheet.

Two PVC couplings with mounted polarizers are connected by approximately 3 inches of PVC tubing. Sand the tubing at one end to permit the easy rotation of the coupling.

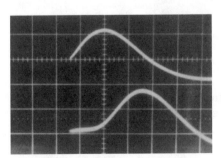

Fig. 4. Typical record showing the delayed response between photodiodes. Horizontal scale is 100 ns/div.

The separation distance of the polarizing films and the size of the aperture make it easy to enclose sealed vials of optically active liquids or to serve as a strain analyzer for thin plastic sheets as they are deformed.

Attaching an angular scale of 10-degree increments to the analyzer coupling facilitates measurement of the amount of angular rotation by the liquid.

The fifth equipment item, which creates much interest and contains some basic mathematics and physics, is a laser-light-show apparatus. Mount two 1.5-VDC motors with mirrors attached at an angle on individual brackets that can pivot in a hole in a pegboard base. The longitudinal vibrations of each mirror causes the laser beam to be reflected on a screen in a Lissajous pattern. The speed of each motor is controlled by a 20-Ω potentiometer. When three mirror/motor units are used, the pattern produced can be very intricate.

Finally by adding a circuit to modulate the intensity from the laser diode, time measurements can be recorded on a

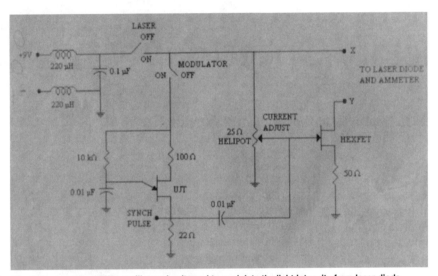

Fig. 3. Inexpensive 1-MHz oscillator circuit used to modulate the light intensity from laser diode.

suitable oscilloscope to measure the speed of light. Figure 3 shows an inexpensive circuit that operates around 1 MHz and produces pulses with smaller rise times than some commercial models. The laser beam passes through a beam splitter. One beam travels a long path, the other a short path, and each is then detected by a photodiode. For optimal use most photodiodes should be biased near –100 V. However, at the level of –9 V available from a typical battery, the rise time produced by the photodiode is still short enough to be comparable to that of the pulsing circuit. Figure 4 shows a typical pulse record from the two detectors when used with the modulator circuit and laser diode.

References

1. For the reader interested in the polarization-emission process of these devices, a good reference is B.M. Yu and J.M. Liu, *J. Appl. Phys.* **69**, 7444 (1991).
2. S. Mak, *Phys. Teach.* **31**, 186 (1993).

Optical Accessories for Optical Bench and Force Table

R.C. Nicklin, Robert Miller, and Andrew Graham, Department of Physics and Astronomy, Appalachian State University, Boone, NC 28608

We have devised some ways to mount standard optical parts that make it far easier to achieve x, y, and z alignment on an optical bench[1] than with the usual three-point lens and mirror mounts. Other accessories adapt a standard force table[2] to some optical experiments. Our department has 16 each of the benches and tables, a considerable investment, and our goal was to improve their usefulness with durable and inexpensive accessories. Most of these parts are easily fabricated using a lathe and common materials.

Laser U supports (Fig. 1a) consist of 0.64-cm (1/4-in, 20) threaded steel rods bent into a U-shape 12.7 cm high by 15.2 cm wide (5 x 6 in) and brazed to a 0.95-cm shaft 15.2 cm long (0.375 x 6 in). Use rubber tubing to cover the U and the 0.32 x 1.27 x 16.5-cm (1/8 x 1/2 x 6.5-in) hold-down strap. Wing nuts secure the strap. This accommodates a wide range of laser sizes and is so secure that alignment is maintained even when the bench is moved around rather roughly.

Horizontal slots (Fig. 1b-f) are made from aluminum channel stock with a 1.27-cm-wide x 0.64-cm-high (1/2 x 1/4-in) channel 12.7 cm long (5 in) screwed to a 0.95-cm shaft 15.2 cm long (0.375 x 6 in). These slots are very handy for supporting a screen, ground glass, mirrors, slits, Polaroids in 35-mm slide mounts and short-focal-length lenses (Fig. 1f). A nylon thumbscrew holds the optical part in place.

An *articulated alligator clip* (Figs. 2a and 3b) is easily adjustable and holds odd-shaped parts such as safety pins, needles, and razor blades at almost any angle for diffraction studies. Use a form tool to make a 0.64-cm (1/4-in) ball radius on a 3-cm-long shaft holding the alligator clip. Use a ball end mill to indent the shaft for the ball and a knurled nut to hold the clip to the 0.95 cm-diam by 15.2-cm-long shaft (0.375 x 6 in).

The *adjustable polarizer-analyzer* (Figs. 2b and 3a) is harder to build but offers an inexpensive[3,4] and effective way to control beam intensity or to do a Malus law experiment. Cut two 2.5-cm lengths (1 in) of 1.90-cm-diam (3/4-in) CPVC pipe. Bore one end of each 2 mm deep and slightly larger than 20 mm diam to allow each Polaroid to rotate freely. In each of two protractors, bore an 11-mm-diam hole to remove the plastic from the optical path. Use an instant adhesive such as Loctite 494 to glue a Polaroid to each protractor, centered over the hole. Machine an aluminum sup-

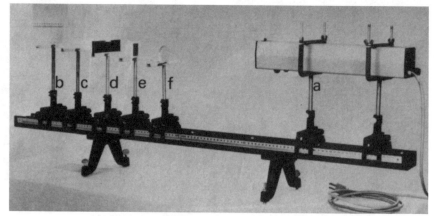

Fig. 1. (a) laser U supports; (b)–(f) horizontal slots to hold screens, slits, and similar items.

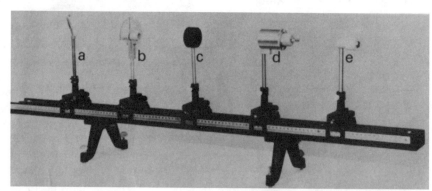

Fig. 2. (a) articulated alligator clip for odd-shaped objects; (b) adjustable polarizer-analyzer; (c) PVC mount for 38-mm-diam lens; (d) 7 1/2-W lamp support and planar object; (e) 2.5-V lamp support (approximate point source).

port, resembling a short tuning fork, to provide a slot for the Polaroids. Attach the CPVC to this support with screws through slotted holes, for easy assembly and adjustment. Both could be allowed to rotate, but we found it better to fix one protractor to the support and glue a small handle to the other one. The relative angle may be read to $\pm$ 0.5°.

Two *38-lens mounts* (Fig. 2c) may be made from a 3.2-cm (1 1/4-in) PVC pipe coupling. Cut the coupling in half, and drill a centered hole in each half to receive a 0.95-cm-

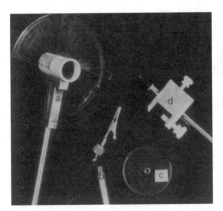

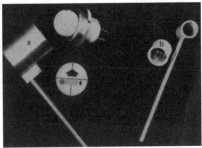

Fig. 4. (a) 7 1/2-W lamp, housing, and planar object; (b) 2.5-V lamp and support, approximate point source when masked with 4-mm hole (also Fig. 2e).

Fig. 3. (a) adjustable polarizer-analyzer; (b) articulated alligator clip; (c) Plexiglas mount for 4.5-mm f/1 lens, flattened for horizontal slot support (Fig. 1f); (d) adjustable clamp, supports photodetector on force table (Fig. 5c).

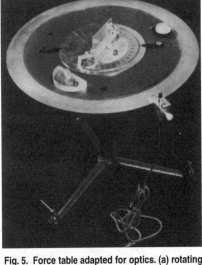

Fig. 5. Force table adapted for optics. (a) rotating circular plate, protractor, and hold-downs for horizontal slot (holds mirrors or plates vertical) for reflection and Brewster's experiments; (b) optical disk, replaces horizontal slot, for careful refraction measurements; (c) photodetector with adjustable clamp, connects to circuit of Fig. 6.

diam (3/8-in) support rod. The coupling is tapered inside, so the lens will rest with a snug fit. Cut a 0.95-cm-long (3/8-in) piece of 3.2-cm (1 1/4-in) pipe and use it to secure the centered lens. These mounts keep a lens on beam center and protect it from fingerprints and breakage.

Construct a *5.7-mm lens mount* (Figs. 1f and 3c) for a 4.5-mm f/1 lens[5] from a 0.63-cm-thick by 5.1-cm-diam (1/4 x 2-in) piece of Plexiglas, flattened at one spot to rest in a horizontal slot support. Bore an undersized hole, then bore two-thirds through with < lens diameter for light press fit. Such a lens is handy for the front end of a cheap laser beam expander but is impossible to use without some such mount.

Here is a *sturdy light source*. Mount a frosted 7 1/2-W bulb in a two-prong socket (Figs. 2d and 4a) in a 5.1-cm (2-in) piece of 3.8-ctn-i.d. (1 1/2-in) aluminum pipe, thinned to 2 mm with a boring tool and drilled top and bottom with 2-mm heat-vent holes. Hold the socket in a threaded fixture machined from a 1.27 x 5.1-cm plate (1/2 x 2 in). Make suitable objects to be illuminated using press-on art materials on bluegrid graph paper. Copy onto transparency material with a copy tnachine, cut to size, and mount between transparent Plexiglas disks. Secure the object with a spring wire retainer aligned with the support stem, so the object position is easy to read from the optical bench.

A *smaller light source* (Figs. 2e and 4b) uses 4 cm of 1.90-cm-diam CPVC pipe (1 1/2 x 3/4-in) and a pipe cap. A low-voltage lamp (e.g., Chicago Miniature 41, 2.5 V, 500 mA) is bright enough to study shadows and illuminate objects for lenses, resulting in bright images over the length of the bench. Since standard bases are too flimsy, we machined a screw-type base with jack for power via a miniature phono plug. When masked with a 4-mm hole in a metal disk or another pipe cap, this lamp makes an adequate point source for an inverse-square law experiment with the phototransistor (described later).

Since the force table has a nice ruled angle scale and is

the right height to receive a laser beam from the optical bench, we made some attachments to adapt it for optics experiments.

The *rotating circular plate* (Fig. 5a) is 18 cm in diam (7 in) and has a 2.5-cm (1-in) centering pin that inserts into the table. Attach a protractor to the plate and two pointers to the table for angle measurements to ± 0.5°. Two hold-down clips with wing nuts secure an optical disk (Fig. 5b) for refraction measurements and also hold a short piece of aluminum channel (another horizontal slot) with nylon thumb-screw to support a front-surface mirror or a glass microscope slide for reflection or Brewster's law measurements. Use a bubble level to make sure the plate rotates in a horizontal plane.

The *photodetector* (Figs. 3d and 5c) clamps to the table's edge. Two nylon thumbscrews allow precise adjustment to capture the reflected or refracted beam. The clamp, machined from a piece of 3.8 x 3.2 x 2.2-cm (1 1/2 x 1 1/4 x 7/8-in) aluminum, is undercut on a radius so it contacts the table at only two points. Otherwise it would rock and confound the angle determination. Mount the detector[5] in a 0.95-cm-diam tube (3/8-in). Secure the cable (1 m, RCA phono plug to stripped ends) with silicone glue to prevent rotation in the

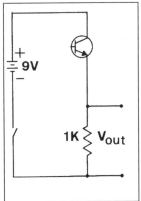

Fig. 6. Circuit for photodetector (Fig. 5c) will fit in a 3.8 x 5.1 x 7.6-cm (1 1/2 x 2 x 3-in) box.

tube. This cable (Fig. 5c) plugs into the supply circuit (Fig. 6), and the output may be read with a digital volt meter. Depending on light intensity, the output will read 0 to about 95 percent of supply voltage.

Acknowledgment

We thank Joe Pollock for the technique for making objects (Fig. 4a) and Bill Sheffield for the photographs.

References

1. Central Scientific Co., 11222 Melrose Ave., Franklin Park, IL 60131-1364; Cenco #85801 (bench), #85808 (carriage), #72288 (lens clamp).
2. Cenco #74285.
3. Edmund Scientific, 101 E. Gloucester Pike, Barrington, NJ 08007-1380; #N36438 20-mm-diam 20 percent Polaroid filters in glass.
4. McMaster-Carr Supply, Box 440, New Brunswick, NJ 08903-0440; #1215T1 4-in protractors.
5. Mouser Electronics, 2401 Highway 287 North, Mansfield, TX 76063; Mouser #551-PH104 phototransistor.

Bright Point Source

Richard E. Berg, University of Maryland, College Park, MD 20742

The University of Maryland physics lecture demonstration facility regularly uses a wide variety of demonstrations involving a bright point source of white light. Some of the important areas include:

1. Shadow projection with white light or with colored light using color filters in front of the lamps
2. Spectra, using prisms or diffraction grating to project white light spectra, line and absorption spectra, rainbows, halos, etc
3. Geometrical optics, showing focal properties, aberrations and distortions of lenses and mirrors
4. Polarization and scattering of light, including wave plates and optical activity
5. Optical board, illustrating ray tracing for lenses and mirrors

We have used a number of different light sources in our large lecture halls (seating up to 320) with mixed degrees of success. Incandescent lamps or wire filaments as objects are often marginally weak and lack intense blue. Projectors often produce a rather broad source, because of the reflector generally built into the lamp, and lack the brightness of an arc lamp. Arc lamps are expensive, require substantial maintenance, and are difficult to operate. Lasers are nice but require precise alignment to function well and cannot be used for showing chromatic effects.

We have recently developed small, bright point sources, which we use for most of our shadow projection and optics applications. Several years ago we began to use 100 W quartz halogen projection lamps as sources for shadow projection. More recently we have discovered similar lamps with 150 W and 250 W power. The 100 W lamp that we use runs at 12 V AC, while the 150 W and 250 W lamps operate at 24 V AC, so each requires only a transformer. The advantages of this type of lamp over other projection lamps are that it does not have a built-in reflector, so it really functions as a point source, plus it is extremely bright and has good blue. The filament size of the 250 W lamp is about 3 mm x 6 mm, and that of the 150 W version is slightly smaller; the 100 W filament is only 2 mm x 4 mm.

We use the 100 W sources for general shadow projection and the 150 W sources for most optics demonstrations. The lamp, lamp holder, transformer, a fuse and the on/off switch are packaged in a black-anodized aluminum sheet metal box about 25-cm high, 15-cm wide, and 28-cm deep (along the optic axis). With one model of the box, we have mounted two 100 W lamps together so it can be used for demonstrations requiring a double source. For the sources used in optics demonstrations, we mount a condenser lens directly onto the front of the box. The 250 W lamp is used for our optical board. We have included a fan with this model, although there seems to be no problem with heat using the smaller models, which are cooled by bottom vent holes optically shielded by the lamp mount and top vent holes with a light shield built onto the top of the box.

Each box is mounted on an adapter, with which the light source is positioned on a triangular optical rail. The filament is located in the box so that it will be on an axis convenient for alignment with the optical elements to be used in the demonstrations. For our spectroscopy demonstrations we mount the filament with the 6-mm dimension vertical and the 3-mm dimension horizontal, so that we get the maximum intensity through a vertical object slit.

Direct visual comparison between the arc lamps and the point sources show striking similarity, with at worst a very slight degradation of the far violet of the point source. We measured the intensity of some sources,[1] and found that the

150 W bulb has the same intensity in the visible as a 330 W (6 amps at 55 V) carbon arc lamp. Approximately 10 percent of the intensity of the arc lamp measured as indicated is ultraviolet. Because there is no ultraviolet with the point source, we retain the arc lamp for special demonstrations involving ultraviolet sensing and for photoelectric effect demonstrations that require high-energy photons.

We do our ray tracing demonstrations using a lecture-hall-size optical board, about 2.1-m long with 45-cm lenses and mirrors. The 250 W lamp provides at least the level of lighting obtained from the arc lamp, allows full-color observations and is operated simply by an on/off switch.

The lamps and lamp holder are available from Microlamp, 1200 Clint Moore Road, Boca Raton, FL 33487 (Phone 1-800-431-4956):
1. FCR Lamp, 100 W at 12 V, approximately $3.10 each.
2. FCS Lamp, 150 W at 24 V, approximately $2.00 each.
3. EHJ Lamp, 250 W at 24 V, approximately $4.50 each.
4. TP17 Lamp holder (fits all lamps), approximately $4.00

each.

To be on the conservative side, we chose the following transformers, all available from Triad-Utrad (through your local electronics parts store):
1. F29U, 12 V, 11 amps for the 100 W lamp, approximately $40 each.
2. F261U, 24 V, 8 amps for the 150 W lamp, approximately $40 each.
3. F226U, 24 V, 12 amps for the 250 W lamp, approximately $50 each.

If you are interested in the drawings for our point-source package, please send a large, self-addressed envelope that will accommodate the six 28-cm x 43.2-cm drawings (11 in x 17 in) to the address above. Fabrication of these boxes requires some skill in sheet metal bending and the appropriate bending machines.

Reference
1. Intensity measurements were made using a Metrologic Model 60-530 radiometer.

Ultraviolet Viewer

Tom Donohue *and* **Howard Wallace,** Corporate Radiation Health Protection, The Boeing Company, P.O. Box 3707, Seattle, WA 98124-2207

Students often have a difficult time conceptualizing invisible radiation. Here is an easy-to-build device that helps them see the effects of the ultraviolet (UV) radiation around them.

Construct the device from a cardboard tube (refer to Fig. 1) by cutting a hole in the top of the tube to hold a filter that passes UV light but is opaque to visible. (Sources for such filters are given in Ref. 1.) Write the letters "UV" on a cardboard oval with a fluorescent highlighting pen. The oval should be placed so that the letters can be seen both through the hole at the front of the tube and through the hole that holds the filter. Tape the filter in place so that no light seeps around the edges. You can also tape the back end of the tube shut so as to block out light.

Look through the front opening of the tube. In the absence of UV light, the interior of the tube will be black. If UV light is present, it will pass through the filter and cause the ink from the highlighter to fluoresce.

Clear plastic is very effective at blocking UV light. Plastic safety glasses placed over the filter will stop the fluorescence and can be used to demonstrate to students that the fluorescence is due to UV radiation and not to visible light getting through the filter.

Students may wish to investigate some of the following

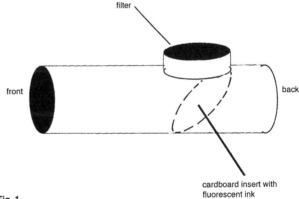

Fig. 1.

questions: How much UV radiation is outside on a sunny day? How much on a cloudy day? Does UV light come through the classroom windows? Do fluorescent lights or video display monitors give off UV radiation? Do expensive UV-blocking sunglasses block better than cheap plastic ones?

Reference
1. UVA filter 4948 from International Light, Dexter Industrial Green, Newburyport, MA 01950; 617-465-5923. Also filter 51124, 1-in diameter, $29 from ORIEL Corp., 250 Long Beach Blvd., P.O. Box 872, Stratford, CT 06497-0872; 203-377-7877.